Science and society

SCIENCE AND SOCIETY
midcentury readings

THOMAS D. CLARESON, college of wooster

Harper & brothers, publishers, new york

Library of Congress catalog card number: 61–6281

Contents

v

III. THE SCIENTIST AND MODERN SOCIETY

IV. SCIENCE AND EDUCATION

V. SCIENCE, PHILOSOPHY, AND RELIGION

VI. THE REFERENCE PAPER

What are the methods of science? How has science influenced contemporary thought? What part should science play in the education of American youth? Has the United States failed to produce an adequate number of research scientists and engineers? What role should the scientist play in a democratic society? How much supervision should government have over scientific research? Is there a quarrel between science and religion? Where is science taking us?

In this period between Hiroshima and space travel such questions have reflected the growing American—indeed, the growing world —concern for the relationship between science and society at midtwentieth century. Moreover, perhaps to an extent not found in previous modern history, the scientists themselves have entered the discussion. That the reactions of both the scientists and the general public to the A-bomb precipitated the widened interest in these issues cannot be doubted. But although the threat of nuclear warfare has remained an important topic, the mushrooming cloud of discussion has shifted its center to a general review of the roles played by science and the scientists as active parts of society, to an examination of the place of science in American education, and to a renewed consideration of the philosophical and religious implications of the new discoveries in such fields as physics.

This volume provides a collection of primary sources taken from books and periodicals of the last decade which the undergraduate student may use either as a reader or as a basis for a reference paper in his freshman or advanced composition course. As a reader, it has a variety of uses. The eight exercises included in the first four parts of the text—two after each one—deal with forms of expository writing and with perennial problems of English composition. Each is directed toward the section of the text it follows, but actually can be used with any of the essays. Each presents the student with a discussion which, although enabling him to begin work on his own, may serve as a point of departure for classroom lecture and discussion. Specific assignments involving the problem discussed have been included after each exercise. The theme topics proposed after each section of the text do not necessarily need annotation and, by and large, will require the student to make some evaluation of material he has read as well as to draw upon his own experience.

As the basis for a reference paper, the text is sufficiently complete to be used alone, although at the discretion of the student and his instructor library research can provide additional material. A bibliographical note heads each entry. To facilitate formal annotation, the original pagination has been indicated in the text. For example, the first selection is the reprint of Margaret Mead and Rhoda Métraux, "Image of the Scientist among High-School Students," *Science*, August 30, 1957, pp. 384–390. Within the text of this article occurs the marking [385] to indicate that the preceding portion of the text originally appeared on page 385, the succeeding on page 386. So it is with each page number in turn. The volume number of periodicals has been omitted from the reproduced text.

At the end of the volume the section entitled "Reference Paper" includes some discussion of the purpose and problems of the undergraduate paper, and indicates a method of documentation based upon the *MLA Style Sheet*. The writing exercises will permit library work and will suggest possible titles for annotated themes of various lengths. By no means are these topics—or the ones included after the earlier sections—exhaustive; reading and class discussion should suggest many others.

The selections included in this volume have been limited to articles and excerpts from books written during the 1950's. This has been done in order to emphasize contemporary issues. In addition, with few exceptions, the material has been taken from the writings of trained scientists, men who are now practicing scientists or administrators in various research and governmental programs or both. The aim here has been to take advantage of both their special knowledge and—whether one agrees or not—their often provocative ideas.

I am especially indebted to Professors Melcher Fobes of the Mathematics Department, William Kieffer of the Chemistry Department,

and Reginald Stephenson of the Physics Department for their aid
with bibliography; to Professor Lowell W. Coolidge of the English
Department for his advice about format and exercises; and to Alice
Super Clareson of the *Journal of Chemical Education* for her copy-
and proofreading.

THOMAS D. CLARESON

The College of Wooster

part I   SCIENCE AND THE STUDENT

Image of the scientist among high-school students

MARGARET MEAD AND RHODA MÉTRAUX
Science, August 30, 1957, pp. 384–390

This study is based on an analysis of a nation-wide sample of essays written by high-school students in response to uncompleted questions. The following explanation was read to all students by each administrator. "The American Association for the Advancement of Science (*1*), a national organization of scientists having over 50,000 members, is interested in finding out confidentially what you think about science and scientists. Therefore, you are asked to write in your own words a statement which tells what you think. What you write is confidential. You are not to sign your name to it. When you have written your statement you are to seal it in an envelope and write the name of school on the envelope. This is not a test in which any one of you will be compared with any other student, either at this school, or at another school. Students at more than 120 schools in the United States are also completing the statement and your answer and theirs will be considered together to really find out what all high-school students think as a group of people."

In general, the study shows that, while an official image of the scientist—that is, an image that is the correct answer to give when the student is asked to speak without personal career involvement—has been built up which is very positive, this is not so when the student's personal choices are involved. Science in general is represented as a good thing: without science we would still be living in caves; science is responsible for progress, is necessary for the defense of the country, is responsible for preserving more lives and for improving the health and comfort of the population. However, when the question becomes one of personal contact with science, as a career choice or involving the choice of a husband, the image is overwhelmingly negative.

This is not a study of what proportion of high-school students are choosing, or will eventually choose, a scientific career. It is a study of the state of mind of the students among whom the occasional future scientist must go to school and of the atmosphere within which the science teacher must teach. It gives us a basis for reexamining the way in which science and the life of the scientist are being presented in the United States today.

OBJECTIVES

Our specific objectives in this study were to learn the following.

1) When American secondary-school students are asked to discuss scientists in general, without specific reference to their own career choices or, among girls, to the career choices of their future husbands, what comes to their minds and how are their ideas expressed in images?

2) When American secondary-school students are asked to think of themselves as becoming scientists (boys and girls) or as married to a scientist (girls), what comes to their minds and how are their ideas expressed in images?

3) When the scientist is considered as a general figure and/or as someone the respondent (that is, the student writer) might like to be (or to marry), or, alternatively, might not like to be (or to marry), how do (i) the postive responses (that is, items or phrases, not answers) cluster, and (ii) the negative responses (that is, items or phrases) cluster?

4) When clusters of positive responses and clusters of negative responses are compared and analyzed, in what respects are the two types of clusters of responses (i) clearly distinguishable, and (ii) overlapping?

5) Is a generally positive attitude to the idea of science, an attitude which we [384] are spending a great deal of money and effort to create, any guarantee of a positive attitude to the idea of science as a career?

SELECTION OF RESPONDENTS

Two separate samples of respondents were used in the study: sample A, a nation-wide sample of high schools, and sample B, a sample of high schools with widely different economic and educational characteristics.

Sample A consisted of 132 public high schools (including one junior high school) that were selected from schools associated with the Traveling High-School Science Library Program sponsored by the National Science Foundation and administered by the American Association for the Advancement of Science. Of these, 118 were drawn from the high schools that participated in this program and an additional 14 from schools that qualified for the program but could not be included in it.

Sample B consisted of 13 special schools: four parochial schools, eight preparatory schools, and one public science high school. All these were from the eastern seaboard, selected to provide contrasts in educational and economic level to the smaller public high schools in the nation-wide sample (sample A). Sample B was collected after the homogeneity of the nation-wide sample had been ascertained.

The total enrollment of the schools participating in the study was 48,000. Schools with an enrollment of less than 300 students were asked to have each student complete one form; schools with an enrollment of more than 300 students were asked to complete 300 forms. The total sample (sample A and sample B) is drawn from the essays written by approximately 35,000 students, and the essays were kept together by the class, grade, and school from which the essays came.

The sample was randomized by drawing envelopes of these replies in groups that included three schools in one state, or three tenth grades, or all the separate classes in three schools, so that no essay was ever separated from the context in which it had been written.

DATA-GATHERING INSTRUMENTS

We asked each high-school student respondent to write a brief essay on a topic set by an incomplete sentence which was printed at the top of a page, on which provision was also made for giving the school, the grade, the class or section, the age and sex of the respondent.

Three different forms were constructed, each with a different incomplete sentence. Each of these three sentences was chosen to elicit one major aspect of the image of the scientist.

Only one form was used in any one school (2), but the forms were so distributed that each form was used by at least one school in each state. These three forms are as follows.

Form I

Complete the following statement in your own words. Write at least a full paragraph, but do not write more than a page.

When I think about a scientist, I think of

Form II

If you are a *boy*, complete the following statement in your own words.

If I were going to be a scientist, I should like to be the kind of scientist who

If you are a *girl*, you may complete either the sentence above or this one.

If I were going to marry a scientist, I should like to marry the kind of scientist who

Form III

If you are a *boy*, complete the following statement in your own words.

If I were going to be a scientist, I would not like to be the kind of scientist who

If you are a *girl*, you may complete either the sentence above or this one.

If I were going to marry a scientist, I would not like to marry the kind of scientist who

Use of the three forms made it possible to distinguish between answers giving official versions of the image of the scientist and those involving the respondents personally, and the use of two forms of the personal question provided material on the links between negative and positive images, since many answers included responses relevant to both. Experience has shown that the way in which a question is phrased—that is, with a positive or with a negative emphasis—affects the phrasing of the answers by the respondents.

ANALYSIS OF MATERIAL AND PROBLEMS OF VALIDATION

This study is based on qualitative data. The material reflects the way individuals feel and think about a subject as well as whether they will answer questions about the subject in the affirmative or the negative. The use of quantitative data, gathered primarily to count the number of individuals in any given group who will respond in one way or in another, is the more desirable technique when one is interested in whether individuals will agree or disagree with some stated opinion rather than how they feel or why they feel as they do. The check marks or brief responses gathered by quantitative studies are generally too sparse in the expression of feeling and imagery to permit the definition, or the redefinition, of shared attitudes; in such studies, attitudes which are assumed to exist are built into the questions.

The relative value of qualitative and quantitative studies has been debated in the behavioral sciences for some time. A resolution generally accepted at the present time is that the qualitative study is the method of choice for generating hypotheses, and the quantitative study the method of choice for testing hypotheses (3). When the problem is one of delineating a shared aspect of a society-wide set of images—rather than of answering questions on which or how many students may be expected to respond in a given way—a qualitative study is preferable.

The identification of the pattern in any large sample of essays and of the cognitive and emotional processes which underlie the attitudes reported by individuals is best accomplished by trained behavioral scientists. Because any one analyst, no matter how well trained, may have some blind spots and biases, and because analysts differ in their types of disciplined perception, we had six different analysts work independently with six subsamples of the total sample drawn from different states. Because one kind of material may be more useful than another in outlining a given area, we used—in addition to the essay samples from the 35,000 students—a variety of other kinds of materials as well.

We are assured that we have identified important themes in the material by the multiplicity of independent analyses and by the use of a variety of data. We are assured of the validity of our conclusions by a comparison of the independent work of the analysts and by the agreement on materials from different parts of the country.

STAGES IN ANALYSIS AND VALIDATION

The stages in analysis and validation were as follows.

1) Sets of data were drawn from the main corpus by envelopes of answers, each set consisting of from 200 to 500 protocols, all from

one state and including envelopes of answers to all three forms. Each of the six senior consultants was given a set of data. They worked in complete independence of one another until they met in conference to pool their results in discussion. This discussion was transcribed. The discussion indicated that the analysts were in agreement on the homogeneity of the attitudes found in the materials from different sections of [385] the country. On the basis of this preliminary working of the material from sample A, further collections for sample B (including provision for a control on the use of the words *American Association for the Advancement of Science*) were planned and carried out.

2) A detailed pattern analysis was performed on 1000 essays, chosen to represent both the homogeneous nation-wide sample of public schools (sample A) and the highly diversified schools (sample B). This analysis of responses (that is, items, phrases) both checked on the patterns identified by the senior analysts (among whom was included the analyst who made the detailed pattern analysis) and provided additional understanding of the patterns.

In making this analysis, essays from classes and schools were still kept together, so that each respondent could be placed and each essay could be placed within the major preoccupations of a class or a school. So some schools provided particularly clear material on the dichotomy between science as a subject for study and the personality of the scientist, or on ways in which an increasing sense of inadequacy was reflected in the rejection of science as a career. Everywhere it was possible to follow the divergent interests of boys and girls—as with the boys' interest in an active outdoor life and the girls' interest in the humanitarian aspects of medicine—but there were underlying assumptions shared by both sexes, such as the great importance of personal interests as a basis for career or marriage choice.

3) Fourteen graduate students were asked to report on smaller independent samples of essays. Graduate students were also enlisted to make collections of visual materials related to the image of the scientist in the culture of the United States today. Examples of this collection are illustrations from selected periodicals which present images of scientists, children's drawings made in response to the instruction "Draw a scientist," and the entire pictorial file from the public relations office of a pharmaceutical company.

4) Still another set of student essays from sample A was given to a seventh senior consultant, who had had no previous contact with any of the materials. Since she had not been involved in the earlier stages of the study, she could bring a fresh point of view to the final conference on the basis of which the report was written.

5) A final conference of the senior consultants was held, at which the preliminary findings were again reviewed, and the findings presented in this article were discussed in detail. There was general agreement that the findings effectively represented the data (4).

THE COMPOSITE IMAGE

In reading the following composite statements, it is important to realize that they do not represent literary descriptions written by the analyst but rather composites of the responses made by the students in their essays, so that each "composite image" is to be understood as being something like a composite photograph which emerges from a very large number of superimposed photographs. Each phrase (response) both stands for a family of phrases (responses) which were used throughout the essays and is itself a recurrently used phrase (response). The phrases have been grouped in relation to themes, as they occur in the essays, but reference to the themes might occur in any order in the essays. It is important to realize that in organizing for presentation here the positive and the negative versions of the composite image of the scientist, the analyst has separated out from the answers the positive phrases (responses), on the one hand, and the negative phrases (responses), on the other hand, as an analytic device, whereas in the essays both occur—or may occur—together in a variety of combinations.

Before the image of the scientist is discussed, it will be useful to look at the way "science" appears in these essays. In the following composite statements, italics indicate the words and phrases (responses) used; detailed examples are given in parentheses, and explanatory notes in square brackets.

SCIENCE

Science is a very broad field which may be seen as a single unit (*science is very important*, or *I am not interested in science*), as a melange (*medicine and gas and electric appliances*), or as composed of

entities (*biology* and *physics* and *chemistry* . . .) linked together by
the personality of the *scientist*.

Science is natural science with little direct reference to man as a
social being except as the products of science—*medicine* and *bombs*—
affect his life. The subjects of science are *chemistry* and *physics* (*laboratories, test tubes, bunsen burners, experiments* and *explosions,
atomic energy, laws* and *formulas* . . .), *biology-botany-zoology*
(*plants* and *animals* [that is, as materials for laboratory work], *microscopes, dissection, the digestive system, creepy* and *crawly things
. . .*), *astronomy* (*the moon, stars, planets, the solar system, outer
space, astronomers, astrologers* [*sic*], *telescopes, space ships* . . .),
geology (*the earth, rocks, mines* and *oil wells, out of doors* . . .),
medicine (*cures for TB, cancer, heart disease,* and *polio, research, se-
rums* . . .); *archeology* (*exploration, ancient cities, early man, fos-
sils, digging* . . .). *Mathematics* is not a science but a tool and a
measure of scientific aptitude.

The methods of science are *research* and *experimentation, invention,
discovery, exploration, finding out new things* and *new ways of improving old ones.* Science means *doing* and *making: hard work*—not
imagination—is the source of knowledge and the means of accomplish-
ment.

The focus of science is upon the present. The past is important only as
it is left behind (*without science we would still be living in caves*) and
the future as a foreseeable goal (when we *find a cure for heart disease,
see if there is life on Mars, discover new fuels* . . .). But as the
past closes in behind us, the future opens to the curious (*there is still
so much to discover*) into the yet unknown.

In thinking about science, different sorts of linked images occur
which may be bracketed together when science is rejected or may be
included when positive preference is expressed for one of a pair. So,
science may be *theoretical* or *applied,* and either of this pair can be
seen as more of a whole and be accepted (that is, the man in the laboratory is visualized as working through the whole problem; or the engineer can see the finished road), while the other is seen as partial and is
rejected (that is, the engineer is visualized as working only on the
end-product; or the man in the laboratory never sees the plan carried
out). Likewise, science can be carried out *in the laboratory* or in a *far
away place;* it may involve large-scale action (*traveling, digging, exploring, constructing, flying through space* . . .) or the skills of fine
detail (*gazing through a telescope, poring over a microscope, dissecting,
solving equations* . . .). The goals of science may be humanitarian

(*working to better mankind, finding cures, making new products,* developing *programs for atoms for peace* . . .), or, in contrast, they may be either individualistic (*making money, gaining fame and glory* . . .) or destructive (*dissecting, destroying enemies, making explosives* that *threaten* the *home,* the *country,* or *all mankind* . . .). Since, by implication, science is the source of unlimited power, its practitioners should have the highest and the most selfless motivations to use only its constructive possibilities—or its destructive possibilities only constructively—for the *welfare of their country* and the *betterment of people, the world,* and *all mankind.*

THE SCIENTIST

THE SHARED IMAGE (5)

The scientist is a man who wears a white coat and works in a laboratory. He is elderly or *middle aged and wears glasses. He is small,* sometimes *small and* [386] *stout, or tall and thin. He may be bald. He* may *wear a beard,* may be *unshaven* and *unkempt. He may be stooped and tired.*

He is surrounded by equipment: test tubes, bunsen burners, flasks and bottles, a jungle gym of blown glass tubes and weird machines with dials. The sparkling white laboratory is full of sounds: the bubbling of liquids in test tubes and flasks, the squeaks and squeals of laboratory animals, the muttering voice of the scientist.

He spends his days doing experiments. He pours chemicals from one test tube into another. He peers raptly through microscopes. He scans the heavens through a telescope [or a *microscope!*]. *He experiments with plants and animals, cutting them apart, injecting serum into animals. He writes neatly in black notebooks.*
The image then diverges.

POSITIVE SIDE OF THE IMAGE OF THE SCIENTIST

He is a very intelligent man—a genius or almost a genius. He has long years of expensive training—in high school, college, or technical school, or perhaps even beyond—during which he studied very hard. He is interested in his work and takes it seriously. He is careful, patient, devoted, courageous, open minded. He knows his subject. He records his experiments carefully, does not jump to conclusions, and stands up for his ideas even when attacked. He works for long hours in the laboratory, sometimes day and night, going without food and sleep. He is prepared to work for years without getting results and face the possibility of failure without discouragement; he will try again. He wants to know the answer. One day he may straighten up and shout: "I've found it! I've found it!"

He is a dedicated man who works not for money or fame or self-glory, but—like Madam Curie, Einstein, Oppenheimer, Salk—for the benefit of mankind and the welfare of his country. Through his work people will be healthier and live longer, they will have new and better products to make life easier and pleasanter at home, and our country will be protected from enemies abroad. He will soon make possible travel to outer space.

The scientist is a truly wonderful man. Where would we be without him? The future rests on his shoulders.

NEGATIVE SIDE OF THE IMAGE OF THE SCIENTIST

The scientist is a brain. He spends his days indoors, sitting in a laboratory, pouring things from one test tube into another. His work is uninteresting, dull, monotonous, tedious, time consuming, and, though he works for years, he may see no results or may fail, and he is likely to receive neither adequate recompense nor recognition. He may live in a cold-water flat; his laboratory may be dingy.

If he works by himself, he is alone and has heavy expenses. If he works for a big company, he has to do as he is told, and his discoveries must be turned over to the company and may not be used; he is just a cog in a machine. If he works for the government, he has to keep dangerous secrets; he is endangered by what he does and by constant surveillance and by continual investigations. If he loses touch with people, he may lose the public's confidence—as did Oppenheimer. If he works for money or self-glory he may take credit for the work of others —as some tried to do to Salk. He may even sell secrets to the enemy.

His work may be dangerous. Chemicals may explode. He may be hurt by radiation, or may die. If he does medical research, he may bring home disease, or may use himself as a guinea pig, or may even accidentally kill someone.

He may not believe in God or may lose his religion. His belief that man is descended from animals is disgusting (6).

He is a brain; he is so involved in his work that he doesn't know what is going on in the world. He has no other interests and neglects his body for his mind. He can only talk, eat, breathe, and sleep science.

He neglects his family—pays no attention to his wife, never plays with his children. He has no social life, no other intellectual interest, no hobbies or relaxations. He bores his wife, his children and their friends—for he has no friends of his own or *knows only other scientists —with incessant talk that no one can understand;* or else *he pays no attention or has secrets he cannot share. He is never home. He is always reading a book. He brings home work and also bugs and creepy things. He is always running off to his laboratory. He may force his children to become scientists also.*

A scientist should not marry. No one wants to be such a scientist or to marry him.

DISCUSSION

The "official" image of the scientist—the answer which will be given without personal involvement—which was evoked primarily in form I, but which recurs in the answers to all three forms, is a positive one.

The scientist is seen as being essential to our national life and to the world; he is a great, brilliant, dedicated human being, with powers far beyond those of ordinary men, whose patient researches without regard to money or fame lead to medical cures, provide for technical progress, and protect us from attack. We need him and we should be grateful for him.

Thus if no more than form I had been asked, it would have been possible to say that the attitude of American high-school students to science is all that might be desired.

But this image in all its aspects, the shared, the positive, and the negative, is one which is likely to invoke a negative attitude as far as personal career or marriage choice is concerned. While the rejection in the negative image is, of course, immediately clear, the positive image of very hard, only occasionally rewarding, very responsible work is also one which, while it is respected, has very little attraction for young Americans today (7). They do not wish to commit themselves to long-time perspectives, to dedication, to single absorbing purposes, to an abnormal relationship to money, or to the risks of great responsibility. These requirements are seen as far too exacting. The present trend is toward earlier marriage, early parenthood, early enjoyment of an adult form of life, with the career choice of the man and the job choice of the woman, if any, subordinated to the main values of life—good human relations, expressed primarily

in terms of the family and of being and associating with the kind of
human being who easily relates to other people.

To the extent that any career—that of diplomat, lawyer, business-
man, artist, aviator—is seen as antithetical to this contemporary set
of values, it will repel male students as a career choice and girls as a
career for their future husbands. But it is important to see also the
particular ways in which the image of a scientific career conflicts
with contemporary values. It divides girls and boys. The boys, when
they react positively, include motives which do not appeal to the girls
—adventure, space travel, delight in speed and propulsion; the girls,
when they react positively, emphasize humanitarianism and self-
sacrifice for humanity, which do not appeal to the boys. The girls reject science, both as a possible form of work for themselves, concerned with things rather than with people, with nonliving things
(laboratory animals, not live animals; parts of anatomy, not living
children), and for their husbands, because it will separate them,
give their husbands absorbing interests which they do not share,
and involve them in various kinds of danger. In earlier periods, when
career choices and marriages occurred later, the girls' attitudes
might not have mattered so much; they are very important today,
on the one hand, because girls represent a principal untapped source
of technical skill, and, on the other hand, because, with present adolescent [387] social patterns, paired boys and girls spend a great
deal of time discussing the style of their impending marriage and
parenthood and the relationship of the boy's career choice to the kind
of home they will have.

The image of the scientist's relationship to money also presents a
problem, in a period of full employment, to young people who think
that an adequate income is something that should be taken for
granted. The scientist is seen as having an abnormal relationship to
money. He is seen either as in danger of yielding to the temptation of
"money and fame," or as starving and poor because of his integrity.
The number of ways in which the image of the scientist contains ex-
tremes which appear to be contradictory—too much contact with
money or too little; being bald or bearded; confined work indoors, or
traveling far away; talking all the time in a boring way, or never
talking at all—all represent deviations from the accepted way of life,

from being a normal friendly human being, who lives like other people and gets along with other people.

SPECIFIC INDICATIONS ABOUT THE TEACHING OF SCIENCE

From the standpoint of teaching, it is important to realize how the present image of scientific work lacks any sense of the delights of intellectual activity; the scientist works patiently and carefully for years, and only when he finds out something does he shout with joy. This lack of any sense that intellectual activity is rewarding in itself can be related to the lack of any mention of living things, plant, animal, or human, in the materials with which the scientist is believed to work. Plants and animals appear only as dead objects for dissection; the human body, as organs or systems studied in the laboratory and treated in medicine; whole human beings appear only as the dead denizens of dead and buried cities, and most of the scientists about whom they read are also dead. The lack of any sense of enjoyment can also be related to the central role given to mathematics as a tool, without any emphasis on the delights of observation, as in early natural history studies or in the perception of regularities and connections in the world around them, or between themselves and the world around them.

Because the materials were analyzed class by class and school by school, the study has also yielded, as a by-product, certain sidelights on science teaching: on the importance of participation as opposed to passive watching, on the role which the personality of the teacher plays in attitudes toward science, on the effect on the rest of the class of the presence in it of one type of exceptionally gifted child.

One of the most recurrent responses is an expression of active boredom, the phrase, "I am not interested in science," or in a particular science course (chemistry or physics), followed occasionally by highly emotional expressions of fury and hatred of particular activities which are being demonstrated. "Interest" and "active enjoyment" seem to be so closely related that the student seated in a classroom who has to watch things being poured from one test tube to another or listen to a string of unrelated facts becomes permanently alienated. General science courses seem to be the ones in which this attitude toward science is characteristically invoked, except when a gifted teacher gives it some special emphasis. When mathematics is seen as the key ability on which all future scientific work is based, not liking and not being able to do mathematics become a specially weak point in the circle of the students' interests.

In contrast, other activities are defined as nonscientific because they are absorbingly interesting: "watching things grow that I have planted," or "working on my hot rod car."

The role of the teacher—as reflected in the comments of a whole class—is an exceedingly interesting one. The disliked teacher is personalized and vivid, but the teacher who has obviously been very successful and has caught the imagination and enthusiasm of the whole class does not emerge as a person at all but, instead, sinks into the background of good classroom conditions, together with "good laboratory equipment." Special aspects of the disliked teacher are commented on in detail. He may be described as an outsider, a stranger, with unusual habits of dress and manner, who does not know his subject well, who cannot talk about anything but his subject, who lives alone without the slightest tie to the community, who is "stuck-up and who is too busy for anyone but himself." It is easy to see how the only male teacher in the school presents special problems to the boys, if he himself is a figure they reject, and how easily the sphere of work for which he stands may be rejected also. So one boy writes, "Anyone who digs our teacher's gab is a square as well as being queer." Some of these consequences undoubtedly flow from the convention in the United States that, ideally, science should be taught by men, with the result that men who might be more successful teachers in some other field are forced into teaching a subject which they dislike and in which they have no special competence. Similarly, foreigners and refugees—if male—may have a better chance to get positions as mathematics and science teachers than they have in other fields (8).

The significance of the lack of particular mention of the good science teacher is equally important, for it is related to the lack of invocation of authority by the students, who state their opinions about science—even those obviously related to a particular teacher—as their own. Only when they disagree, when they wish to attack the current image of science as a good thing from a minority position—that is, from the viewpoint of some fundamentalist religious position which they accept—do they invoke authority. It is related also to the situation in American culture where, through generations, there has been a break between immigrant parent and native-born child. In this new setting, the European tendency for children to identify with the personality and occupation of the parents has been replaced by a tendency to follow the style set by members of one's own generation, especially those in one's own local school clique.

In the classroom, a disliked fellow-student who is regarded as a future scientist may also be described in some detail, as students say they do not want to be the kind of scientists who "go about with their noses in a book, looking superior." But in those classrooms where everyone has been committed to the joy of some experiment or project, no individuals emerge: it is impossible to say what is the sex, age, nationality, and personality of the teacher.

In summary, it may be said that where science teaching is successful, the teacher has created a situation in which his or her (one does not know which) personality sinks into the background, and in which no one student stands out as so especially gifted and preoccupied as to rouse annoyance in the class. Students and teacher appear to have worked as a group, accepting science as a part of *their* lives, preoccupied with no specific identified individuals.

RECOMMENDATIONS

Mass media. Straight across the country there is a reflection of the mass media image of the scientist, which shares with the school materials the responsibility for the present image. Alterations in the mass media can have important consequences in correcting the present distorted image if such changes are related to real conditions. Attempts to alter the image, in which the public relations department of a particular company represents its research personnel with crew cuts and five children may improve the recruitment program of single companies, [388] but do so only at the expense of intensifying the negative aspects of the image for the country as a whole.

What is needed in the mass media is more emphasis on the real, human rewards of science—on the way in which scientists today work in groups, share common problems, and are neither "cogs in a machine" nor "lonely" and "isolated." Pictures of scientific activities of groups, working together, drawing in people of different nations, of both sexes and all ages, people who take delight in their work, could do a great deal of good.

The mass media could also help to break down the sense of discontinuity between *the scientist* and other men, by showing science as a field of endeavor in which many skills, applied and pure, skills of observation and of patient, exact tabulation, flashes of insight, delight in the pure detail of handling a substance or a material, skills in orchestrating many talents and temperaments, are all important. This would help to bring about an understanding of science as a part of life, not divorced from it, a vineyard in which there is a place for many kinds of workers.

The schools. The material suggests the following changes which might be introduced in educational planning.

1) Encourage more participation and less passive watching in the classroom, less repeating of experiments the answers to which are known; give more chance to the students to feel that they are doing it themselves. A decrease in the passive type of experience found in many general science courses seems particularly necessary.

2) Begin in the kindergarten and elementary grades to open children's eyes to the wonder and delight in the natural world, which can then supply the motive power for enjoyment of intellectual life later. This would also establish the idea of science as concerned with living things and with immediate—as contrasted with distant—human values.

3) Teach mathematical principles much earlier, and throughout the teaching of mathematics emphasize nonverbal awareness (9): let children have an opportunity to rediscover mathematical principles for themselves.

4) Emphasize group projects; let the students have an opportunity to see science as team work, where minds and skills of different sorts complement one another.

5) Emphasize the need for the teacher who enjoys and is proficient in science subjects, irrespective of that teacher's sex; this would mean that good women teachers could be enlisted instead of

depending on men, irrespective of their proficiency. Since it would seem that the boys do not need to identify with an adult male as a teacher, this should leave us free to draw on women as a source of science teachers.

6) Change the teaching and counseling emphasis in schools which now discourages girls who are interested in science. This would have many diffuse effects: on the supply of women teachers and of women in engineering, on the attitudes of girls who are helping boys to choose careers, and on the attitudes of mothers who are educating their small children in ways which may make or mar their ability to deal with the world in scientific terms.

7) Deemphasize individual representatives of science, both outstanding individuals like Einstein—whose uniqueness simply convinces most students that they can never be scientists—and the occasional genius-type child in a class. (This type of child, who represents only one kind of future scientist and who is often in very special need of protection from the brutalities of his age mates, should probably be taken out of small, low-level schools, and placed in a more protected and intellectual environment.) Instead, emphasize the sciences as fields, and the history of science as a great adventure of mankind as a whole. (The monotonously recurrent statement "if it weren't for scientists we would still be living in caves" is an insult to the memory of millions of anonymous men who have—each in his way—made further advances possible.)

8) Avoid talking about *the scientist, science,* and *the scientific method.* Use instead the names of the sciences—biology, physics, physiology, psychology—and speak of what a biologist or a physicist does and what the many different methods of science are—observation, measurement, hypotheses-generating, hypotheses-testing, experiment.

9) Emphasize the life sciences and living things—not just laboratory animals, but also plants and animals in nature—and living human beings, contemporary peoples, living children—not the bones and dust of dead cities and records in crumbling manuscripts. Living things give an opportunity for wonder and humility, necessarily less present in the laboratory where students deal with the inanimate and the known, and contact with living things counteracts the troubling implication that the scientist is all powerful.

CONCLUSION

This report is not in any way a statement of the proportion of high-school students who will choose science as a career. It is a discussion of the state of mind of fellow-students, among whom the occasional future scientist must go to school, of the degree of personal motivation necessary to commit oneself to science, and of the atmosphere within which the science teacher must teach. Since most high-school students' attitudes closely reflect those of their parents, it is also an indication of the climate of opinion in which parents may be expected to back up their children in choosing science as a career, citizens may be expected to vote funds for new laboratories, and voters may be expected to judge Congressional appropriations for science education.

References and Notes

1. To control any possible influence which the wording of this statement might have, part of sample B was collected without reference to the association. No difference in the formulation of the replies was found when the association was mentioned and when the association was not mentioned.
2. In six of the schools included in sample B, all three forms—to be used by different classes—were sent to the same school.
3. There are a number of different quantitative studies of the broader subject under way: those directed by H. H. Remmers in the Division of Educational Reference at Purdue University, on high-school students' attitudes toward science; a study at the Survey Research Center at the University of Michigan on attitudes of the public toward science writing; two studies under the Science Manpower Project at Teachers College, Columbia University, one by Hugh Allen, on "Attitudes toward science and scientific careers: a research inventory for New Jersey high-school seniors," and a second by Frances Hall, on science teachers' attitudes toward science. The Interim Committee on Studies on the Social Perception of the Satellite Program and Personnel, under the chairmanship of Donald Michael of Dunlap Associates, Stamford, will also cover some overlapping areas.
4. For assistance in this study through the Institute for Intercultural Studies, which cooperated with the American Association for the Advancement of Science, we wish to thank Ruth Bunzel, Edith Cobb,

Natalie Joffe, Martha Wolfenstein, Mark Zborowsky, also graduate students in Columbia University anthropology courses GS 271–2 and GS 198, and, for criticism of the report, Robert Weiss of the Survey Research Center, University of Michigan.

5. A few of the more mature students realize that this picture is stereotyped and incomplete. So, for instance, having described the scientist as the "man in the white coat," students continue: "On second thought—he might equally well be seining a small stream, feeding facts into an electronic computer, or injecting a radioactive fluid into the veins of a monkey" (boy, 17, 12th grade). "I realize that there is more than microbiology [that is, the man in the white coat] to science. Therefore, I think of the atom, and somehow always of old men, working on various bombs and reactors. When I think of the use of atoms for peace, I think of young men working in offices. I don't know why" (girl, 14, 10th grade). "At the word *science*, I can imagine so much. The scope is unlimited and I sometimes do not connect the two words [*science* and *scientist*] any further than the laboratory. But if I could put the two together, a scientist would become more of an adventurer, a romanticist, than a figure who is nothing but a human IBM machine" (boy, 15, 10th grade).

6. When evolution is mentioned, it is mentioned negatively. It is impossible to tell what the absence of other than negative references to evolution means. In Remmers' study [H. H. Remmers and D. H. Radler, *The American Teenager* (Bobbs-Merrill, Indianapolis, Ind., 1957), p. 171] 40 percent of the teenagers checked "No," to the statement "Man has [389] evolved from lower forms of animals"; another 24 percent checked "Don't know"; 35 percent checked "Yes."

7. In this statement, we draw not only on the attitudes in this study but on a wide variety of other materials on the attitudes of contemporary young Americans.

8. The other side of this picture is sometimes seen in comments made by foreigners who have entered the sciences because Americans think they require less of a knowledge of the culture, and who because of their science training can get teaching positions in the schools. After a year or two of teaching in small-town schools, the foreign-born teacher flees back to the cities where he has friends or at least can live anonymously. (Based on life-history data from Chinese informants in the Chinese section of the Study Program in Human Health and the Ecology of Man, New York Hospital—Cornell Medical College, New York.)

9. Studies of the College Entrance Examination Board Commission on
   Mathematics and the University of Illinois Committee on School
   Mathematics give promise of bringing about improvement in mathematics instruction. A study of junior-high-school mathematics will
   be undertaken at the University of Maryland this fall. There is
   more to be done, especially in the elementary grades, and state departments of education should be encouraged to establish state committees which can determine how work now in progress at the
   national level can be made effective in local schools. The Poloidi-
   blocs, developed by Margaret Lowenfeld of the Institute of Child
   Psychology, 6 Pembridge Villas, London, W.11, are an important
   addition to the equipment for teaching young children mathematics.

Science and the high-school student

LETTERS TO THE EDITOR OF *SCIENCE*
Science, December 6, 1957, pp. 1200–1201

There seems to be much likelihood that the definitive results of Mead and Métraux's study of the "Image of the Scientist Among High-School Students" [*Science* 126, 384 (1957)] will be considered as applying only to high-school students and scientists. Since almost all the appropriate age group attends high school these days, Mead and Métraux's sample is essentially a sample of that age group of the whole population. It is unlikely that this image of the scientist changes much with age. Hence, one concludes that the man in the street has very much the same image. Let us not censure high-school students, even by implication only, for sharing public opinion. The high-schooler who plans to become a scientist has about the same relation to his fellow students as the adult scientist has to his fellow citizens. He may as well get used to it while he is young.

It is likely that the same sort of results would have been obtained regarding physicians, ministers, nurses, or any other dedicated group of people. This not-for-me attitude is directed at the dedication, not at the profession. In view of the fact that about 90 percent of the population has an IQ of less than 120, the not-for-me attitude is common-sense realism, and the high-schoolers are to be congratulated on their good sense.

I suggest an unscientific generalization of the title to "Image of the Dedicated Minority as Seen by the Undedicated Majority."

M. J. Walker

Storrs, Connecticut

In his comment on our article, M. J. Walker has combined three themes—the rejection of dedication, the extent to which the high-school student's attitude coincides with that of the man in the street, and the reasonableness of students with an IQ of less than 120 rejecting science as a career. As we pointed out, rejection of dedication in all fields of science is a characteristic of the attitude of post-World War II youth; it would extend to any profession which was seen as requiring an extreme degree of commitment. We know of no material that suggests that rejection of dedication and low IQ are systematically related [1200] and believe that there would be variations as the career in question was phrased as more or less intellectually demanding. While the attitude of today's high-school students may be said to prefigure the attitudes of the man in the street tomorrow, it is necessary also to recognize that these students have been exposed, rather more than their forebears, to articulate and concerted attempts to involve them in scientific careers, and so they may differ somewhat from their seniors today. The report is not in any sense designed to blame the high-school students but rather to focus attention on the one-sidedness of a picture of the scientific life which overemphasizes the gap between those who do and those who do not participate in it.

Margaret Mead
Rhoda Métraux

New York, New York

Exercises and theme topics

EXERCISE I. STATEMENT OF PURPOSE, THESIS SENTENCE, AND TOPIC SENTENCE

Any example of expository writing, whether it be your own theme or an article such as those included in this volume, concentrates upon a central idea, or thesis, which the author wants to discuss. To introduce this central idea, the writer may use one (or both) of two methods early in his paper. He may make a *statement of purpose* that will describe and set forth the limitations of his topic, or he may present a *thesis sentence* that he proceeds to develop. For example, in "Science —The Endless Adventure" (see p. 163), Lee A. DuBridge states the purpose and limitations of his article when he explains:

I propose to examine not the superstructure that men have erected on the foundation of knowledge, but the foundation itself. I am not going to explore the glittering upper rooms and towering pinnacles of technology—I propose to go to the basement and examine the foundations of science on which all technology is based.

And I propose to discuss first about science not in the light of the new technology to which it may lead, but to talk about science for its own sake—science as a method of thinking, science as a method of acquiring new knowledge, science as the key to understanding, the road to comprehension of the physical world. I am going to discuss science, the endless adventure.[1]

Immediately the readers know not only the subject matter of the article, but also Du Bridge's attitude toward his topic. This *statement of purpose* is of particular value to the student working on a reference paper, for he can tell at once if the article will be relevant to his own project.

In "Responsibilities of Scientists in the Atomic Age" (see p. 117), Eugene Rabinowitch achieves the same result by employing a *thesis sentence:*

[1] Lee A. DuBridge, "Science—The Endless Adventure," *Bulletin of the Atomic Scientists,* XIII (March 1957), 74.

In our time, when science has become an important force, affecting both the life of the individual and the fate of society, scientists have acquired a peculiar responsibility, originating from their special knowledge and the power associated with it. What is it?[2]

Notice how the question emphasizes the statement; the remainder of the paper answers the question and thereby elaborates upon the *thesis sentence*. Notice, however, that both the *statement of purpose* and the *thesis sentence* merely introduce, focus upon, the central idea of the article; they do not present the author's conclusions.

The central idea of any expository paper divides into a number of organic parts—the exact number depending upon the manner in which the writer organizes and presents his material—each of which he indicates by a *topic sentence*. Each part of the paper will thus become an elaboration of the topic (or phase of the whole). In your own shorter papers, these divisions may serve as the basis for paragraphing. In longer selections, each may be made up of a number of paragraphs. Indeed, even then each paragraph may have a *topic sentence*, although often it may be omitted at that level.

For the reader and student taking notes on an article the value of discovering these constructions lies in that they provide the skeleton, the outline, of the article.

Assignments

1. What *statement of purpose* and/or *thesis sentence* do Mead and Métraux make in "Image of the Scientist Among High-School Students"? What are their *topic sentences*?
2. Examine the essays in Part II, "The Nature of Science and the Scientific Method," to find which authors use a *statement of purpose*, a *thesis sentence*, or both. In any one essay find the *topic sentences*.
3. Write a *statement of purpose* for an article in Part II which does not use one. Write a *thesis sentence* for an article which does not use one.

EXERCISE II. PROCESS: HOW TO DO IT AND HOW IT IS DONE

Because expository writing involves essentially explanation—the giving of information about your subject—one of its special func-

---

[2] Eugene Rabinowitch, "Responsibilities of Scientists in the Atomic Age," *Bulletin of the Atomic Scientists*, XV (January 1959), 2.

tions is to give directions. This type of exposition is known as the *process* paper. Each time someone asks you how to find a highway, a street, an address, you answer by outlining a *process*. First, he must go to the second stoplight; then turn right; third; fourth; and so on. Whether you tell someone how to follow a recipe, how to improve his golf game, or how to dissect a frog, you deal with *process*. Notice, as in the example above, that the basic feature of this type of exposition is its chronological organization—first, second, third—for each step must be taken in its proper order. Notice also that at this level you deal with personal experience; by and large, you delineate some relatively complex action which you yourself have performed.

This personal element provides at once the strength and possible weakness of the *process* paper. Keep in mind that your reader may not have had the same or similar experience; you must discuss each step fully and clearly so that no confusion results. All too often familiarity with the subject breeds lack of clarity, overconciseness, and the use of technical terms that are not defined. Since the ideas and actions are clear in your own mind, you assume wrongly that mere mention of them to the reader will call forth your own body of experience. This is, of course, impossible. Remembering this potential difficulty, you should be sure to include complete details and necessary definitions. Most important, however, explain each step of the procedure so that your reader will understand *why* certain actions must be taken at a given time.

On many occasions you will wish to discuss more complicated *processes* with which you have little or no direct experience. For example, you may choose to report upon the *process* by which candidates are selected at the conventions of political parties; upon steps necessary in preparing and launching an ICBM or a satellite; or upon the steps taken in producing some finished product, like a TV set or aluminum. This type of paper is called the "how it is done" paper, and its chief function is to inform its readers, for in all probability neither you nor the readers will ever perform all of the actions involved. The same suggestions regarding effectiveness apply to this paper, even more so perhaps, because you must substitute fullness of detail for the vividness of personal experience. Again the basic organization is chronological, and the understanding of each step remains essential.

Notice that before Mead and Métraux present the findings of their survey of high school students, they devote nearly half of the article to a discussion of their aims and methods. Here, too, is a *process*. As in any simple or complex action, it has its objectives (to bake a cake, to launch a missile, to find out certain information) and its procedures. Moreover, as in the delineation of any *process*, the presentation of step-by-step procedure helps the reader to judge the effectiveness and validity of the results. It is perhaps not only as a report, a description, of procedure but also as a basis for evaluation of procedure and results that the *process* theme has its greatest value.

Assignments

1. In carrying through their survey, what steps did Mead and Métraux take? Is each one reported effectively? Could any one (or more) be omitted from the article without damaging the article's effectiveness? Should any steps have been added?
2. Draw upon your personal experience to write a "how to do it" paper. Choose a topic such as setting up an experiment in a laboratory, writing an outside theme, or performing some action connected with a particular interest of yours.
3. Write a "how it is done" theme.
4. In discussing the scientific method, do the authors of the selections in Part II describe a *process*? Analyze one such account in the manner suggested for the Mead-Métraux article in Assignment 1 above.

THEME TOPICS

1. Does your personal attitude and that of your friends agree or disagree with the findings of Mead and Métraux? (This paper should be limited to a discussion either of the image of the scientist or of the criticism and recommendations regarding the teaching of science.)
2. From the Mead and Métraux article and articles in Part IV, "Science and Education," what picture do you gain of the American student? Do you believe that this portrait is justified? Why is it adequate or inadequate?
3. Assuming that you have an interest in and talent for scientific research and mathematics, why would you choose or reject a career in science?

4. Why would you marry or not marry a scientist?
5. Are M. J. Walker's inferences regarding the man in the street justified? Why are they adequate or inadequate? Do Mead and Métraux answer him effectively?
6. Mead and Métraux speak of "an official image of the scientist" [p. 384] which differs from the students' personal views of the scientist. Do you agree or disagree that such an "official image" exists in the mind of the American public? If you do agree, what sources (for example, newspapers, movies, government agencies) have created it? How does it differ from your personal image of the scientist?
7. Are the problems cited in the section of the article entitled "Specific Indications About the Teaching of Science" the same ones emphasized by the authors represented in Part IV? If there are differences, how do you account for them?
8. Are the recommendations made in the article regarding the teaching of science in the future the same ones made by the authors represented in Part IV? If there are differences, how do you account for them?

part II — THE NATURE OF SCIENCE AND
THE SCIENTIFIC METHOD

Science and technology in the last decade

JAMES B. CONANT

Modern Science and Modern Man. New York: Columbia University Press, 1952, pp. 18–30*

. . . Now I should like to examine a little more closely the procedures employed by the scientists today in physics, [18] in chemistry, in biology, and in the application of science for practical ends in the whole area of the natural sciences. If in so doing, I appear to be underlining the obvious, I hope I shall be forgiven; for although a discussion of the so-called scientific method is almost a standard topic in a university, what I have to say is so antithetical to much of the current doctrine that I venture to present it in some detail here.

It would be my thesis that those historians of science, and I might add philosophers as well, who emphasize that there is no such thing as *the* scientific method are doing a public service. To my mind, some of the oversimplified accounts of science and its workings to be found in the elementary texts in high schools, for example, are based on a fallacious reading of the history of physics, chemistry, and biology. I will not attempt to trace back the sources of what seems to some of us a set of erroneous conclusions. Let me rather present my own analysis of the nature of science, if I may.

In order to produce a straw man that I may knock down, let me quote a definition of the scientific method written some years ago in an elementary text of chemistry of which I am a joint author: "The scientific way of thinking requires the habit of facing reality quite unprejudiced by any earlier conceptions. Accurate observation and dependence upon experiments are the guiding principles. The watchword is not 'what does the book say about this or that, but let's try to find out for ourselves.' " Then follows an account of the steps in the process of finding out. Such accounts in many textbooks, including the one [19] I helped to write, usually run as follows: "Scientists collect their facts by carefully observing what is happening. They group them and try to interpret them in the light of other facts that are already known. Then a scientist sets up a theory or picture that will explain the newly discovered facts, and finally he tests out his theory by getting more data of a similar kind and comparing them with the facts he got through the earlier experiments. When his theory does not quite fit the facts, he must modify it and at the same time verify the facts by getting more data."

Another and more sophisticated account by a biologist is entitled "Steps in the Scientific Method." Note the use of the word "the" rather than the plural "scientific methods." Here the steps are listed: "Recognize that an indeterminate situation exists. This is a conflicting or obscure situation demanding inquiry. Two, state the problem in specific terms. Three, formulate a working hypothesis. Four, devise a controlled method of investigation by observation . . . or by experimentation or both. Five, gather and record the testimony or 'raw data.' Six, transform these raw data into a statement having meaning and significance. Seven, arrive at an assertion which appears to be warranted. If the assertion is correct, predictions may be made from it. Eight, unify the warranted assertion, if it proves to be new knowledge in science, with the body of knowledge already established."

The simplified account from my own elementary textbook and the more sophisticated version of the biologist, I have become convinced, serve only to confuse a layman. [20] The basic fault is a failure to distinguish between two closely related activities which together have made the history of science possible. As I now read the story of the advances that have been made in the natural sciences since the time of Galileo, what has happened is essentially this. An age-old process of inquiry by which artisans and skillful workers improved the methods of handling inanimate nature became gradually associated with the type of thinking up to then characteristic of mathematics. Another way of putting it is to say that two streams of human activity, separated until the sixteenth century, gradually came together. These were abstract reasoning, as represented by Euclidian geometry, and experimentation, as represented by the work of the metallurgists who over the generations had improved the methods of winning metals from the ores.

Closely related to abstract reasoning were the broad speculative ideas of philosophers about the nature of the universe: of these the Aristotelian picture was predominant in the Middle Ages. A rival conceptual scheme associated with the name of Democritus was never wholly lost to view. Those who followed this line of thought imagined that the world was composed of corpuscles or atoms.

The usual descriptions of "the scientific method" are descriptions actually of the very limited procedure by which a person can improve a particular practical art. Indeed, if we take any one of these descriptions, we can apply it to almost any practical problems that arise in this mechanized age at home. Take the eight steps so [21] carefully set forth by the biologist and apply them to the failure of an electric light to go on in one's country house. Certainly there is an indeterminate situation—something is wrong. The problem can be stated in specific terms, namely, when I turn the switch, the light does not work. What can be found that can be changed in order to make the light work when I turn it on? As to the working hypotheses, the first one will perhaps be that the bulb is burned out. The method of investigation is obvious: you try replacing the bulb with another—and the controlled experiment here is to see that the other bulb does light in a proper socket—you arrive at an assertion that is warranted, and the new knowledge easily fits into what you had before. Or you know by experience that it is more likely that the fuse is blown out, in which case you formulate another working hypothesis and make the test by turning on another light on the same circuit. In short, much of the so-called scientific method consists of rational experimentation or well-ordered inquiry directed towards solving a specific practical problem.

Now more than one teacher has pointed out to his or her class that, after all, the scientific method can be applied to everyday life and has used examples such as I have given. But I think this form of exposition is really putting the cart before the horse. The point is that what the scientist does in his laboratory is simply to carry over, into another frame of reference, habits that go back to the caveman. We can imagine, for example, that one of our early ancestors tried the impact of fire on various kinds of minerals, probably starting from a chance observation, [22] and so gradually evolved a process of making a metal from an ore.

All this information is conveniently called "empirical," which means essentially cookbook information. John Tyndall, in a famous address[3] of a popular nature on fermentation, wrote, "Hitherto the art and practice of the brewer have resembled those of the physician, both being founded on empirical observation." (And I am giving this quotation to define my use of the word "empirical.") "By this is meant the observation of facts apart from the principles which explain them, and which give the mind an intelligent mastery over them. The brewer learned from long experience the conditions, not the reasons, of success. But he had to contend, and has still to contend, against unexplained perplexities."

At the time Tyndall was writing one could say that the art of wine making and beer manufacture was empirical. The work of Pasteur and subsequent microbiologists and chemists has greatly lowered the degree of empiricism. Still, even today, there are many procedures in these industries which are simply based on experience and cannot be related to the concepts or theories of chemistry or biology. It is convenient to characterize a given practical art or a branch of science by assigning to it a degree of empiricism. If one wants to find an activity where the degree of empiricism is very low, I suggest turning to the work of the surveyor. Long ago the science of optics was developed so that it is possible to [23] calculate by mathematical formulas the shapes of mirrors and lenses and to construct the optical part of a surveyor's instruments. Furthermore, Euclidian geometry provides a mathematical framework for the observations of the surveyor. Therefore, one can say that the surveyor's work represents an applied science in which the degree of empiricism is essentially zero. At the other end of the scale I would put the labors of any excellent cook, for in spite of all our knowledge of the chemistry of proteins, fats, and carbohydrates, the recipe for a good sauce or a good dessert is still entirely empirical.

I shall use this idea of the degree of empiricism repeatedly throughout these lectures. I introduce it at this time in order to tie

---

[3] Published in *Essays on the Floating-Matter of the Air in Relation to Putrefaction and Infection* (London: Longmans and Co., 1881), p. 238.

[Throughout the text footnotes are numbered as in the original articles. Therefore, where material has been omitted, the footnotes may not begin with number 1 (as here) or may not be consecutive.—EDITOR.]

together the work of the scientist and the inventor. In the heyday of the inventor, which I regard as being the nineteenth century, the elements of science at his disposal were relatively rudimentary and he was able, operating with those and with the aid of very little mathematics or elaborate theory, to apply the new knowledge by a series of largely empirical procedures.

Earlier I was dwelling on the new and revolutionary aspects of the relation between society and science. I pointed out that the man in the street—the public at large—had come to see that the scientist is today taking the place of the inventor; that the "long-haired" professors who were elaborating highly abstruse mathematical theories had been able to play an important part in the extraordinary development of the atomic bomb. Also, people are beginning to realize that in other fields as well, the lowering of the degree of empiricism of which [24] I have just spoken, that is, the application of theory to practice, has paid enormous dividends in terms of actual control of inanimate nature. Many hours could be spent relating the story of modern chemistry or our triumphs in electricity which follow this same pattern. The discovery of Wallace Carruthers which led to nylon fabric, the story of the development of various electronic devices, including the new solid material as a substitute for a vacuum tube—all these would illustrate the same point.

In emphasizing the distinction between developments in which new theories have played an important part and those based on essentially empirical procedures, I have perhaps done less than justice to one change which has been going on during the whole period of the growth of modern science. We have learned that there are ways in which empirical procedures can be improved without the introduction of theory. We have, as it were, empirically improved empiricism. The inventor in the last century working in his attic might more or less erratically try first this procedure and then that in order to get a better way of carrying out a step in his process, for there was no one to criticize him; if his methods were far from being effective, that was no one's business but his own. But when invention was replaced by the work of scientists in laboratories, then self-criticism was replaced by group criticism. People learned that if a specific problem is to be solved as rapidly as possible, accurate observations of each experiment should be kept; furthermore, even in trial-

and-error procedures there is a difference between well-ordered and disordered empiricism. Take the [25] simple homely example of finding out what is wrong with the electric light; we can all imagine procedures which systematically test one limited working hypothesis and then another or helter-skelter methods of operating where the same trial is repeated several times to no purpose.

What is often defined as the scientific method is nothing more or less than an approximate description of a well-ordered, systematized empirical[4] inquiry. Now, systematized or well-ordered empirical inquiries are one element in the advance of science; the other element is the use of new concepts, new conceptual schemes that serve as working hypotheses on a grand scale. Only by the introduction of a theoretical element can the degree of empiricism be reduced. Only by the use of new ideas of broad significance has science advanced—such ideas as those embodied in Newton's laws, as the notion that the earth is surrounded by a sea of air which exerts pressure, that light is a vibratory motion in an all-pervading ether, that matter is composed of atoms that unite in definite proportions to form compounds. The essential element in the advance of modern science has been the curious interplay between such theoretical notions and the experimentation of the artisan; through such an interplay scientists have built up a fabric of interconnected concepts and conceptual schemes.

Without unduly laboring the obvious, let me repeat: by well-ordered empirical procedures it has been possible [26] to make great progress in the practical arts. Such procedures are still being used in almost all branches of applied science. In metallurgy and organic chemistry, for example, the degree of empiricism is still high, but the development of new concepts and wide conceptual schemes was essential to the progress of physics, chemistry, and biology in the last three hundred and fifty years. As these sciences became equipped with more and more satisfactory theories, the degree of empiricism in the arts related to these sciences diminished. As a consequence, in these practical endeavors it became more and

---

[4] Any philosopher who happens to read these lectures will note that throughout I am using "empirical" and "empiricism" in a sense other than that to which he is accustomed; I am using these words as they are commonly employed by scientists (see p. 23).

more possible to attain the accuracy of prediction of such undertakings as those of the surveyor. The practical significance of the advance in theoretical science lies right here. The history of the last hundred and fifty years in particular shows what occurs when advances are made in pure science. New principles evolve which can be related to empirical observations; at that point it becomes possible to control with far greater accuracy than before what one is doing in the practical arts and to predict the outcome of a large-scale operation directed towards making a commercial product.

No better illustration of this can be found than in applied biology, the very field that John Tyndall was discussing. I referred to Tyndall's words which were concerned with the practical art of brewing. Explaining why the brewer could not proceed as long as his art was founded entirely upon empirical observations, he said, "But he had to contend and still has to contend against unexplained perplexities. Over and over again his care [27] has been rendered nugatory; his beer has fallen into acidity or rottenness and disastrous losses have been sustained of which he has been unable to assign the cause. It is the hidden enemies against which the physician and the brewer have hitherto contended that recent researches are dragging into the light of day, thus preparing the way for their final extermination." These researches had been instituted by Louis Pasteur in his study of fermentation. He had shown that living microorganisms were the "hidden enemies" with which the brewer had contended without knowing it. This knowledge was the consequence of a bold working hypothesis on a grand scale by Pasteur, namely, that fermentation and putrefaction were the consequences of the growth of microorganisms. Armed with his theory, Pasteur reduced the degree of empiricism in the whole range of fermentation industries. We accept the working hypothesis of Pasteur today as an established principle; we base all our procedures for handling food on the assumption of its correctness. Furthermore, this theory or principle is basic to medicine and public health. One need elaborate no further on this example of what theory can do to practice.

Let me give a reverse case where the failure to have any satisfactory theory has led to surprising consequences. I refer to the question of the action of chemicals on living organisms. In spite of an enormous amount of experimentation by chemists in making new substances and pharmacologists in testing them on animals and on men, one can say that it is almost impossible to predict the action of a chemical substance of a given structure on a [28] human being or on a microorganism. An adequate theory would enable one to write down the molecular architecture of a substance and from this structure predict the effect of the compound on a living organism. Such predictions are possible today only within very narrow limits and with very special classes of substances. And even here the correlation is essentially empirical—we have no broad, overall theory of drug action. Only within the last half a dozen years has some glimmering of hope appeared that chemotherapy can become a science.

To recapitulate, the inventor was largely an empiricist; he continued the tradition of the ingenious artisan. His place today has largely been taken by teams of scientists and engineers. To a considerable degree they likewise operate empirically; but their procedures are well ordered and systematized; they are disciplined by experience. In almost every field into which theory has been introduced, the degree of empiricism has been lessened. The teams of scientists in industry and in medicine are engaged both in reducing further the degree of empiricism and in applying the theories of science as they now stand. All this has become an organized social undertaking. As a sociological phenomenon modern science deserves careful study. Agriculture, medicine, public health, and the production of raw materials and their processing in industry are all interpenetrated heavily by well-trained empiricists using modern instruments to assist their trial-and-error experimentations. For the most part their success in advancing science, that is to say, developing new theories and testing these theories by experiment, are publicly recorded. Scientific [29] societies and scientific journals make this intercommunication possible. Destroy the social nature of scientific research in the sense of destroying the intercommunication of scientists, and the advance of science would almost cease. Recognizing this fact, one must ponder on the consequences of the vast sums of money now being spent on secret military research and development undertakings. One cannot help wondering how long a large fraction of our scientific manpower can be employed in this atypical scientific work without threatening the traditions that have made science possible.

The history of science demonstrates beyond a doubt that the really revolutionary and significant advances come not from empiricism but from new theories. The development of these theories, in turn, has in the past depended on free discussion of their consequences. How much can be accomplished behind a wall of secrecy remains to be determined. This wall represents public policy. I do not question its necessity in these grim years of rearmament. But it is essential that the public in free countries be aware constantly of its existence and understand the special conditions now imposed on some phases of an activity that industrialized societies can ill afford to damage: the advance of science. If this be fully realized, then the significance of one phase of the "recent developments in the physical sciences" can be better understood.

On "scientific method"

PERCY WILLIAMS BRIDGMAN

Reflections of a Physicist. New York: Philosophical Library, 1955, pp. 81–83

It seems to me that there is a good deal of ballyhoo about scientific method. I venture to think that the people who talk most about it are the people who do least about it. Scientific method is what working scientists do, not what other people or even they themselves may say about it. No working scientist, when he plans an experiment in the laboratory, asks himself whether he is being properly scientific, nor is he interested in whatever method he may be using *as method*. When the scientist ventures to criticize the work of his fellow scientist, as is not uncommon, he does not base his criticism on such glittering generalities as failure to follow the "scientific method," but his criticism is specific, based upon some feature characteristic of the particular situation. The working scientist is always too much concerned with getting down to brass tacks to be willing to spend his time on generalities.

Scientific method is something talked about by people standing on the outside and wondering how the scientist manages to do it. These people have been able to uncover various generalities applicable to at least most of what the scientist does, but it seems to me that these generalities are not very profound, [81] and could have been anticipated by anyone who knew enough about scientists to know what is their primary objective. I think that the objectives of all scientists have this in common—that they are all trying to get the correct answer to the particular problem in hand. This may be expressed in more pretentious language as the pursuit of truth. Now if the answer to the problem is correct there must be some way of knowing and proving that it is correct—the very meaning of truth implies the possibility of checking or verification. Hence the necessity for checking his results always inheres in what the scientist does. Furthermore, this checking must be exhaustive, for the truth of a general proposition may be disproved by a single exceptional case. A long experience has shown the scientist that various things are inimical to getting the correct answer. He has found that it is not sufficient to trust the word of his neighbor, but that if he wants to be sure, he must be able to check a result for himself. Hence the scientist is the enemy of all authoritarianism. Furthermore, he finds that he often makes mistakes himself and he must learn how to guard against them. He cannot permit himself any preconception as to what sort of results he will get, nor must he allow himself to be influenced by wishful thinking or any personal bias. All these things together give that "objectivity" to science which is often thought to be the essence of the scientific method.

But to the working scientist himself all this appears obvious and trite. What appears to him as [82] the essence of the situation is that he is not consciously following any prescribed course of action, but feels complete freedom to utilize any method or device whatever which in the particular situation before him seems likely to yield the correct answer. In his attack on his specific problem he suffers no inhibitions of precedent or authority, but is completely free to adopt any course that his ingenuity is capable of suggesting to him. No one standing on the outside can predict what the individual scientist will do or what method he will follow. In short, science is what scientists do, and there are as many scientific methods as there are individual scientists.

Is there a scientific method?

J. TURNER

Science, September 6, 1957, p. 431

The question of whether there is a scientific method produces a game that any number can play. If philosophers—with a knowledge of science limited for the most part to the finished product—can speak of a method, or even *the* method, then scientists—with first-hand experience in groping for new scientific ideas—can speak of as many methods as there are problems or even deny that in discovery there is such a thing as method at all. Yet, perhaps, a careful answer to the question would reveal that, despite differences in interest and emphasis, all the players are on the same side.

In broadest outline, science has as its purpose the discovery of true generalizations or laws of nature, these generalizations being used to explain particular happenings. For example, you explain the bursting of a particular water pipe in a particular house during a particular winter in terms of the severity of that winter and the generalization that water always expands on freezing. Or you explain the occurrence of a particular eclipse in terms of earlier positions and velocities of the planets and Newton's law of universal gravitation.

Method enters science in the business of how you go about increasing the probability that a given generalization is true. If you merely reel off a greater and greater number of positive instances, then you are using the wrong method. The unity underlying all inquiries is that to turn the trick you must seek other kinds of instances as well. Thus, to increase the probability that all A's are B's, you must not only examine joint occurrences of A and B but must seek out circumstances in which at least A is not present and circumstances in which at least B is not present. The classic, if not altogether complete, formulation of method in this sense was given by the 19th-century philosopher John Stuart Mill in his five canons of inductive inference.

44

An illustration in miniature of scientific method is Edward Whymper's explanation of the curious evaporation that invariably holds in the high Alps. Whymper, who is better known as the first man to scale the Matterhorn, would awake in the morning to discover that a considerable quantity of wine had disappeared from his flask during the night. Since the Chamonix porters in his party always vigorously denied having seen anyone touch the flask, there seemed no explanation of the event other than the unusual dryness of the high mountain air. But Whymper, by examining a circumstance in which, so to speak, neither A nor B was present, found a way to increase the probability of the truth of his suspicions, and, incidentally, to save his wine. He showed that the evaporation ceased completely when he used the flask as a pillow during the night.

In this illustration, there is reference to an underlying method, but there is no claim to an automatic procedure for solving problems. Of course, given a set of variables, A, B, C, and D, you can examine mechanically all possible combinations in a search for invariable relationships. But, to decide in the first place what variables are relevant to the problem requires an insight for which no rules are available.

The creative process

J. BRONOWSKI

Scientific American, 199 (September 1958), 59–65

The most remarkable discovery made by scientists is science it-self. The discovery must be compared in importance with the invention of cave-painting and of writing. Like these earlier human creations, science is an attempt to control our surroundings by entering into them and understanding them from inside. And like them, science has surely made a critical step in human development which cannot be reversed. We cannot conceive a future society without science.

I have used three words to describe these far-reaching changes: discovery, invention and creation. There are contexts in which one of these words is more appropriate than the others. Christopher Columbus discovered the West Indies, and Alexander Graham Bell invented the telephone. We do not call their achievements creations because they are not personal enough. The West Indies were there all the time; as for the telephone, we feel that Bell's ingenious thought was somehow not fundamental. The groundwork was there, and if not Bell then someone else would have stumbled on the telephone as casually as on the West Indies.

By contrast, we feel that *Othello* is genuinely a creation. This is not because *Othello* came out of a clear sky; it did not. There were Elizabethan dramatists before Shakespeare, and without them he could not have written as he did. Yet within their tradition *Othello* remains profoundly personal; and though every element in the play has been a theme of other poets, we know that the amalgam of these elements is Shakespeare's; we feel the presence of his single mind. The Elizabethan drama would have gone on without Shakespeare, but no one else would have written *Othello*.

There are discoveries in science like Columbus's, of something which was always there: the discovery of sex in plants, for example.

46

There are tidy inventions like Bell's, which combine a set of known principles: the use of a beam of electrons as a microscope, for example. In this article I ask the question: Is there anything more? Does a scientific theory, however deep, ever reach the roundness, the expression of a whole personality that we get from *Othello?*

A fact is discovered, a theory is invented; is any theory ever deep enough for it to be truly called a creation? Most nonscientists would answer: No! Science, they would say, engages only part of the mind—the rational intellect—but creation must engage the whole mind. Science demands none of that groundswell of emotion, none of that rich bottom of personality, which fills out the work of art.

This picture by the nonscientist of how a scientist works is of course mistaken. A gifted man cannot handle bacteria or equations without taking fire from what he does and having his emotions engaged. It may happen that his emotions are immature, but then so are the intellects of many poets. When Ella Wheeler Wilcox died, having published poems from the age of seven, *The Times* of London wrote that she was "the most popular poet of either sex and of any age, read by thousands who never open Shakespeare." A scientist who is emotionally immature is like a poet who is intellectually backward: both produce work which appeals to others like them, but which is second-rate.

I am not discussing the second-rate, and neither am I discussing all that useful but commonplace work which fills most of our lives, whether we are chemists or architects. There are in my laboratory of the British National Coal Board about 200 industrial scientists— pleasant, intelligent, sprightly people who thoroughly earn their pay. It is ridiculous to ask whether they are creators who produce works that could be compared with *Othello*. They are men with [59] the same ambitions as other university graduates, and their work is most like the work of a college department of Greek or of English. When the Greek departments produce a Sophocles, or the English departments produce a Shakespeare, then I shall begin to look in my laboratory for a Newton.

Literature ranges from Shakespeare to Ella Wheeler Wilcox, and science ranges from relativity to market research. A comparison must be of the best with the best. We must look for what is created

in the deep scientific theories: in Copernicus and Darwin, in
Thomas Young's theory of light and in William Rowan Hamilton's
equations, in the pioneering concepts of Freud, of Bohr and of
Pavlov.

The most remarkable discovery made by scientists, I have said, is
science itself. It is therefore worth considering the history of this discovery, which was not made all at once but in two periods. The first
period falls in the great age of Greece, between 600 B.C. and
300 B.C. The second period begins roughly with the Renaissance,
and is given impetus at several points by the rediscovery of Greek
mathematics and philosophy.

When one looks at these two periods of history, it leaps to the eye
that they were not specifically scientific. On the contrary: Greece between Pythagoras and Aristotle is still, in the minds of most scholars,
a shining sequence of classical texts. The Renaissance is still thought
of as a rebirth of art, and only specialists are uncouth enough to
link it also with what is at last being called, reluctantly, the Scientific Revolution. The accepted view of Greece and of the Renaissance is that they were the great creative periods of literature and
art. Now that we recognize in them also the two periods in which
science was born, we must surely ask whether this conjunction is accidental. Is it a coincidence that Phidias and the Greek dramatists
lived in the time of Socrates? Is it a coincidence that Galileo shared
the patronage of the Venetian republic with sculptors and painters?
Is it a coincidence that, when Galileo was at the height of his intellectual power, there were published in England in the span of 12 years
the following three works: the Authorized Version of the Bible, the
First Folio of Shakespeare and the first table of logarithms?

The sciences and the arts have flourished together. And they have
been fixed together as sharply in place as in time. In some way both
spring from one civilization: the civilization of the Mediterranean,
[60] which expresses itself in action. There are civilizations which
have a different outlook; they express themselves in contemplation,
and in them neither science nor the arts are practiced as such. For a
civilization which expresses itself in contemplation values no
creative activity. What it values is a mystic immersion in nature,
the union with what already exists.

The contemplative civilization we know best is that of the Middle Ages. It has left its own monuments, from the Bayeux Tapestry to the cathedrals; and characteristically they are anonymous. The Middle Ages did not value the cathedrals, but only the act of worship which they served. It seems to me that the works of Asia Minor and of India (if I understand them) have the same anonymous quality of contemplation, and like the cathedrals were made by craftsmen rather than by artists. For the artist as a creator is personal; he cannot drop his work and have it taken up by another without doing it violence. It may be odd to claim the same personal engagement for the scientist; yet in this the scientist stands to the technician much as the artist stands to the craftsman. It is at least remarkable that science has not flourished either in an anonymous age, such as the age of medieval crafts, or in an anonymous place, such as the craftsmanlike countries of the East.

The change from an outlook of contemplation to one of action is striking in the long transition of the Renaissance and the Scientific Revolution. The new men, even when they are churchmen, have ideals which are flatly opposed to the monastic and withdrawn ideals of the Middle Ages. Their outlook is active, whether they are artists, humanist scholars or scientists.

The new man is represented by Leonardo da Vinci, whose achievement has never, I think, been rightly understood. There is an obvious difference between Leonardo's painting and that of his elders— between, for example, an angel painted by him and one by Verrocchio. It is usual to say that Leonardo's angel is more human and more tender; and this is true, but it misses the point. Leonardo's pictures of children and of women are human and tender; yet the evidence is powerful that Leonardo liked neither children nor women. Why then did he paint them as if he were entering their lives? Not because he saw them as people, but because he saw them as expressive parts of nature. We do not understand the luminous and transparent affection with which Leonardo lingers on a head or a hand until we look at the equal affection with which he paints the grass and the flowers in the same picture.

To call Leonardo either a human or a naturalist painter does not go to the root of his mind. He is a painter to whom the detail of nature speaks aloud; for him, nature expresses herself in the detail. This is a view which other Renaissance artists had; they lavished care on perspective and on flesh tones because these seemed to them (as they had not seemed in the Bayeux Tapestry) to carry the message of nature. But Leonardo went further; he took this artist's vision into science. He understood that science as much as painting has to find the design of nature in her detail.

When Leonardo was born in 1452, science was still Aristotle's structure of cosmic theories, and the criticism of Aristotle in Paris and Padua was equally grandiose. Leonardo distrusted all large theories, and this is one reason why his experiments and machines have been forgotten. Yet he gave science what it most needed, the artist's sense that the detail of nature is significant. Until science had this sense, no one could care—or could think that it mattered—how fast two unequal masses fall and whether the orbits of the planets are accurately circles or ellipses.

The power which the scientific method has developed has grown from a procedure which the Greeks did not discover: the procedure of induction. This procedure is useless unless it is followed into the detail of nature; its discovery therefore flows from Leonardo's vision.

Francis Bacon in 1620 and Christian Huygens in 1690 set down the intellectual bases of induction. They saw that it is not possible to reach an explanation of what happens in nature by deductive steps. Every explanation goes beyond our experience and thereby becomes a speculation. Huygens says, and philosophers have sheepishly followed him in this, that an explanation should therefore be called probable. He means that no induction is unique; there is always a set—an infinite set—of alternatives between which we must choose.

The man who proposes a theory makes a choice—an imaginative choice which outstrips the facts. The creative activity of science lies here, in the process of induction. For induction imagines more than there is ground for and creates relations which at bottom can never be verified. Every induction is a speculation and it guesses at a unity which the facts present but do not strictly imply.

To put the matter more formally: A scientific theory cannot be constructed from the facts by any procedure which can be laid down in advance, as if for a machine. To the man who makes the theory, it may seem as inevitable as the ending of *Othello* must have seemed to Shakespeare. But the theory is inevitable only to him; it is his choice, as a mind and as a person, among the alternatives which are open to everyone.

There are scientists who deny what I have said—that we are free to choose between alternative theories. They grant that there are alternative theories, but they hold that the choice between them is made mechanically. The principle of choice, in their view, is Occam's Razor: we choose, among the theories which fit the facts we know now, that one which is simplest. On this view, Newton's laws were the simplest theory which covered the facts of gravitation as they were then [62]* known; and general relativity is not a new conception but is the simplest theory which fits the additional facts.

This would be a plausible view if it had a meaning. Alas, it turns out to be a verbal deception, for we cannot define simplicity; we cannot even say what we mean by the simpler of two inductions. The tests which have been proposed are hopelessly artificial and, for example, can compare theories only if they can be expressed in differential equations of the same kind. Simplicity itself turns out to be a principle of choice which cannot be mechanized.

Of course every innovator has thought that his way of arranging the facts is particularly simple, but this is a delusion. Copernicus's theory in his day was not simple to others, because it demanded two rotations of the earth—a daily one and a yearly one—in place of one rotation of the sun. What made his theory seem simple to Copernicus was something else: an esthetic sense of unity. The motion of all the planets around the sun was both simple and beautiful to him, because it expressed the unity of God's design. The same thought has moved scientists ever since: that nature has a unity, and that this unity makes her laws seem beautiful in simplicity.

The scientist's demand that nature shall be lawful is a demand for unity. When he frames a new law, he links and organizes phenomena which were thought different in kind; for example, general relativity links light with gravitation. In such a law we feel that the disorder of nature has been made to reveal a pattern, and that under the colored chaos there rules a more profound unity.

A man becomes creative, whether he is an artist or a scientist,

* Page 61 of the original text is a full-page illustration.—EDITOR

when he finds a new unity in the variety of nature. He does so by finding a likeness between things which were not thought alike before,
and this gives him a sense both of richness and of understanding.
The creative mind is a mind that looks for unexpected likenesses.
This is not a mechanical procedure, and I believe that it engages the whole personality in science as in the arts. Certainly I
cannot separate the abounding mind of Thomas Young (which
all but read the Rosetta Stone) from his recovery of the wave theory
of light, or the awkwardness of J. J. Thomson in experiment from his
discovery of the electron. To me, William Rowan Hamilton drinking
himself to death is as much part of his prodigal work as is any
drunken young poet; and the childlike vision of Einstein has a
poet's innocence.

When Max Planck proposed that the radiation of heat is discon-
tinuous, he seems to us now to have been driven by nothing but the
facts of experiment. But we are deceived; the facts did not go so
[63] far as this. The facts showed that the radiation is not continuous; they did not show that the only alternative is Planck's hail
of quanta. This is an analogy which imagination and history
brought into Planck's mind. So the later conflict in quantum physics
between the behavior of matter as a wave and as a particle is a conflict between analogies, between poetic metaphors; and each metaphor enriches our understanding of the world without completing it.

In *Auguries of Innocence* William Blake wrote:

> A dog starv'd at his Master's gate
> Predicts the ruin of the State.

This seems to me to have the same imaginative incisiveness, the
same understanding crowded into metaphor, that Planck had. And
the imagery is as factual, as exact in observation, as that on which
Planck built; the poetry would be meaningless if Blake used the
words "dog," "master" and "state" less robustly than he does.
Why does Blake say dog and not cat? Why does he say master and
not mistress? Because the picture he is creating depends on our factual grasp of the relation between dog and master. Blake is saying
that when the master's conscience no longer urges him to respect his
dog, the whole society is in decay. This profound thought came to
Blake again and again: that a morality expresses itself in what he

called its Minute Particulars—that the moral detail is significant of a society. As for the emotional power of the couplet, it comes, I think, from the change of scale between the metaphor and its application: between the dog at the gate and the ruined state. This is why Blake, in writing it, seems to me to transmit the same excitement that Planck felt when he discovered, no, when he created, the quantum.

One of the values which science has made natural to us is originality; as I said earlier, in spite of appearances science is not anonymous. The growing tradition of science has now influenced the appreciation of works of art, so that we expect both to be original in the same way. We expect artists as well as scientists to be forward-looking, to fly in the face of what is established, and to create not what is acceptable but what will become accepted. One result of this prizing of originality is that the artist now shares the unpopularity of the scientist: the large public dislikes and fears the way that both of them look at the world.

As a more important result, the way in which the artist looks at the world has come close to the scientist's. For example, in what I have written science is pictured as preoccupied less with facts than with relations, less with numbers than with arrangement. This new vision, the search for structure, is marked throughout the other articles in this issue of *Scientific American;* and it is also marked in modern art. Abstract sculpture often looks like an exercise in topology, exactly because the sculptor shares the vision of the topologist.

In each of the articles which follow I find again my view, that a theory is the creation of unity in what is diverse by the discovery of unexpected likenesses. In all of them innovation is pictured as an act of imagination, a seeing of what others do not see; indeed, Dr. Pierce uses the phrase "creative observation," which would outrage many theoretical scientists, but which exactly describes the pioneer vision of Leonardo. And Dr. Eccles gives me almost a physical feeling of creation, as if the structure of a theory reproduces the pattern of interlacing paths engaged in the brain.

There is, however, one striking division in these articles, between those [64] which treat the physical and those which treat the biological sciences. The physical scientists have more fun. Their theories are more eccentric; they live in a world in which the unexpected is everyday. This is a strange inversion of the way that we usually picture the dead and the living, and it reflects the age of these sciences. The physical sciences are old, and in that time the distance between fact and explanation has lengthened; their very concepts are unrealistic. The biological sciences are young, so that fact and theory look alike; the new entities which have been created to underlie the facts are still representational rather than abstract. One of the pleasant thoughts that these articles prompt is: How much more extravagant the biological sciences will become when they are as old as the physical sciences.

Exercises and theme topics

After reading an article or book, even though you have made detailed notes on it, you will want to have at hand a brief reference to its essential facts. Not only will you find such a record valuable during your research and the early organization of your paper, but also you may keep it permanently for use in other reports or class work. A *précis* provides a concise statement in your own words of the author's central thesis and conclusion(s). It does not interpret or evaluate, but merely reports the basic facts. In its simplest form it may do no more than state the thesis and conclusion in two or three sentences. For example, in "Liberal Education in a Scientific Age" (see p. 180), after Bentley Glass begins with an anecdote from Carl Becker's *Progress and Power,* he continues by giving a *précis* of that book:

Progress may be defined in terms of power, the augmentation of which was very slow in prehistoric times, developed rapidly after the advent of sword and pen, even more rapidly after the introduction of gunpowder and printing, and today, in the age of atomic energy and satellites, is accelerating exponentially into outer space. This augmentation of power is the principal theme of history—indeed, it may be essential to history.[1]

This idea provides the core of Becker's book. All else that he introduces grows out of it. So concise a *précis* as Glass's will be of value to you during the period of your research by recalling the writer's fundamental concept. After a period of time, however, it may lose much of its value because of its brevity. It is better, therefore, to augment such a statement with some presentation of the writer's supporting evidence, his line of reasoning, and his attitude toward his subject. Yet you must remember that you are not rewriting the book or article. You are condensing it into a brief summary. For

[1] Bentley Glass, "Liberal Education in a Scientific Age," *Bulletin of the Atomic Scientists,* XIV (November 1958), 346.

example, you might make a more fully developed *précis* of Percy W. Bridgman's "On 'Scientific Method' " in the following manner:

> In "On 'Scientific Method,' " Percy W. Bridgman asserts that the working scientist is too concerned with solving particular problems to generalize about *the* scientific method. The non-scientist, the "outsider" who does not fully understand the objective of science, has been the one to dogmatize about method. By emphasizing his categorical distinction between scientist and non-scientist, Bridgman frees the scientist to use any procedure that will help him find the correct answer to a problem. For Bridgman, then, the essence of scientific procedure lies in the scientist's ability to check, to verify, his results exhaustively since "a single exceptional case" may disprove a general proposition. In addition, any preconceptions or personal bias must be avoided in order to attain objectivity. As a result of this freedom, "there are as many scientific methods as there are individual scientists" (p. 83).

In contrast to the *précis*, the *critical summary* contains your evaluation of the book or article. Besides stating the essential facts, you should also give attention to such matters as the adequacy of the writer's evidence and illustrations, the logic of his arguments and conclusions, his objectivity or bias, and his qualification to write on the subject. When dealing with a technical or scholarly article or book, you may wish to refer to other works treating the same subject, although such reference is not always regarded as necessary.

Compare the following *critical summary* of Bridgman's article and the *précis* of it. Notice that the addition of your evaluation will of necessity lengthen your summary and make it more complex because of the difference in purpose and in presentation of material.

> In "On 'Scientific Method,' " the distinguished physicist, Percy W. Bridgman, wishes to destroy the oversimplified concept of *the* scientific method which the public has learned from its elementary textbooks. He maintains that the scientist is too concerned with solving particular problems to be interested in method "*as* method." Thus, far from being a rigid procedure, scientific method may vary with each individual scientist. What remains essential to the procedure is the scientist's ability to check, to verify, his results exhaustively. Also, he must rid himself of any preconceptions or personal bias in order to attain objectivity.
>
> Bridgman lessens the effectiveness of much of what he says by re-

peating certain generalizations. Granted individual differences among workers, still the necessity of verification must demand some pattern of activity. Of this there is nothing. Nowhere does Bridgman explain; nowhere does he deal in concrete illustrations. Moreover, by implication at least, he reduces science to empirical laboratory work, whereas James B. Conant has stressed the lowering of the degree of empiricism in science during the last half century.

Perhaps the most serious flaw of the article results from its tone. From the beginning, Bridgman asserts that non-scientists are the ones who dogmatize about *the* scientific method; he pictures them as "outsiders" who "wonder how the scientist manages to do it" (p. 81) and produce "not very profound" generalities because they do not understand the objective of science. By emphasizing his categorical distinction between the non-scientist and scientist throughout the article, Bridgman implies that science and scientists are set apart from other men and activities. As a result, his tone is that of someone reprimanding the uninitiated for speaking of mysteries they cannot comprehend.

Nevertheless, the article has value because of Bridgman's attack upon the oversimplified, "textbook" concept of *the* scientific method.

Assignments

1. Explain the differences between the *précis* and *critical summary* of Bridgman's article. What would you add to each of them? What would you omit? Explain your additions and omissions.
2. Write a *précis* of James B. Conant's "Science and Technology in the Last Decade."
3. Write a *critical summary* of J. Bronowski's "The Creative Process."
4. Write both a *précis* and a *critical summary* of one of the articles in Part III, "The Scientist and Modern Society."

EXERCISE IV. DEFINITION

Just as the essential question of process is "how," so the essential question of definition is "what." In its most simple form, as occurs in dictionaries, a definition places the term to be defined in its proper class (*genus*) and then describes the characteristics which make it individual (*differentiae*). Thus, for example, a bicycle is "a light vehicle having two wheels one behind the other, a steering handle, a saddle seat or seats, and pedals by which it is propelled" (*Webster's New Collegiate Dictionary*). For a person who has seen a bi-

cycle or is at least vaguely familiar with the concept, such a definition is adequate; but imagine the effect of it upon someone who has
never seen a bicycle or someone who is a member of a culture that
has not developed the wheel, such as the ancient Mayans. At best,
other questions immediately arise: what is its form, what is its use,
who uses it? Try the same thing with another familiar term: oxygen.
Oxygen is "an element occurring free as a colorless, tasteless, odor-
less gas (ordinary oxygen) in the atmosphere, of which it forms
about 23 percent by weight and about 21 percent by volume, being
slightly heavier than nitrogen." Once more, try it with an abstract
concept like love.

These examples are not intended to question the need for, or the
validity of, such brief definitions; but rather, to suggest, as do many
of the writers included in this volume, the difficulty of communicating even simple, everyday ideas and the need for full and exact
definition. The above examples rely basically on classification; they
assume, and *must* assume, that the reader is a member of twentieth
century society and therefore has at least a speaking acquaintance
with many phases of that society. In other words, they rely upon the
reader's frame of reference.

The greatest difficulty arises, of course, from terms having a
technical meaning in special fields. In your literature classes, you
will need to know the meaning of such terms as *epic, elegy, omniscient author, imagery,* and *local color,* to cite but a few. Some
words are additionally difficult because they are open to interpretation; in literature, for example, *romanticism* and *myth* provide special bugaboos, for in the former case especially there are almost as
many interpretations as there are English teachers. But terms must
be defined if there is to be communication.

Perhaps the cardinal rule of definition should be to state the unknown, the unfamiliar, in terms of the familiar. Moreover, as much
as possible, to bring the abstract down to the concrete. Notice how
Turner reduces the abstraction "scientific method" to "an illustration in miniature" which is an anecdote taken from everyday experience. Notice, too, that in addition to giving concrete illustrations,
Conant begins his discussion by telling you what scientific method is
not; that is, by dismissing the conventional high-school textbook
definitions as inadequate. To defend his thesis that science is a crea-

tive activity, Bronowski relies upon a comparison of scientific theory to a work of art like *Othello*, of a modern scientist to a Renaissance painter like Leonardo da Vinci (who was also a scientist). (Comparison and contrast as a form of exposition may serve as the basis for an entire paper.) What each of these writers has done is to state, to define, his concept in terms of the familiar. They have employed such methods as detail, illustration and anecdote, comparison and contrast, negation, and classification. They might also have used analysis, a discussion of origins and causes, or a discussion of results, effects, and uses. Had they wished to, they might have centered their articles around a brief, formal definition: *term, genus, differentiae*. But always they have been guided by the single principle: define the unknown in terms of the known, the familiar.

Assignments

1. Examine both Conant's and Bronowski's articles to find all of the methods they use in making their definitions. What methods are common to both writers? What methods are different?
2. Drawing in part at least upon Conant's article, define the term *empiricism*.
3. Drawing in part at least upon Bronowski's article, distinguish between the scientist and the technician by defining each.
4. Select a technical term from some field you are interested in and write a definition of it. Be prepared to explain what methods you used and why you used them.
5. Write a brief, formal definition of both science and scientific method, employing *term, genus, differentiae*.

THEME TOPICS

1. Why does Conant believe that the textbook definitions of scientific method are inadequate?
2. Which author has added most to your understanding of the nature of science and the scientific method? Why is his presentation particularly effective?
3. Is Bronowski persuasive in his argument that the development of a scientific theory is a creative action?
4. Conant suggests that "the really revolutionary and significant advances come not from empiricism but from new theories" (p.

30). Write a paper exemplifying or denying this principle, drawing upon a field with which you are acquainted to prove your assertion.

5. Does Bronowski's emphasis upon induction deny or confirm Conant's thesis regarding the lowering of the degree of empiricism during the present century?

6. On the basis of all the essays in Part II, write a definition of the scientific method (or science). What do all of the writers' definitions have in common? How do they differ? Can these differences, if they exist, be reconciled?

7. On the basis of all the essays in Part II, what part does verification play in scientific method? Is it the essential feature as Bridgman asserts?

part III   THE SCIENTIST AND MODERN SOCIETY

The scientist in society

J. ROBERT OPPENHEIMER

The Open Mind. New York: Simon and Schuster, 1955, pp. 119–129*

There is something inherently comforting about a panel of experts. One knows that the partial and inadequate and slanted and personal views that he expresses will be corrected by the less partial, less personal views of everyone else on the panel; it is not unlike the experience of the professor who always is glad that he has to meet his class again because he can correct the mistakes that he made the last time. It is with such tentativeness that I am going to talk to you.

This is a vast terrain—one full of strange precipices, [119] chasms and terrors. What I thought I would do first is to run over in a quite synoptic way a few general opinions, almost words only, which seem to me involved in the relations between science and man's life. It is my hope that I will do this with enough baldness so that you will pick up some of these words and deal with them more fully and more wisely than in this summary. I will then devote a little time to one problem which seems to me singularly fit in this hall and in this company, which worries me a great deal, and as to a resolution for which I have only the most rudimentary notions.

For one thing, we have changed the face of the earth; we have changed the way men live. We may not change the condition of man's life, but we have changed all modes in which that condition occurs. I do not by this mean to say that from the existence of science, from the discovery, knowledge, technique and power of science the particularities of the present time follow. But we all know that if life today is very different from what it was two hundred years ago, if we meet our human and political problems in a quite new form, that has much to do with the fact that we know how to do a great many things, and that there are people who are eager to do them, not typically scientists, but people who are glad to use the knowledge and with it the control which science has made available.

I need not belittle two points. One is that the effect of science on the condition of man's life is also in part a cultural and intellectual one. I shall return to that because it is my persuasion that this is largely a happy symbiosis of the past; today we have very little of it. The ideas which have changed [120] the thinking caps of men and which derived from experience in science are really not contemporary ideas but go back a century or two centuries or more.

The second, of course, is not to try to give to scientific life an autonomy of society. It is possible, manifestly, for society so to arrange things that there is no science. The Nazis made a good start in that direction; maybe the Communists will achieve it; and there is not one of us free of the worry that this flourishing tree may someday not be alive any more.

But nonetheless we *have* changed the face of the earth; any beginning of a talk about science and society must take that as a fact.

There is another theme. This is a time that tends to believe in progress. Our ways of thought, our ways of arranging our personal lives, our political forms, point to the future, point not merely to change, to decay, to alteration, but point with a hopeful note of improvement that our progress is inevitable. In the acquisition of knowledge, in the very notion of a cumulative discipline, tomorrow in a certain sense comprises today and yesterday. How much this built-in sense of progress in man's life—which is, I think, not a religious notion, not a Christian notion—how much this derives from the effects of science on philosophical and political thought I would leave to historians of ideas. It is probably not wholly trivial.

A third theme is that science in a certain sense is universal. It is not universal in the sense that all men participate in it. It is universal in the sense that all men can participate in it. It is nonnational, nonlocal and, although one would not say noncultural, singularly independent of the form of government, [121] the immediate tradition, or the affective life of a people. It has to do with *humanitas*. This universality is not a trivial thing at a time when forms of unity, large forms of unity in the world, appear to be for other reasons rather necessary. This has been very much in all our minds in the years since the last war. I remember that on one occasion when I was in this hall, at the Bicentennial of the University, we were talking about the universality of science; and at that very moment the Soviet delegate to the United Nations Atomic Energy Commission was imploring his government for permission to accept the scientific and technical report of the subcommittee of this commission. This, I think, is the last time—the last time I remember— that the Soviet government has said *yes* to anything, has said *yes* to an agreement of fact. I know how bitterly disappointing the experiences of these years have been as to universality of science, but we all know that this is bad politics but not bad science. We all know that there is no such thing as German physics or Soviet genetics or American astronomy. These fields can open themselves to all reasonable men willing to take the trouble to inquire.

There is also what may first seem like the opposite of universality; I hope you will bear that in mind when I talk of science as a great and beautiful word. There *is* a unity to it; but there is also an even more striking and immense diversity. Both of your speakers this morning are physicists, and I think we are very different from our brothers the chemists and our brothers the mathematicians. In our values, in our style, we are different. Physics is perhaps the branch of science which [122] has been most concerned to keep itself one. The Physical Society splits off divisions from time to time but is reluctant to do so; and the divisions largely have to do with semi-applied science. Physics has a history of close association with mathematics, with astronomy, with epistemology and cosmology too. And yet we do not know very much about the rest of the scientists. I know that it is a very happy occasion at the Institute when some piece of work turns up which is of interest to both the mathematicians and the physicists. It is a very rare occasion and we tend to ring bells when a small bit of cement can be found between their interests. I would stress especially that there is no systematic unity of techniques, of appreciation, of values, of style between the many things that we call science. There is a lot of difference between the nuclear physicist and the agricultural scientist exploring the possibility of improving crops in some poor island in the Caribbean. They are scientists, and they understand each other, and we hope love each other. But they are not very much alike.

There are perhaps two or three other general things. One I believe may be of more importance to some of the other panels than to this. This is one of the by-products of the great flowering of science that dates back to the time when science did have an effect on culture and on ideas. We have been impressed, and I must say I never stopped being impressed, by the great sweep of general order in which particulars are recognized as united. You know the examples: electricity and light, the quantum theory and the theory of valence, places where things that appeared to be separate, and each having [123] its own order, appear as illustrations of a more general order. And one may say, I suppose, that science is a search for regularity and order in those domains of experience which have proven accessible to it.

I am not sure that the effect of the impressive victory of man's mind in this enterprise has not been to make us a little obtuse to the role of the contingent and the particular in life. It is true that many particulars can be understood and subsumed by a general order. But it is probably no less a great truth that elements of abstractly irreconcilable general orders can be subsumed by a particular. And this notion might be more useful to our friends who study man and his life than an insistence on following the lines which in natural science have been so overwhelmingly successful.

There is another great complex of questions. These I feel reassured to mention hardly at all because my friend and successor Dr. Waterman has thought so deeply about them; he is perhaps as well informed as any man in the world. This has to do with the great variety of means whereby society patronizes science, whereby it is possible for the scientist to operate and live and eat and do his work, get in some sense a bit of encouragement and in some sense a bit of nourishment. The problem of patronage is a complex one; it is changing; it has changed enormously in the last decade in this country. I leave it with a good conscience to Alan Waterman that he may deal with it wisely.

What is it, then, that bothers me especially, that I want not merely to mention but to worry about here? I think that in this matter perhaps this panel is not so different than the [124] panel on the role of the artist, or the panel on the role of the philosopher. To put it with great brutality, the point is that the scientist is not in society today, any more than is the artist or the philosopher.

Of course, he does get paid, he does get patronized and even, for odd reasons that he sometimes does not understand, respected. But he is not in society, in the sense that the ideas he has, the work he is doing, stop really rather short with the limits of his profession. They are not part of the intellectual and cultural life of the times. I am over and over again appalled by how ignorant, how incredibly ignorant of the most rudimentary things about my subject are my fellows the historians, my acquaintances the statesmen, my friends the men of affairs. They have no notion of what cooks in physics; I think that they have very little notion of what cooks in any other science. And I know that only by good luck and some hard work do I have even a rudimentary notion of what cooks in other parts of the house called science than the one that I live in. I read the *Physical Review* and work very hard to catch up with it every two weeks; and I think maybe I have some notion of what is going on in some parts of physics; but by and large we know little about one another, and the world outside knows nothing about us. I think this may vary a little from place to place. Perhaps it is tradition in Britain, where there is a sort of deliberate tendency, a national tendency, to refuse to let things become obscure and recondite, that there is a little more effort to see that civilized men have a notion of what the mathematicians and astronomers and physicists are doing—not merely to know the by-products of [125] their works, the practical products, but what they are thinking.

This is in very sharp contrast, this startling general ignorance of scientific ideas and discoveries at the edge of the technical disciplines, in very sharp contrast to the state of affairs two or three centuries ago; and some of the reasons for this are manifest. But I believe that the science of today is subtler, richer, more relevant to man's life and more useful to man's dignity than the science which had such a great effect on the age of the enlightenment, had such a great effect, among other things, on the forms and patterns, traditions and hopes—reflected in our Constitution—of human society. Science is not retrograde; and there is no doubt that the quantum mechanics represents a more interesting, more instructive, richer analogy of human life than Newtonian mechanics could conceivably be. There is no doubt that even the theory of relativity, which has been so much vulgarized and so little understood, that even the theory of relativity is a matter which would be of real inter-

est to people at large. There is no doubt that the findings of biology
and astronomy and chemistry are discoveries that would enrich our whole culture if they were understood. And what is perhaps
more troublesome, there is a gulf between the life of the scientist and
the life of a man who isn't actively a scientist, dangerously deep.
The experience of science—to stub your toe hard and then notice
that it was really a rock on which you stubbed it—this experience is
something that is hard to communicate by popularization, by education, or by talk. It is almost as hard to tell a man what it is like to find
out something new [126] about the world as it is to describe a
mystical experience to a chap who has never had any hint of such an
experience.

The enlightenment was a peculiar time; it was hopeful, and superficial, and humane; and how much of the ideas of the enlightenment
derived from an appreciation of science, it is perhaps not right for
anyone but a careful historian to say. But we know that the same
men who wrote about politics and philosophy—not very good philosophy, and not too good politics—also wrote about natural science,
about physics, and astronomy, and mathematics. We know that on
two very different planes Franklin and Jefferson managed to span
the whole way from a living, and in some cases even practicing, interest in science to the world of affairs. And we know how full their
writings are of the illumination which one sheds on the other.

Science in those days was connected with the practical arts; it was
very close to common sense. Yet always there is in science little more
than the infinitely diligent and patient and unremitting application
of the practical arts and common sense. By now it has come to be a
long chain. The mere process of carrying a boy through the elementary steps of this chain consumes so much of his life and is such an
exhausting operation, to the teacher and student alike, that the simple means of communication and understanding, which sufficed in
the seventeenth and eighteenth centuries, are clearly not good
enough.

This is a problem that has had the thought of many wise people; I
do not pretend to be talking of anything new or strange. I suppose
the notion of having laboratory courses [127] was an attempt to
bring the young man and woman into this experience of really discovering something; yet my fear is that by the time it gets into the

laboratory and the professor knows the answer, the whole operation is different; it is an imitation and not the real thing. I suppose all of you have read the eloquent pleas which a number of scientists, of whom perhaps President Conant is the best known, have made for attempting to communicate some understanding of science by what is essentially the historical method. These do, I think, establish the fact that science as a human activity is treatable by the historical method. They do not, I think, establish that a scientific method, or a scientific discovery, is communicable by these means. I have a great anxiety that our educational directions, far from making us a part of the world we live in, in this very special sense that we share ideas and some bit of experience with our fellow men, may even be moving rather in the opposite direction.

This is odd: we live in the world very much affected by science, and even our thinking caps, and our ideas and the terms in which we tend to talk about things, the notion of progress, the notion of a fraternity of scholars and scientists which is so familiar to a Christian life and which has a new twist because of the spread of science —all of these we can see originally at a time when science was understood by men of affairs, by artists, by poets. We live today in a world in which poets and historians and men of affairs are proud that they wouldn't even begin to consider thinking about learning anything of science, regarding it as the far end of a tunnel too long for any wise man to put his head into. We therefore [128] have, in so far as we have at all, a philosophy that is quite anachronistic and, I am convinced, quite inadequate to our times. I think that whatever may have been thought of Cartesian and Newtonian reforms in the intellectual life of Europe, the time when these were what the doctor ordered—all that the doctor ordered—is long past. Far more subtle recognition of the nature of man's knowledge and of his relations to the universe is certainly long overdue, if we are to do justice to the wisdom which our tradition has in it and to the brilliant and ever-changing flower of discovery which is modern science.

Research is action; and the question I want to leave in a very raw and uncomfortable form with you is how to communicate this sense of action to our fellow men who are not destined to devote their lives to the professional pursuit of new knowledge.

The real responsibilities of the scientist

J. BRONOWSKI

Bulletin of the Atomic Scientists, XII (January 1956), 10–13, 20

We live in times of very difficult decisions for scientists, for states-men, and for the lay public. Many of these decisions are forced on us by new scientific discoveries, and the difficulties in making them are created by the distance between the scientist and the pub-lic. (Indeed, there is a frightening distance even between scien-tists in one field and those in another.) This sense of distance is, I think, a grave threat to the survival of the kind of society in which science can flourish at all.

People hate scientists. There is no use in beating about the bush here. The scientist is in danger of becoming the scapegoat for the helplessness which the public feels. And if an immense revulsion of public feeling does lead to the destruction of the scientific tradition, then the world may again enter a dark age as it did after the Goths destroyed Rome. It is not impossible that the whole mechanical and intellectual society which we know could be abolished by a great wave of fanaticism.

That is the danger which faces us, because people hate scien-tists. But even if this danger does not materialize, something as ter-rible can happen—and is happening. This is that the scientist is forced, by the hatred of public opinion, to side with established au-thority and government. He becomes a prisoner of the hatred of the lay public, and by that becomes the tool of authority.

My purpose is not to underline these obvious dangers, which we may hide from ourselves but which in our hearts we all know to exist. My purpose is to try to give a picture, as I see it, of the real responsi-bilities of scientists, government, and public, in order that, beginning from this diagnosis, we may begin to cure the great and threatening division between them.

THE ABUSE OF SCIENCE

What the lay public does when it hates the scientist is what it does also when it hates policemen and ministers of state and all symbols of authority. It tries to shift the responsibility for decisions from its own shoulders to the shoulders of other people. "They have done this," it says. And "They" is always the law, the government—or in this case, the scientist.

You must allow me here to make a digression which is not strictly part of my theme, but which I think needs saying. It is this: that we must not forget that scientists do bear a heavy responsibility. I am of course about to explain that really the public and governments bear the main responsibility. But this does not shift from us, the scientists, the grave onus of having acquiesced in the abuse of science. We have contrived weapons and policies with our public conscience, which each of us individually would never have undertaken with his private conscience. Men are only murderers in large groups. They do not individually go out and strangle their neighbor. And scientists are only murderers in large groups—collectively. For scientists are very ordinary human beings. Any collection of people in any laboratory contains good and bad, people with consciences and without, and what we have allowed to happen is the conquest of science by the minority without conscience which exists in every group.

It is sad that scientists have been exceptionally corruptible. Look into your own experience. Most of us have come from poor parents. We have worked our own way up. The practice of science has enabled us to earn salaries which would be unthinkable to us if we had stayed peddling whatever our fathers peddled. Quite suddenly, the possession of a special skill has opened to us a blue door in the antechambers of prime ministers. We sit at conference tables, we have become important people, because we happen to be able to be murderers. And therefore scientists have been bought with large salaries and fellowships and rewards quite inappropriate to their merits, because a policy was furthered by their techniques. The scientist has proved to be the easiest of all men to blind with the attractions of public life.

Having said this I now propose to stop abusing the scientist. I

think it is right that we should all make this confession of guilt—I
have been as guilty as anyone else—but this is all spilt milk, this is
all water over the dam. We must now look toward what we can do to
remedy what has happened. And it cannot be remedied by a gigantic strike of scientists, who will suddenly refuse to have anything
to do with commercial or war research, because the society of scientists contains [10] too many fallible human beings to make this
practicable.

When the public dreams of such a strike, when it says: "scientists
ought not to have invented this or disclosed that secret," it is already
demanding something of the individual scientist which lies beyond
his personal responsibility.

The voters of Great Britain elect for the purpose of making their
policy six hundred and thirty members of Parliament. They do not
elect the people who go to Harwell or the people who go to my own
research laboratory. That is: we have already deputed to those
whom we elect the responsibility for framing policy in peace and
war, and it is quite wrong to ask a body of professional experts like
the scientists to take this responsibility from the men whom our
society has named.

The individual scientist is not the keeper of the public conscience,
because that is not what he was chosen for. The population at
large, through its deputed ministers, has chosen scientists to ex-
ecute certain public orders which are thought to represent the public will. And you cannot ask the scientist to be executioner of this
will, and judge as well. If you have given a body of scientists this
particular hangman's task, you cannot ask them also to form a collective opposition to it. The collective responsibility belongs to the
lay public and through that, to those who were elected by that public to carry it out.

Thus when Einstein on August 2, 1939, wrote a letter to President
Roosevelt in order to draw his attention to the possibility of an
atomic bomb, he was acting with exemplary correctness. He was
disclosing to the elected head of government a matter of public importance on which the decision was not his, the writer's, but was
the President's to make.

We must explain to people that they are asking of scientists quite
the wrong collective decision when they say, "you should not have

invented this" or "you should not have disclosed that." This is asking us all to betray the public in the same way as Dr. Klaus Fuchs did, by asking scientists to make decisions which are for the nation to make. The only man who ever, on his own responsibility, was willing to shoulder public responsibility in this way, was Dr. Fuchs. But so far from being hailed as the only sane scientist, he was treated as quite the opposite—as of course he was, since scientists have no right to betray the will of the nation. Yet Fuchs did just what the public asks of every scientist—he decided what to do with a scientific invention.

THE PRIVATE CONSCIENCE

Very well. We will agree that the scientist is not the keeper of the nation's policy. Then what is he the keeper of? He is the keeper of his own private conscience. His responsibility is not to be seduced as a person. He has the right to act individually as a conscientious objector. Indeed, I believe he has the duty to act as a conscientious objector. I would like to repeat this point. It is in this country an offense to betray the armed forces or to seduce their members from their allegiance. It is not an offense to refuse to be a soldier. And I believe that this is exactly like the position of the scientist. He has no business to act as if he commands the army, but he has a business to settle with his own conscience: the serious business whether he personally will engage in forms of research of which he does not morally approve?

My claim then is that the individual scientist should exercise his own personal conscience. This is his duty. What is the duty of governments in this respect? It is to make it possible for him to exercise his conscience. The responsibility of governments in this is to create the conditions in which a scientist can say: No! to projects in which he does not want to take part. He must even be able to give advice which is distasteful to those in authority, and still must not be hounded out of public life or prevented from making a living.

In all countries the serious threat to scientists who have once touched the fringes of secret subjects is that they are then caught in something from which they can never escape again. They do not get a passport, in case somebody captures them. They cannot get a job because, if they do not want to do this, then they are too dangerous or awkward to be trusted with anything else. This is what we must prevent governments from doing, and this can only be prevented by the opinion of quite ordinary citizens. This is the duty which citizens owe to scientists, to insist that governments shall make it possible for scientists to be conscientious objectors if they wish.

I have explored this subject in general terms, and I would now like to be specific. I would like to tell you precisely what I think is the responsibility of the public, of the scientists, and of governments.

The responsibility of the public is to make the decisions of policy on which their future depends, and to make them themselves. And in a democracy the apparatus for this is to elect those people in whose judgment you have confidence—and to elect them on the issues which in fact face the world. Now you can only elect such people, you can only put pressure on them about public issues, if you are well informed. The greatest lack in public opinion today is lack of information about what is possible and not possible in science. This sets my teeth on edge every time I read a scientific newsflash. I will quote one of many instances which I find distasteful: the use of the phrase "cobalt bomb." This is a technical term for a piece of medical equipment, but has suddenly become transformed into something to describe how a hydrogen bomb might be clothed. As a result, of the fifty million people in this country, forty-nine million nine hundred odd thousand have heard the words "cobalt bomb," but are helplessly confused between radioactive treatment and something that you blow people up with. The public must be well informed; and the public gets not only the government it deserves, but the newspapers it deserves.

If this is once granted, the next step I think is simple. If it is once granted that we believe in democratic election, and that in our generation this can only be carried out by a public [11] informed on the scientific issues on which the fate of nations hangs, then the duty of the scientist is clear. The duty of the scientist is to inform the public. The duty of the scientist is to create the public opinion for right policies, and this he can only create if the public shares his knowledge.

My generation has a heavy task here, because it ought to spend the bulk of its time—alas—not in the laboratories at all, but in explaining to the voting public what is going on in the laboratories. What are the choices which face us? What could be done with anti- biotics, with new materials, with coal (if you like), and with al- ternative forms of energy? These are urgent questions and yet, however many times we raise them, the layman still does not understand the scale of the changes which our work is making, and on which the answers must hang.

There is a slightly irreverent story about this. At the time the Smyth Report was published in America there was published in this country a White Paper on the British contribution to atomic energy. One of the documents in it is the directive which Mr. Winston Churchill, as he then was, gave about the setting up of an atomic energy project. This directive begins with the words, "though per- sonally satisfied with the power of existing explosives . . ." This bland phrase is a monument to a nonscientific education. For it could only have been written by a man, an intelligent man, who sim- ply does not understand how big a million is. The difference be- tween atomic explosives and ordinary explosives is the difference between the length of a nuclear bond and a molecular bond; and this is a factor of more than a million. To suppose somehow that in mul- tiplying the energy of an explosive by a million, you are doing nothing very different from multiplying it by two, or five, or ten— this is simply not to grasp the scale of the world.

And the public does not grasp it. To say "ten to the sixth" to any- body, however educated, is still to invite the reproof today that one is stressing mere numerical details. One of our tasks, as scientists, must be to educate people in the scale of things.

While I am telling improper stories—improper only in the amus- ing sense—I will tell you that everybody who works in industrial re- search has this trouble all the time, when he discusses the economics of new processes. We put forward the result of research, or we sim- ply estimate what would happen if a piece of research proved suc- cessful. And at once we get back a balance sheet from the finance department which says: The current process makes a profit of $2/2d$ a ton, and what you have in mind might take a loss of $8d$ a ton; it is therefore not worth pursuing. This, if you please, is the comment on a piece of research which, if it works on the full scale, might cut costs by a factor of five. But no accountant understands a factor of five; he budgets in shillings and pence, and what is liable to loss is to him as good as lost. One cannot explain a factor of five, or a factor of a million, to people who have not been brought up in a scientific tradition. This is what I mean when I say that the scientist has a duty to become a teacher to the public in understanding the pace, the nature, the scale of the changes which are possible in our lifetime.

GOVERNMENT AND OPPORTUNITY

I have detailed the duties of the public and of the scientist. What are the duties of government? The duties of government are to give its public the opportunity to learn, and therefore to give scientists the opportunity to teach. And I have already suggested that these duties are twofold. One is to give scientists freedom to live their own lives if they do not want to go on with research projects which seem to them without conscience. The other is the duty to allow scientists to speak freely on subjects of world importance.

As for the second, everyone who has ever been connected with the atomic energy projects knows how it is met today. We spend our time waiting for some American journalist to publish some piece of information which we know to be accurate, so that we may then quote it as being the opinion of the *New York Times*. I am being frank about this: I do it all the time. I read what the greatest indiscreet senator said to the small indiscreet reporters, and I know that nine statements are nonsense and one statement is accurate. Then I quote the one that is accurate—but not as my opinion.

Of course it is natural that governments resist the explosive opinions of scientists. All governments, all societies are resistant to change. Rather over two thousand years ago, Plato was anxious to exile poets from his society; and in our lifetime, for the same reason, governments are in effect anxious to exile or at least silence scientists. They are anxious to exile all dissidents, because dissidents are the people who will change society.

There is a simple difference between governments and scientists. Governments believe that society ought to stay the way it is for good—and particularly, that there ought to be no more elections. Scientists believe that society ought to be stable, but this does not mean the same thing to them as being static. We scientists want to see an *evolving* society, because when the physical world is evolving (and we are helping to evolve it) the forms of society and government cannot be kept the same.

THE MORAL CONTRACT

Having described the duties of the public, of scientists, and of governments, let me now underline what I have said by describing what happens in all three cases if these duties are not kept. If governments do not allow scientists freedom of conscience, to work at what they like and to refuse to work at what they do not like, and to speak freely about why they do so, then you get the gravest of all disasters—the disaster of state intolerance. This is a disaster because it saps both sides of the moral contract. For there is a moral contract between society and its individuals which allows the individual to be a dissident; and if the state breaks this moral contract, then it leaves the individual no alternative but to become a terrorist. I do not know whether the great state trials in Russia were just or were false. But I know that if they were just, if men like Radek and Trotsky and Zinoviev really committed those enormities, then this in itself condemns the system of government which does not allow any other form of protest than such a form. The grave danger to our society too is that this becomes the only choice which is left open to scientists, if state intolerance imprisons them and tries to turn them into a secret Egyptian priestcraft.

The great sin of the public is acquiescence in this secrecy. I am horrified by the feeling that I get, from such trifling things as American advertisements, that people really enjoy the sense that they are not to be trusted. There is an advertisement running in the *New Yorker* at the moment (I think for a clothing firm) which shows a man who has just got out of an airplane. He has a face like a prize-fighter, he is well-dressed and wears what in New York is called a sharp hat, and he carries a bag in one hand which is chained to his wrist. He is [12] carrying secret documents. This is the holy of holies. This is what we are to admire—the man with his mouth shut tight who is not trusting you and me, because of course you and I are not to be trusted. When people come to believe this, when they themselves believe that it is better for them not to know, then totalitarianism is on the doorstep. Then you are ready for Hitler to get up and say: "I am the man who will take your communal responsibilities. I will make your decisions for you."

And the third in our scheme, the scientist, must preserve the tradition of quarreling, of questioning, and of dissent on which science (and I believe all post-Renaissance civilization) has been built. He must do this for two reasons. First, there is the mundane reason which is obvious in the failure of German research after Hitler took power. It is this: that you do not get good science as soon as you have reduced the scientists to yes-men. It is the nature of scientists to be thoroughly contrary people—let us own up to that. It is the nature of science as an activity to doubt your word and mine. As soon as you get a science, such as atomic energy research in totalitarian Germany, in which the young men are no longer allowed to question what the great men have said, then that science is dead. You can find in the files of the German Atomic Energy Commission that several young men made what I suppose must be called very good suggestions, but they were not followed because (such is the influence of totalitarianism) Heisenberg always knew the answers already.

This does not happen in English laboratories yet. Mr. Churchill begins by saying that he is satisfied with existing explosives, but after the comma he does give scientists the opportunity to be dissatisfied. This tradition, this independence and tolerance, is I believe the base of all our values; and this is what we as scientists must preserve.

THE DUTY OF HERESY

I have given you the simple practical grounds for allowing scientists to be awkward, but I believe also that imaginatively and intellectually this is equally important. The sense of intellectual heresy is the lifeblood of our civilization. And the heresy of scientists cannot be confined to their science. Newton was thoroughly and [13] rightly contrary in science, and he was also a thorough heretic in religious matters. For the same reason, people like Oppenheimer and Einstein are found to associate with such unreliable characters. You cannot say to scientists: "When you get into the laboratory at nine in the morning you are going to become a dissenter; and when you go out at five-thirty you are going to become a citizen who touches his cap and who is politically sound." The intellect is not divided into these simple categories.

I have said that the duty of the scientist is today publicly to become a teacher. Let me end by saying something of what he is to teach. There is, of course, the scientific method. There are things about the scale and order of size, of which I have spoken. There are the possibilities which are open to us in controlling nature and ourselves. Above all, he can teach men to ask whether the distance between promise and achievement in our age need be quite so large; whether there must be such a gap between what society is capable of doing and what it does. All this, every scientist can teach.

But every scientist can also teach something deeper. He can teach men to resist all forms of acquiescence, of indifference, and all imposition of secrecy and denial. We must resist the attitude of officials, that there ought to be a good reason why something should be published before you allow it. We must teach even officials that there will have to be a very good reason indeed before anyone is silenced by secrecy.

Mr. Gordon Dean, former chairman of the American Atomic Energy Commission, has just been complaining against secrecy on practical grounds. He says that the commercial reactors which are being built in America are still on the secret list and that this is handicapping American business in its competition with English business for world reactor markets. God works in a mysterious way and it may be that by this anxiety to sell atomic power, science will be liberated. At any rate, let us not look askance at any ally in the drive against silence. My message, in this and in all else, has been the scientist's duty to speak. There is one thing above all others that the scientist has a duty to teach to the public and to governments: it is the duty of heresy.

Government and the expert

HERMAN FINER

Bulletin of the Atomic Scientists, XII (November 1956), 329–332

All history is the record of the struggle of the political sovereign to be absolute against spiritual and intellectual experts who seek freedom of discovery and testimony and sometimes have sought to master political sovereignty itself. The former has wanted its will carried out; the latter, science brought in.

The expert has his limitations, which are the obverse of his contributions to government. His expertise is bound to be minute in proportion to its depth. He is not an elected person clothed with the authority inherent in the democracy. He has no political responsibility. His narrowness must leave him as only one small ingredient among many in the statesman's policy. Having no authority, he must be subservient to those who have. Bearing no responsibility, in the political sense, he must take orders and, possibly, suffer frustrations. Outside his specialism he is no wiser than other men.

Claims to know the way of human salvation or to impose damnation, exercised through prophecy, ritual, charms, oracles, and portents, have, over the millennia, been more fearful to societies than the nuclear weapons so far. The priests who could sway human obedience, fought with the kings for plenary authority; and the kings fought back, making themselves the High Priests, or *pontifex maximus,* or Augustus the God, to leave no doubt about who was supreme.

The spiritual experts, by fighting back, impressed society and its rulers with the necessity of a large zone of freedom. And this not only added to human happiness, but it kept the society an open one in general. It gave the tyrants or demagogues pause. According to their degree of civilization, the nations have been induced to drop religious tests for their experts.

The various states have been adamant with their intellectual experts. For the latter were needed, but were always suspected of wanting to pervert their indispensable contribution of intellectual power into domination of policy. We could note the long succession of struggles between democracies or kings and their *strategoi*, their *majordomos;* their Cardinal Wolseys; their Richelieus and Colberts. Weak states, like France, succumbed to bureaucracy, that is, government by experts undirected, unspurred, and uninspired by a wise and energetic political superior. This is where the word "bureaucracy" originated.

Even today the weak body politic in France, breaking the national vision by a conflict of many political parties, with legislative power over the executive unchecked, has left the great corps of experts— career civil servants, administrators, and natural scientists—largely ungeared to the community, in spite of France's brilliant intellectual society and its many consultative councils serving the government. The expert needs a master, a strong master, but a wise master, to set him the problems of human usefulness. So ferocious have been French sovereign political wills, that the experts have been politicized. The high army chiefs have in recent years divulged secrets; even the secrets of the National Defense Council have been passed out to politicians.

The subjection of the German experts (they connived in the expulsion of Einstein) by the political sovereign, was so abjectedly accepted by those who entered the service, that Hitler had only to purge the service of a comparatively small proportion. They would not face the loss of their pensions, even when they execrated him. At the Nuremburg trials, the higher experts claimed that they merely stayed to avert what might be worse in Hitler's evil intentions, and that international law did not impose on them any responsibility for assisting the *political* leaders in making war or committing crimes against humanity.

Is the expert, then, to be a will-less instrument? Or, in critical situations, is he to refuse obedience or advice, and to lose his livelihood, and his access to the equipment, plant and laboratories, and data, in the possession of the government? One thing is notable in the wretched [329] story of the German experts' subservience: at least the political sovereign, whether royal, Bismarckian, or Hitlerian, did relieve the expert of punishment for political error, by making *clear-cut* the narrow range of his specialist responsibilities.

BRITISH EXPERTS AND GOVERNMENT

It would seem that in Britain, an intelligent balance has been established between the sovereign Parliament and the expert, while in the U.S. a struggle still proceeds agonizingly intensified by the pressures of international insecurity and weapons of mass destruction.

The characteristics which have been, in general, extremely beneficial for the British experts and the people who benefit from their most diverse expertise are as follows.

1. The legislature is sovereign. There is no confusion in the mind of the experts between loyalty to the "Constitution," or the "country" or their governmental superiors. The sovereignty of Parliament is delegated to the ministers, who are the superiors of the experts, in statutes which are their blueprints of operation.

2. Parliament is tethered to the community by political parties which are based on principle; which are coherent; which are responsible-minded; which discipline their own members from the standpoint of the public good as well as party advantage.

Indeed, in all the bitter debates since the first nuclear fission, Parliament has been not a man-hunting assembly with the experts in government service as the exterminable wolves, but has been the forum for the protection of the experts' jobs and the implementing of decent procedure where "sensitive" situations exist.

3. Ministers, subjected to daily criticism and influence by Parliament and themselves members of Parliament, are sole and undisputed chiefs of the departmental pyramid of officials, i.e., the experts who advise and the experts who carry out the laws. The departments are linked with scientific bodies outside the government career service in various patterns of advisory nexus, similar to American contractual arrangements.

4. The career experts fall into various classes of which the two most important are (*a*) the Administrative Class and (*b*) the Professional, Scientific, and Technical Class. The former number 3,500; the latter, about 115,000, if the auxiliary experts are included. The Administrative Class is headed in each department by their career chief, the Permanent Secretary. They and he are the advisers and counsellors, the "brains trust" of the minister, that is, the politician, who is the political head of the department.

The British doctrine and practice require that the professional, scientific, and technical class experts reach the minister, not directly, nor through their own superiors in their own class, but indirectly, through the Administrative Class.

For many years, the scientists have been very restive on two grounds. Firstly, they have objected to their exclusion from the hierarchy which would allow those with administrative ability to enter the Administrative Class. This is now taken care of, more or less satisfactorily, by arrangements for promotion and transfer where such abilities are evinced, and adequate salary scales.

Secondly, the scientists have felt that their views may not have a due impact on the political minister, and therefore on the Parliament and the public, if the data are collated by the Administrative Class and then relayed by these to the minister. The official answer to this is a firm one: the political minister is an amateur in his department; the advice of any scientist, however important his science, is but one ingredient among many in the formation of policy; the minister could not possibly understand the crude data (because of lack of time, type of education, etc.), whereas the career administrator has been educated to enable himself to understand the scientists and to bring together with their direct help the diverse elements of advice, the fragments of science, in an integrated pattern.

Thus, there is a kind of buffer—an intermediate level—between the "scientist" and the politicians. But it is a curious buffer. It turns into an administrative statesmanship serving the minister, and it is a powerful safeguard for the *independence of mind* of the scientist. For it makes reasonably sure that he will not have a Sinclair Weeks seeking the dismissal of a Dr. Astin, the director of the National Bureau of Standards, because he has dared to be a faithful scientist. It safeguards his independence of mind because it relieves him of direct political direction. He can get on with his discoveries without being called a security risk or a menace to private enterprise, because even if he wished to raise "political" or "moral" matters (such as were raised by the General Advisory Committee under Robert Oppenheimer's gifted chairmanship), it would be known to the Administrative Class that these views were either *obiter dicta*, and hence immune from *post facto* persecution, or were asked for, and therefore, again, immune from inquisition.

But, more usually, the Administrative Class will have thought out the problem to be put to the scientist for solution, so that it is stripped of political integuments, and so will save him, at any rate, from accidental, or unwitting, or involuntary, immixture in "politics." He will not be liable to be bullied as Robert Oppenheimer was (*Hearing*, p. 959) for having felt "that having played an active part in promoting a revolution in warfare, I needed to be responsible as I could with regard to what came of this revolution."

Parliament and the ministers actively seek expert *independence of mind*. They want all the benefits of existent and emergent social and natural science. This desire is [330] shared and implemented by the Administrative Class who are recruited by the most rigorous competitive examination based on the best general education Britain provides. To enable this system to work for the commonweal, certain principles must be observed: The *anonymity* and the *impartiality* of the civil service, that is, the government's experts.

Anonymity means that no official employed by the government is to make a public claim to friends, press, or Parliament, that he has advised the government or carried out its orders in such and such particulars. It also means that neither Parliament nor the public will presume to know the identity of the expert who gave advice—not Oppenheimer, not Fermi, not Rabi, not Teller, not the Pentagon politicians, not General Zwicker and the scores of others—nor praise or blame him for it.

This is administrative *detachment* for the freedom of exploration. The only person held to public responsibility is the minister of the department, the politician, or, if the matter transcends one department, the Prime Minister. It is the business of the minister to see that his department, through the Administrative Class, does its job properly. The convention of anonymity allows the expert to get on with his own specific job. It shields his independence of mind. It relieves him of political onus. It excludes the claim of either political party, on reaching office, to conduct a manhunt against the experts who have been pilloried or praised in public to its distaste. The convention therefore assists the other twin part of the principle, which is impartiality.

Impartiality. Experts in the employ of the British government are expected to serve the minister with impartial zeal no matter to what party he belongs. Impartiality does not mean listless or perfunctory collaboration. Experts are firmly expected, *if they are to remain in the public service,* to offer the minister nay, even to press upon him, all the expert advice relevant to his *political* problem that they can muster in themselves and their departmental colleagues and subordinates, all the alternatives of benefit and loss inherent in the assembled data. They could even say that it is immoral to manufacture the H-bomb—so long as this were an honest opinion. The minister would not be punitive, but grateful. He could still reject the idea. The Permanent Secretary of the relevant department could be relied on to vouch for the expert's disinterestedness. If there were differences of opinion within the administrative-scientific hierarchy, the merit and intention of the advice would be assayed there, in the calm and quiet.

Thus, the merit of the British system of political-expert relationships, is evident in a clear distinction between expertness and policy, *or* the expert's impunity if the two are mixed—and it avoids excessive responsibility on the expert, for excessive responsibility is paralytic to thought. Frankness is regarded as the highest virtue and is worshipped and rewarded, and this is why impeachment went out in the 18th century.

THE U.S.A. AND ITS EXPERTS

The advent of the nuclear weapons, the sudden thrust of the U.S.A. into the limelight of world leadership, the ruthlessness of imperialistic and barbarous communism, found the U.S.A. gravely unready to meet the problem of its experts with intelligence, firmness, composure, and democratic decency.

The U.S.A. still has an extremely strong impulse hostile to the nonpartisanship of experts. This is far less the fault of the scientists and career administrators than it is of the politicians. Paradoxically and unconsciously, American politicians are very similar to Soviet Communist ones, almost Marxist, in fact, they would be horrified to realize, in their disbelief in the nonpartisanship of government advisers. Is it so strange? A "perfect" democracy may be as furiously partisan as a zealous Communist party—both are despotic in temper. As Jefferson observed in his *Notes On Virginia* (1781),

"One hundred and seventy-three despots would surely be as oppressive as one."

Each American party is exigent for its own "experts" when it gets into office. It ejects the suspects and continues to suspect those who are not ejected. The development of the merit service since the 1870's is amazing considering the politicians' voracity for jobs and jealousy of intellectual ability, yet the number of jobs still under the "spoils" system weakens the contribution of science and the responsible freedom of scientists.

There is no hierarchical pyramid in each government department with a career service from top to bottom. What situation could better breed informers, envy, and insubordination?

American public administration has refused to make the distinction between the career administrators and the scientists, the former to be the "intervening layer," between the latter and the politicians. In American government departments, scientists, professionally trained men, technologists, get to the highest posts in the departmental hierarchy, as heads of the bureaus. This inevitably affects the scientist's impartiality. His contact with politics is immediate: with the political assistant secretaries and chief. But these have not anything like the qualities required for the comprehensive, intelligent, and comparative appraisal of the data—they have not the education nor the experience, nor sufficient time in office. Hence the shocking clashes of interest and purpose on the Vista Project. Hence the perennial farce of trying to get a Defense Department to integrate the three services and their warring divisions. What expert would feel free to give his utmost to the politicians who man the committees, considering what happened to others who have given their best conscience and mind in the past? Would the case of Oppenheimer [331] be an encouragement to be frank and original?

The arguments for still leaving the scientists without a protective shield of the kind supplied by the British Administrative Class are plausible, but feeble and hardly relevant.

1. Scientifically trained men can go right up to the top of their bureau and be administrators as well as mere technicians, and this opens employment opportunity. Yes; and it does damage to science and to administration.

2. The government is more assured of diversified talent. The answer is that other governments are so assured also, *but* they divide the labor and responsibilities rationally.

3. Scientifically trained people are less likely to be hidebound with traditions. They are innovators. Maybe. But their speciality may also make them spoilers by their narrowness.

4. In order to secure benefits which are alternatively described as weak government and individual freedom, the Constitution has established the separation of powers, that is, institutionalized jealousy between the Congress and the Executive, regardless of the party composition of either.

What kind of life can experts hope for under the friction and raids on each others' territory in such a system? They are not anonymous; they are out in the open field with all guns trained on them.

5. This takes us back to the want of principles in American political parties. For even if the parties were alike in principles, so long as they possessed them and were possessed by them, we should expect their caucuses to curb the ugly excesses of their most unvirtuous colleagues, and even never to let them into their fold. One feature of the feebleness of principle in the parties is the advancement to powerful committee chairmanships simply by seniority with no specific consideration of appropriate merit and character.

The life of the scientist in the U.S. government service will continue to be hard, even unbearable, unless weighty reforms are undertaken, and weighty reforms are undertaken only when it is plainly admitted that they need to be made for powerful reasons of public benefit.

6. It is a misfortune that Congress confuses the expert it does not like by playing a kind of three-card or pea-under-which-thimble trick on him. It baits and bedevils him with the question, "To what are you loyal—the country, the Constitution, or your superior in office?" If the government and administration were rationally organized, e.g., in the British-type arrangement, then it would be extremely unusual that an expert need worry more than to be loyal to his official superiors. The confusion of tongues in the American system actually invites insubordination, informers, guerilla warfare in and between the departments and Congress.

CONCLUSIONS

1. The expert must bow to the fact that the political sovereign is, indeed, sovereign; or he should seek other work.

2. The expert ought to have ample political freedom as a citizen, exercising it with such tact as to avoid the charge of partisanship.

3. Political parties must learn to discipline their partisanship and, even more, not to foment trouble.

4. The departmental and advisory organizations in government must institute the distinction between the natural and social scientist, administrative liaison and command, and policy-making.

5. If the scientists are invited into policy-formulation, then they should be given a waiver of vindictiveness against them.

6. The maximum procedural safeguards are needed for the vindication of the individual against charges by the security agencies, especially in a governmental system where the state of the public mind, the leadership of the legislature and the parties are often in a state of distemper, and where the Executive is unschooled and badly articulated.

7. Loyalty to the chief of the department must be the first rule of the expert, through the levels to the top. *On the whole*, this is the best general rule. Only necessity knows no law; exceptions may be pardoned *post facto*, not made into an established system of mental reservations.

8. There is dire need, especially in the American government, for "an intervening layer" of career servants between scientists and politicians. Much as in Britain (the French have now followed this method, and the Germans have long had it), this group should be recruited, in the main, from the best minds and characters of the *young* graduates. They should have a modern liberal education, which would include a scientific orientation. They should be recruited in early manhood, so that they are nurtured in the spirit of governmental equity. They will take off the shoulders of the "pure" scientists the job of fighting for appropriations, of justifying departmental policy and briefing their own political chiefs, and taking up arms in the struggle between departments and bureaus and agencies for authority and decisions.

A nation needs to be civilized to treat its intellectual assistants to freedom and respect. The gravest problem for governments is how to encourage them to pioneer and adventure into strange realms of thought. There is enough and to spare of discouragement: derision for the prophecies that fail, diffidence, want of courage, malicious sneers at the wild surmise, embarrassment when ideas have been botched. The scientist needs security and loyalty from government as much as it needs it from him.

Dare we admit the truth?

EDITORIAL FROM *THE CHRISTIAN CENTURY*
The Christian Century, October 23, 1957, pp. 1251–1252*

In the U.S.A., scapegoat-hunting was more popular than breast-beating in the first week after the Russians launched their earth satellite. Partisans sought to pin blame on their opposition, with the chief fire directed at cuts in the defense budget. Standing at $38 billion, the budget is probably the largest in the world, but there are always voices that cry havoc if more money does not gush forth from a supposedly bottomless treasury at every crisis or threat. However, as time wears on, the suspicion grows that something is required far more difficult to achieve than increases in defense spending. We have been starving our schools and neglecting the education of the young, not only in science but even more importantly in the humanities. The result which we are compelled bitterly to recognize in the skies is not as important as another consequence: the shrinking of human purpose, the diminution of human dignity, the reduction of the American's conception of his own and his country's mission. In recent years we have trained fewer than half as many scientists and engineers as Russia has, but this has more than one interpretation. A comparatively undeveloped Russia needs more such people than we do; Russia has had a longer way to come to the present. The difficulty here is not that we lack scientists, but that our scientists have lately lacked freedom to do their patient, reflective work without fear or harassment. Hard as it is for us to admit, the results of the satellite program indicate that at least some scientists [1251] in Russia are given more freedom (even in their isolation) than their counterparts are in this country. Before we reject this thesis, let us remember what mccarthyism did to Director Condon of the United States Bureau of Standards and to Director Oppenheimer of the Institute of

Advanced Studies at Princeton. Let us reflect on what public ignorance, superstition and fear did to other scientists, who severed all
connection with government service rather than subject themselves
and their families to the risk of character assassination. Beyond the
circle of men of science were the administrators on whose efforts
scientific advance has always to depend; high government officials who met frustration, harassment and often defeat. And beyond
these were patriotic citizens who were treated with contumely just
because they denounced hysteria-induced tyranny: Mildred McAfee
Horton, former head of Wellesley College and prominent church-
woman, because she criticized the House committee on un-American activities; Bishop G. Bromley Oxnam, because he demanded
that the same committee stop circulating untruths concerning himself. It will be a sign of returning health if we admit that we have
been a sick country, that we have believed the worst about our best,
that we have been ill with suspicion, dread and terrors created
by our own diseased imaginations, that we have particularly sinned
against sound learning, creative freedom and the courage which has
stood and still stands against mob rule.

The waste of scientists

L. V. HEILBRUNN
The Nation, December 7, 1957, pp. 426–427

During the past few months there has been an increasing demand for improvement in American science. We are told that the Russians are training many more scientists than we are and that, perhaps, their young scientists receive better instruction than do ours. In a world in which national supremacy and national survival depend to such a large extent on scientific superiority, this is indeed a serious matter.

What is to be done? Spokesmen for science and influential legislators are demanding that the government spend more money in support of science; an all-out effort is being made to attract our intelligent young men and women into scientific careers.

Thus far all the planning has been done by various prominent citizens in and out of science. Might it not be wise to consult to a greater extent the laboratory scientists, the men primarily responsible for scientific advances?

No one scientist can hope to know more than his own particular field, and anything I have to say concerns primarily the field of biology and physiology. Herein I have, perhaps, a right to express an opinion, for as far as I know, I have trained more biologists and physiologists than anyone else now actively engaged in teaching, and many of the men I trained are now leaders in the field.

In the first place, we biologists do not feel that our science is inferior to that of the Russians'; indeed we [426] believe that it is vastly superior. And we think, too, that applied biology—medical science, for example—is in a much better state in America than it is in Russia. We sometimes wonder why the fact of this superiority in "peaceful" science has not been used as a basis for counter-propaganda.

But though the United States may be superior in various sciences concerned more with human betterment than with human destruction, there is certainly room for improvement. And money alone will not solve the problems involved. It is true that two billion dollars produced the atom bomb. But two billions, or even ten billions, might not produce a cure for cancer, especially if the money were not wisely spent. Great advances in science are made by men with ability and imagination. We scientists are—or should be—creative workers. If you were to give a would-be poet a million dollars to write sonnets equal to those of Shakespeare, there is but an infinitesimal chance that he would succeed. And if millions or billions of dollars of cancer money are given to men without ideas or understanding, it is very doubtful if success can be obtained.

Ask any working biologist about how money is now spent in support of scientific effort and he is very likely to be critical. Never has so much money been spent with so little return. The men on the committees or panels which allocate the funds are on the whole sincere and honest. But they are human and often enough they give large sums to their friends or to each other. I could cite many instances in which many thousands of dollars have been allocated to workers who, instead of advancing science, have published erroneous results that have retarded progress.

Not long ago a man whom I had trained applied for a grant of $45,000 from a governmental agency interested in the study of cancer. The proposed research was at best only vaguely related to cancer, but because it was in a field in which I have achieved prominence, I was asked to pass judgment on it. I found the proposal unworthy and the applicant guilty of overstatement and misstatement; I expressed the opinion that he was not capable of carrying on properly the work he wanted to do. The panel examining the proposal suggested that the applicant be given only a part of the funds requested; yet, in the end, the $45,000 request was approved in full. Apparently my former student had been successful in making friends in high places. As a result, after he had started on his work, I had to take time from my own cancer studies to straighten him out, losing the better part of a month in the effort. This is by no means an isolated case. A month or two ago, a leading authority in the field of photosynthesis told me that although he had strongly criticized an application for research in his field which had been submitted to him for review, the applicant, whom he called a "swindler," got the money he asked for.

The sad thing about all this is not the fact that some thousands or perhaps even some millions of dollars are wasted, but that sincere, hard-working biologists who are dedicating their lives to laboratory research, lose out and to some extent are ploughed under. To these honest workers it is discouraging to see the rewards that accrue to flatterers, overstaters and even charlatans. Once a man gets sufficient funds, he can hire young men to do his work for him; he can hire not only skills but often brains as well. I have heard a successful scientific promoter and politician, a man of little scientific achievement but nevertheless the recipient of vast sums of money, urge publicly that young investigators be trained to be "slick operators." Young scientists are learning that "it pays to advertise" even at a risk of absolute honesty. To some extent Madison Avenue has moved in.

And worst of all there never has been a time when so much power has been in the hands of men who long since have abandoned active participation in scientific inquiry for the field of scientific politics. Years ago the influential leaders in the field of biology were men of great achievement and splendid character. Now, to some extent at least, the "leaders"—the men who wield great power and can influence the allocation of research funds—are cordially hated by the active workers in the field. It is not too much to say that some are, in a sense, petty racketeers.

If the situation in biology is not healthy, I have reason to believe that in what concerns military effort, the situation may in some areas be even worse. Some of my former students who tried to do research in military establishments found themselves under the control of Army and Navy men who had little understanding of the ways of science. Apparently the curricula at West Point and Annapolis are somewhat lacking in this respect. When the atom bomb was developed, one of the leaders of the scientific team which produced it was quoted as saying that he thought that the general in charge had not delayed the successful outcome by more than six months. I have heard even harsher criticism.

What we need in this country is a better understanding of science on the part of those who control its destinies. With a greater awareness of our deficiencies, perhaps there may be improvement.

Science and the citizen

Bulletin of the Atomic Scientists, XIII (December 1957), 361–365

On each Thursday afternoon some three hundred years ago, a group of gentlemen gathered at the Bull-Head Tavern in Cheapside, London: Sir Christopher Wren, who was primarily professor of astronomy at Oxford, but who also designed the military defenses of London and many famous and lovely buildings, including St. Paul's Cathedral; Robert Boyle, who was a great physicist and who also was the author of the *Defense of Christianity;* Lord Brounker, a patron of all the branches of learning; Bishop Wilkins, who in addition to being a cleric was Master of Trinity College and an expert on Copernican theory; Sir William Petty, who was a political economist, a professor of anatomy at Oxford, and a professor of music at Gresham College; Pepys, the diarist and man-about-town; and at a later time our two great American Benjamins—Franklin and Thompson, the latter better known as Count Rumford. There were in this group members of Parliament, critics, civil servants, and pamphleteers. There were explorers and travellers, antiquarians, and *bon vivants.* They were obviously men of wide interests: men of both intellectual and physical vigor. These were men of curiosity, and men of parts. They met there, every Thursday afternoon, to carry out experiments, to eat and drink together, but primarily *they met there to discuss science.*

This was the beginning of the Royal Society Club, a group which, together with others, received from the King on July 15, 1662, the charter of The Royal Society, that great organization which has been the center of British—and for that matter, much of Western— science for nearly three centuries.

It is good for us to think about this group of men. They were no sheltered scholars, no narrow specialists. They were men of varied and of important affairs. They devoted themselves to an activity—the serious study of science—which is today less common and at the same time more important than it was then.

For to these lively spirits of the seventeenth century, observing as they currently could the great beginnings of modern science, it was nothing much more than an intellectual luxury to know something about the then new ways of testing, of analyzing, and of understanding nature. Science had as yet so little touched their daily lives and works that they could have, in fact, known essentially nothing about science and still lived well-balanced and useful lives. The Industrial Revolution was to be faced by their great-great-grandchildren, not by them. One could appreciate the epoch-making character of the Bill of Rights of 1689, and could have his opinions about the personal government of Louis XIV without making use of any facts from physics or chemistry. They could trim the candle or saddle the horse or dispatch a servant with a handwritten note without getting involved in any scientific equipment.

SCIENCE IN OUR LIVES TODAY

But for us it is a different story. The most superficial, even if the most multitudinous, aspect of the contrast is that each one of us now makes constant use of devices that are essentially scientific in character—the telephone, radio, and television; the automobile and the airplane; the air conditioner and the electric blanket; electrically driven and largely automatic washing machines, dryers, refrigerators. Not long ago I counted the number of electric motors in our house. There are thirty-two.

Our clothes closets are filled with suits and dresses whose fibers come not from cotton plants or off the [361] backs of sheep, but from test tubes. Our medicine cabinets are filled with drugs that have been produced not by the herbalist, but by the organic and biochemist. In our own living rooms we look at and listen to far-distant events. We are warm when it is cold, and cool when it is hot. Our health is protected and restored by the exquisite skill of modern medicine and surgery. Even our worries are calmed by chemicals.

We are starting to utilize solar energy, and we are beginning to understand the way in which the green plant converts the energy of sunlight into a chemically stored form. We talk about making rain, and with the vast energy now at our disposal we even consider the possibility of affecting climate on a world-wide scale. We have learned how to tear apart and glue together the nuclei of atoms; and as a result we have an array of man-made radioactive isotopes which constitute powerful new tools of research. We have a future in which the supply of energy is essentially unlimited, and we have weapons of such destructiveness that we are quite capable of destroying civilization. Indeed when we entered the nucleus of the atom we opened a Pandora's box of problems of the most complex and formidable kind.

I read in a recent article in *Harper's*[1] that "most people don't give a damn about most things, unless those things are part and parcel of their concrete lives." But don't you think that science *is:* don't you think that the time has come when you *must* give a damn about science?

The atom, the cell, the star—the mind of modern man has invaded all of these. This new knowledge has brought new beauty into life, new satisfaction of understanding, and new power over nature. But it has also brought great and unavoidable problems. Many of these are economic, social, political, and moral problems: but they are also inescapably scientific problems. Thus these are not isolated problems for a few queer specialists. They are problems for every citizen.

No longer is it an intellectual luxury to know a little about this great new tool of the mind called science. It has become a simple and plain necessity that people in general have some understanding of this, one of the greatest of the forces that shapes our modern lives. We must know—all of us must know—more about what science is and what it is not. We must appreciate its strength and value, and we must be aware of its limitations. We must realize what conditions of freedom and flexibility of support must be maintained for pure scientific research, in order to assure a flow of imaginative and basic new ideas. Without some of this understanding we simply cannot be

[1] R. L. Heilbroner, "Public Relations: The Invisible Cell," *Harper's Magazine*, June 1957, pp. 23–31.

intelligent citizens of a modern free democracy, served and protected by science. Without this we will not know how to face the modern problems of our home, our school, our village, state, or nation.

KNOWLEDGE OF SCIENCE A NECESSITY

Our daily lives are surrounded by problems with scientific implications. When do we—or do we not—consult the psychiatrist or accept a free shot of a new serum? How about vitamins, hormones, sleeping pills, and tranquilizers? How about nutritional regimens and slimming schedules? How about the emotional and psychological problems of present-day children? How about birth rates, death rates, population increases, and food supplies? How about cigarette smoking and lung cancer? How about secrecy in science? How about visas for foreign scientists?

How can we as a nation keep a healthy balance between pure science and applied science? How can we recruit and train enough good scientists, and at the same time not interfere with the recruitment and training of enough good philosophers, businessmen, poets, doctors, musicologists, lawyers, theologians, etc.?

How about the more scientific aspects of foreign technical aid? How about automation? How about nuclear power and weapons testing and radiation damage and induced mutations and the future genetic purity of the race?

Who, in a democracy, really makes the decisions; and how can the decisions, in a modern scientific world, be made wisely and decently unless the public does have some real understanding of science?

The challenge to know something about science, moreover, is by no means limited to these practical questions, important as they are. For if we restricted our interest to motors and drugs, to electronic computers and guided missiles, to radiation genetics and atom bombs, we would move step by ugly step toward a mechanized future in which the purpose of our lives would be nothing much more than a rather selfish sort of convenience and safety precariously posited on power. It is therefore of even more basic necessity that we understand the deeper aspects of science—its capacity to release the mind from its ancient restraints, its ability to deepen our appreciation of the orderly beauty of nature, the essential and underlying humbleness of its position, the emphasis it places upon clarity and honesty of thinking, the richness of the partnership which it offers to the arts and to moral philosophy.

What, then, is science? Being an operationalist, I can only reply that science is the activity practiced by scientists. But this is only the start of an answer. Who and what are scientists? How do they act? What motivates them? Do they all have beards and wild eyes? Can you spot one on the street? To what extent and in what way are they different from nonscientists? When you prick them, do they not bleed? When you tickle them, [362] do they not laugh? When you poison them, do they not die?

Scientists are men and women, not gods, not freaks, not magicians, not monsters. "To think of science as a set of special tricks, to see the scientist as the manipulator of outlandish skills—this," as Bronowski has said, "is the root of the poison mandrake which flourishes rank in the comic strips."

On the average, scientists tend to be pretty bright, and a very few of them are so exceedingly bright that they must be called geniuses. But, by and large, scientists are very much like other folks. They doubtless have rather more than the average curiosity about the insides of things, and they may perhaps have a rather special natural appetite for sharply focused and logical thinking as contrasted with intuitive, artistic, and emotional reactions. But their one really basic difference, I believe, is an intellectual inheritance, transmitted to them in their education as scientists, from the centuries of tradition about the scientific method and the scientific attitude toward the world. To understand what I mean by this we must make a considerable diversion, eventually coming back to the scientist.

ADVANTAGES OF PHYSICAL SCIENCE

The physical world happens to be put together in such a way (I consider this one of God's really bright ideas) that one can usefully take it apart and study an isolated bit of it at a time. Such a study then reveals useful and analytically describable uniformities. For example, pull a spring with a force of one pound and it stretches two inches. Pull with two pounds and it stretches four inches. The generalization (Hooke's law) is that for all springs (all elastic material, in fact) the stretch is directly proportional to the pull.

Now why do I interrupt remarks about the nature of scientists to talk about springs? Because of this remarkable fact that when you stretch them, all springs behave the same way. Stop and think how strange and useful this is! For when you stretch the credulities of a lot of persons, they behave in all sorts of ways. You can, moreover, take a spring out of a watch, and usefully study it as a spring, forgetting its origin. But you can't take the pituitary gland out of a man, or a child out of its home, or a line out of a poem, or a spot of color out of a painting, or a note out of a symphony, and usefully study these isolated bits, neglecting origins.

It is this dissectability of the physical world which permitted science—primarily physical science—to get such a good start so long ago. It was for this reason that Galileo could learn all about pendulums and the laws followed by *all* objects when they fall, whether these objects be lead balls or bird feathers. Newton could discover a *universal* law of gravitation. Ampere could find out the *basic* laws for electric currents—laws which continue to be true in modern electrical devices that Ampere could not have dreamed of.

Thus this way of analyzing nature—of designing experiments to learn the facts, of formulating general rules for describing nature's uniformities, of dreaming up possible new and even more general rules, and then testing by experiment to see if the rules are valid— this scientific way proved to be tremendously powerful. It worked. Step by step and accumulatively it gave men an understanding of physical nature, and along with that understanding, the power to control and, in the good senses of that word, to exploit.

In the world of living things, the progress of science was not so rapid, and we ought to be able to surmise why this was bound to be so. One single number describes how hard, so to speak, it is for direct current to pass through a certain wire. One concise law states the gravitational attraction between all particles of matter in the entire cosmos. Although there are indeed great complications and refinements in modern physical and chemical theories, the amazing fact is that enormous and very practical progress could be achieved with exceedingly simple and yet exceedingly general laws.

But how many variables does it take to describe a flower, an insect, or a man? How many subtly interacting and essentially interlocked factors must be taken into account to understand an emotional state? How complicated is the set of influences that affect behavior?

In other words, physical science was able to get started several centuries ago primarily because the world is so built that physics is relatively easy. There are, at the center of physical theories, a few general laws of great simplicity and generality and power; and these laws are relatively accessible to man because they are clearly and individually exhibited in rather simple examples. Biology, broadly speaking, is several cuts harder. A living organism is essentially more complicated and has many more interacting characteristics. It is much more restrictive (and can be wholly misleading) to study these characteristics one or two at a time, and underneath all is the massive fact, at once mystical and practical, that when one takes a live organism apart to study it, an essential aspect of the problem has vanished, in that what is on the experimenter's table is no longer an organism and is no longer alive.

There is a second—really a closely related—reason why the life sciences could begin to flower only after the [363] physical sciences had borne considerable fruit. For, as we are seeing more and more clearly today, a real understanding of life processes often requires a study at a submicroscopic or even molecular scale of dimension, using tools and techniques that have only recently been developed in the physical sciences. An illustration will clarify this point. In 1910 a disease was identified, hereditary in nature and confined to Negroes, which had a clear external pattern of fever, cough, headache, ulcers on the extremities, and sometimes eventual death. Little by little we have closed in on this disorder until it is now known to be caused by a purely *molecular* abnormality—the hemoglobin molecule in the red blood cells of the affected person possess an abnormally high positive electrical charge. This causes these hemoglobin molecules to link up together in a way that distorts the external shape of the red blood cells—makes them sickle shaped rather than doughnut shaped—and this in turn lowers the physiological effectiveness of the red blood cells and causes a special kind of anemia. The point of the illustration is that the cough, the fever, the decline, and death are obvious facts of the ordinary large-scale world: but the explanation could be found only when science had devised tools which could explore inside molecules.

When we pass further up the scale of complexity, subtlety, and essential interrelatedness, and consider the field of the mental sciences—normal and abnormal psychology, psychiatry, etc.—and ask questions concerning memory, the subconscious, the learning process, the relation between the mind and the brain, etc.—then we should not be surprised that the answers are on the whole still more tentative, the basic generalizations still fewer, the dependability and utility of the relevant knowledge still more questionable.

It is tempting to go one further stage and consider the realm of human behavior including all those social, economic, and political aspects of individual, group, and mass actions which constitute the social sciences; and to comfort oneself with the assurance that progress in understanding, and eventually in controlling, these phenomena is just as sure to occur as its progress in understanding the cell. We must not be impatient, or critical, surely we should not be contemptuous, of the tentative and fragmentary nature of the successes to date.

USES OF SCIENCE

So we have this great pageant of scientific progress, beginning with the austere precision of mathematics, the grandeur of astronomy, the great conquests of physics and chemistry together with the impressive technologies they have made possible, the marvelous although still partial progress made in understanding the living world together with beneficient applications of this biological knowledge to medicine and agriculture, and finally the first exciting invasions into the world of the mind and of behavior.

This—in necessarily sweeping and approximate terms—is what the scientists have been doing since those memorable Thursdays at the Bull-Head. One stubborn and complicated problem after another has given way before the evolving techniques of science. These techniques, which sometimes seem so specialized and formidable, with a baffling private language, with concepts of great abstractness, and with instrumentation that not even Hollywood can exaggerate, are in simple fact but highly purified forms of the methods of inquiry and reasoning which homo sapiens has used ever since he first began to become sapiens.

Thus the scientists have learned by experience that it pays to stop and think; that it is sensible to suspend one's prejudices and try to find out what the relevant facts are; that trying to decide what *is* relevant is of itself an illuminating procedure; that if the facts, as determined under sensibly controlled conditions and by competent persons, run contrary to tradition or hearsay or the position of arbitrary authority, then it is necessary to face and accept the story which is told by the facts; that logical precision in thinking is very useful when one is dealing with the more quantitative aspects of experience; that high standards of personal honesty, open-mindedness, focused vision, and love of truth are a practical necessity if one is going to be successful in dealing with nature; that curiosity is a worthy and a rewarding incentive; that nature is orderly and reasonable, not capricious and mad, with the result that it is possible to attain greater and ever greater understanding of the world about us.

These attitudes—usually phrased more formally—just about cover what is ordinarily called "the scientific method." But I have purposely used terminology that on the one hand makes it clear that science has no exclusive claim on these useful procedures; and which, on the other hand, should make it clear that persons in all fields of activity ought to inform themselves about the way in which science uses these procedures, since they obviously have validity in many other fields.

SCIENTISTS ARE HUMAN

Having listed some of the best characteristics of the scientific method we should, at least parenthetically, take note of the fact that scientists, being mortal, very frequently fail to utilize these valuable techniques when they step outside of their professional specialties. We have all too frequent examples of the over-emotional, poorly informed, and indeed sometimes quite nonsensical behavior of scientists when they express themselves on business, social, or political affairs.

And at this point I must indeed return to the scientists, whom we left waiting in the lobby several pages back. We said that science is what scientists do. We [364] said that scientists are on the whole pretty normal folks, eating and sleeping, laughing and loving and dying like all the rest of us. But we said that they do differ from other persons in one way, this being the intellectual inheritance which they receive from their schooling in scientific method, their knowledge of the vast successes which science has had, their proud partnership in the profession that has measured the star, split the atom, and probed the cell.

This inheritance is, I am bound to tell you, magnificent but dangerous. To too great an extent the word "science" has been identified with the more technological aspects of man's conquest of physical nature. To too great an extent we associate this noble word with the mechanical, deterministic, physical science of fifty years ago. Too little do we remember—because the subject is essentially not simple, and too few scientists spend the energy to try to be clear and too few citizens spend the energy to try to understand—that as thinking has progressed, the earlier rigid mechanical determinism has vanished out of science, so that the science of today deals with concepts that involve abstractness, imagination, the beauty of conciseness, and at the very core of the subject something which can properly only be called faith.

Overawed by electronic computers and atom bombs, appreciative of all the material comforts science has made possible, humbly thankful for the skill and tools of the modern doctor, misled by the mechanically complicated but intellectually simple gadgetry which is so often falsely paraded as science, confused by strange symbols and formidable looking apparatus, the average citizen has, I fear, established an uncomfortable relation to science. He tends to think of it as all-powerful and unchallengeable, because ultimately exact and perfect. The really great scientists never fooled themselves on this matter of exactness. Newton would have been the first to welcome and praise the corrections Einstein brought to gravitational theory, for Newton himself, speaking of the check with which he calculated two aspects of the force of gravity, first as necessary to hold the moon in its orbit, and second as necessary to make an apple fall to the ground, remarked simply, "I found them answer *pretty nearly*."

SCIENCE AND THE AVERAGE CITIZEN

The fact is that the average citizen tends to fear science; when he should of course learn about it, so that it can be an exciting intellectual companion and a useful servant. He tends to think that science is entirely mechanistic, and that its successes in the biological field depress the dignity of the inner man; whereas, as Robert Oppenheimer has said he should have known that "human life was far too broad, deep, subtle, and rich to be exhausted by anything the scientist would find out in his own field."

Rather than pretending to be perfect and ultimate, any scientific theory represents only a stage of progress in successively better approximations. Concerning one of the most basic theories in physics, Oppenheimer said ". . . it is a theory which is almost closed, almost self-sufficient, and almost perfect. Yet it has one odd feature: if you try to make it quite perfect, then it is nonsense." I would suggest that an absolutely critical distinction between science and religion may be that science never will and never can actually reach the final goal of perfection, whereas religion can do so and has done so.

The average citizen tends to think that science has destroyed the element of faith in religion; when he should realize that science is itself founded on faith. He tends to think that science is an ugly sort of foe of the gentler arts; when he should recognize that, as Bronowski has said[2] "There is a likeness between the creative acts of the mind in art and in science. . . . The scientist or the artist takes two facts or experiences which are separate; he finds in them a likeness which had not been seen before; and he creates a unity by showing the likeness." This discovery of unity is at the center of science, and it is also at the center of art. Whenever Coleridge tried to define beauty he returned to a central deep thought. Beauty, he said, is "unity in variety."

[2] J. Bronowski, "Science and Human Values," *Universities Quarterly*, 1956, p. 247 *et seq*.

We, of course, are not average citizens. We are determined to understand this great modern intellectual force, to utilize it properly so that it may serve our lives and may enrich our appreciation of the world around us, to respect the abilities of science at the same time that we realize its limitations, to know enough about science so as to be able intelligently to meet the responsibilities of modern citizenship. "I am strongly of the opinion," wrote Sir Edward V. Appleton, "that it is the scientist's mission not only to uncover nature but also to interpret his results to his fellow men. Scientific knowledge is itself neutral. It is the use that is made of it that is good or evil. Decisions concerning that use are not for the scientist alone. The layman must therefore make his own efforts at understanding. To assist him, the scientist must, in turn, be ready to leave his laboratory to act as a guide."

What we don't know hurts us

CHAUNCEY D. LEAKE
Saturday Review, January 4, 1958, pp. 38–40*

Today, for the first time since John Quincy Adams was in the White House and speaking directly to the Congress in his Presidential messages on behalf of science, the fine art of disciplined curiosity about the world we live in has an officially responsible voice in the top councils of the United States government. We now have what is in effect an Assistant President for Science and Technology.

Yet while we rejoice at this deserved state of dignity for science, the spirit of inquiry asks, "How come?"

With all respect to the Presidency, it seems clear that Dr. James R. Killian's appointment was a response to popular clamor.

How did the clamor arise?

The people clamored at omens in the skies.

There was public assurance from Presidential Press Secretary James Hagerty, and others, that neither Sputnik nor Muttnik surprised the White House. Regular readers of these pages were in part psychologically prepared. But to most Americans the rising of the Russian moons was a stunning shock, as big black newspaper headlines have shown.

To be blunt, then, the main reason why this country now has an Assistant President for Science and Technology is that our people learned the unwelcome truth of Russian scientific skill from a source beyond our borders. Under the force of this surprise the winds of U.S. opinion suddenly shifted from smug unconcern about science to a near hurricane of anxiety about our scientific prestige.

Can our democracy afford such blind shiftings and major policy decisions based on sudden emotional shocks? Indeed, without fully informed and deliberately weighed opinion, have we a democracy in reality? Are we not at last confronted by the tragic consequence

* Originally published in the Science and Humanity Section of *Saturday Review.*

of a false feeling of security given by authoritarian attempts to preserve "secrets" of scientific effort? Before this bureaucratically imposed secrecy destroys what it purports to preserve, would we not be wise to reconsider it as a national policy, and try instead to restore science to its traditional free, open, and democratic state, so that scientists may really help to protect and to extend those freedoms which we profess to cherish?

Such a change in national policy cannot come overnight. We need much personal and group soul-searching about what the concept of science implies. Then we might realize what scientists are trying to do, and how we may all help.

Before Sputnik, many Americans believed that whatever progress was made in Russia was accomplished by stealing our "secrets." Actually, no scientific "secrets" were ever involved. The essential scientific principles have been known to scientists everywhere. The important matter was choice of purpose to which the scientific knowledge might be applied, and then the technical knowhow to accomplish the chosen purpose. The belief that such knowhow could be handed over to an enemy by some spy whispering words on a street corner, or by passing secret documents, has little justification. In every previous case of Russian advance our well-intentioned but unwise advocates of secrecy could point to our previous possession of some technical advantage that might have been stolen. Only since the Niks rose into a sky empty of any moon of our modeling have our people had a chance to see how our own scientific progress can be retarded by interfering with the free exchange of scientific ideas. Only after the ballyhooed test flight of our own space rocket ended in smoke four feet off the ground was it clear to our people how little we had for anyone else to pirate. Our current timetables for reaching the moon are merely more smoke taking our attention from the basic requirements we need in science to assure our survival as a self-governing people.

Consider the paradox from which the Niks sprang. In the USSR, we are told by Dr. Nicholas DeWitt of Harvard's Russian Research Center, youngsters seek a scientific career because it is a safe refuge from the constant pressure of the Party line. In every form of intellectual activity in Russia, except science, one has to be dishonest with oneself in order to conform to the prevailing Marxism-Leninism. Scientific endeavor is self-defeating if it is dishonest. Dr. DeWitt goes on to say, "In the Soviet setting, the creatively inclined individual is most likely to seek escape . . . from political and social reality . . . in a scientific or engineering career. . . . Many good men . . . flock to (science) . . . to preserve the tiny bits of human honesty and dignity largely destroyed or shattered in the hypocrisy of Communist tyranny."

And while this scientific island of free expression exists in the midst of the sea of suppression surrounding the Kremlin, what have we in the United States? Our youth shuns science in resistance against demands for conformity in thinking. The Purdue Opinion Panel's poll of a nationwide sample of high school pupils in 1956 showed a twenty-seven per cent belief that science expects its practitioners to be "willing to sacrifice the welfare of others to further their own interests," a fourteen per cent belief that "there is something evil about scientists" and a nine per cent belief that "one can't be a scientist and be honest." Margaret Mead's study also revealed the low opinions held of scientists by American youngsters.

American scientists have been particularly harassed by ill-advised security [38] regulations which have hampered their scientific activities, inhibited their scientific interests, and given them a serious sense of anxiety and frustration. Our country has lost the services of many outstanding scientists as a result of narrow interpretation of security regulations. In comparison, the experience in Russia of Dr. Peter Kapitsa, one of the world's great physicists, is illuminating: When he refused on principle to work on nuclear weapons, he was allowed to pursue such scientific studies as would be of interest to him.

Our scientists have been fearful of being stigmatized by showing any interest in Russian science. The result is that we are painfully ignorant of what Russian scientists have been accomplishing, although their reports have been made openly available, in many instances with English summaries. Thus has American science suffered from the authoritarian administration of security regulations. Individual and responsible freedom is as essential to scientific progress as it is to the survival of democracy.

Because of the delusion that has been perpetrated upon him, it is

unreasonable to expect the citizen-at-large to initiate the change toward greater freedom. How, then, do we bring about the return to
sanity? Have not our scientists a special obligation here? It was our
scientists who set the pattern by imposing secrecy upon themselves
in atomic research well before the American government invoked
the censorship of World War II. Dr. Arthur H. Compton leaves no
doubt of this in his book, "Atomic Quest." The argument behind it
—fear that Hitler's racial bigots would turn their perverted intelligence to making the A-bomb first—proved unfounded, but it seemed
convincing at the time. No one then supposed that our free-wheeling
democracy would ever succumb to its own peculiar hunt for witches
dressed as scientists.

How can scientists begin to undo what we never intended to be
done? The National Science Foundation would seem to have provided us with an answer. In its report entitled, "Basic Research: A
National Resource" (in preparation for two years, it was dispatched
to the White House just eleven days after Sputnik's unexpected appearance in the heavens), NSF declares it to be "in the national interest that all results of basic research, wherever it is done, be published promptly. This applies to basic research in industrial laboratories as well as laboratories of universities or government." Should
Assistant President Killian adopt this policy as his own and persuade President Eisenhower to throw his weight behind it, scores if
not hundreds of research findings that are now locked up under one
pretext or another would fly like seed pods on the wind.
A second policy suggestion of the NSF study calls for "recognition of the requirement that federal grants for research . . . should
carry a minimum of restrictions on the freedom of the scientist."
The effect of such a proposal, conscientiously pursued, would reach
far beyond the limits of research itself into the social and political
consequences of science. There would be little compulsion for a sci-
ence-statesman like Dr. Vannevar Bush to tell the press, as he did
tell it at the close of last October: "The whole story (of our lagging
behind Russian science) hasn't been told and I can't break security
to tell it. . . . Many of the things I know were learned while in
scientific research for the government. I've got to hold them in confidence. I wish I were in a position to say more."

There is yet a third proposal in the NSF report which provides, in essence, a kind of enforcement for the other two. It advocates the return of as many as possible of our fundamental inquiries into nature and nature's laws to our universities, the historic defenders of freedom of thought. "It would contribute to the same end," the report observes, "if the policy were adopted by all research-supporting federal agencies to make contracts for applied research and development at such institutions if and only if the following conditions were met. First, the work must be demonstrably essential to national defense or welfare. Second, the work cannot adequately be done by industrial laboratories, federal laboratories, research institutes or research centers—approached in that order; or a selected university has unique competence in the area of interest." The extent to which the traditionally free exchange of information in university laboratories has been compromised by secret technological work is evident in the NSF caution that a change back to the older, preferred order of things must be undertaken gradually "so as to minimize any unfavorable effects," *i.e.*, wrecking of school budgets now dependent on contracts for "classified" experiments.

It is precisely at this point of delicate balance that the individual scientist can most effectively make his weight felt. As was noted by Dr. Charles V. Kidd, of the National Institutes of Health, at an American Political Science Association symposium last fall, "It is difficult to find a scientist of any stature" in the country who is not in some manner an advisor to the federal government. But the advice is often given in an atmosphere of political naivete. Dr. Kidd explained: "An advisor from a university who is serving on a policy advisory group may . . . feel that the federal agency is asking universities to undertake work of a routine nature which is, in his opinion, inappropriate. But if the full-time staff of the [39] agency strongly urges that such work be contracted out to a university the advisor is not likely to interpose strong objections. He is likely to remain silent on such questions, at least in formal meetings. He may believe that he should hold his fire for more significant issues. But these significant issues are seldom presented in a clear-cut manner. . . . 'Policy' is often not the adoption of carefully considered action formulated before the fact and near the top of the administrative hierarchy. . . . (It is most often) the accretion of . . . a long series of apparently trivial decisions made near the bottom of the . . . hierarchy . . . over a long period of time and viewed retrospectively. By reason of the nature of this process, it is often difficult for consultants to advise effectively on policy even when they are asked to do so. They hesitate to object to (the) small decisions . . . (whose) accumulation . . . is . . . policy making . . . (and so) the scientific advisor is at times and in a certain sense a captive."

Scientific advisors are captive not only to their political naivete but to something else that they are only now and very slowly becoming aware of. After many years of feeling unappreciated by their non-scientific fellows, the scientists suddenly find themselves lionized. They enjoy the experience, proving once again that they are human. There is a warm sensation of prestige in being consulted by one's government. Sputnik has brusquely interrupted this pleasant reverie by reminding independent thinkers that their silence, or to put it charitably, their true opinions, is in part responsible for the country's present state of shock and humiliation.

Having said as much, I am clearly obligated to speak unequivocably in favor of a reform in which I have been personally concerned. As chairman of the Committee on the Social Aspects of Science of the American Association for the Advancement of Science, I am one of a group of scientists who have advocated the abolition of administrative regulations which restrict publication and free exchange of information on the hazards of atomic radiation to public health. This group of scientists also believes, in company with Congressman Chet Holifield of California (see SR/Research, August 3, 1957) that the Atomic Energy Commission, being primarily responsible for maintenance of American supremacy in atomic weapons, should be relieved of the conflicting responsibility for evaluating the radiation dangers of wastes from atomic disintegrations.

I cannot and do not speak as Committee Chairman because the Committee wisely has concluded that it is not appropriate for such a scientific group as it represents to attempt to issue statements on social problems involving science, but rather to help furnish the information necessary for wise public policy decisions. The Committee hopes to deal with such general social problems involving science as air and water pollution, over-population, authoritarianism, optimum nutrition, and hazards to the common human gene pool. Protection of humanity from the danger of war may become a major consideration for the Committee, and here secrecy matters may again interfere. How, for example, can many people be protected against nerve gases, radiation hazards, or biological warfare, when no free person is allowed access to the classified information available on these matters? I speak as an individual who believes in unfettered knowledge.

I trust that nothing written here will be read to imply that I foresee a millennium in which the word "secret" disappears entirely from official documents. Given the present grave divisions among nations, classified experiments in military technology seem inevitable, transitory though the secrets prove in practice. Even in dealing with them, however, I would hope that we have learned that we simply cannot enforce loyalty by lining up those we suspect and purging them from us. Loyalty depends on a vast complex of interpersonal relations involving common standards and ideals. For us in the United States this means loyalty to the democratic way of life as exemplified in the history and traditions of the American people. One of these traditions is the tradition of science to find the truth about ourselves and the world about us. Our concept of national security must develop toward maximizing scientific gains rather than minimizing losses.

Now that we are face to face with unassailable evidence that the withholding of publication of our basic research findings does not prevent others from overtaking us, we may be able to look at secrecy in reverse. It is quite possible that by reporting our experiments openly we could work a deterrent effect on irresponsible politicians abroad. The men in the Kremlin are just as dependent on science as is the man in the White House. The elite character of the scientist in Soviet society is well known. If the Russian researchers could read for themselves the fundamental discoveries that we make, their knowledge of the implications would almost certainly serve as some brake on adventures in conquest. And there is always the hope that, with time, exchange of scientific intelligence may become a bridge for peaceful intercourse between eastern and western civilizations.

Here is a case history

JOHN LEAR
Saturday Review, January 4, 1958, p. 41*

On a preceding page Dr. Chauncey Leake has described the treatment the Soviet government accorded to Dr. Peter Kapitsa, a Russian scientist who refused to work on nuclear weapons. Dr. Kapitsa was held under house arrest for years, but was paid all the while and was permitted to follow a line of experimentation of his own choosing, which turned out to do with space rockets. Meanwhile, in the United States, Dr. Edward O. Condon, a past president of the American Association for the Advancement of Science, was driven from his job as director of the Bureau of Standards because people less well informed than he thought there was something suspicious about the intensity of his interest in Communist scientific literature. What follows is Dr. Condon's own story as he told it to a meeting of the American Physical Society in St. Louis and as it has been reproduced in *Science*, the AAAS journal:

During the last two months there has come about a general public awareness that America is not automatically, and effortlessly, and unquestionably the leader of the world in science and technology. This comes as no surprise to those of us who have watched and tried to warn against the steady deterioration in the teaching of science and mathematics in the schools for the past quarter century. It comes as no surprise to those who have known dozens of cases of scientists who have been hounded out of jobs by silly disloyalty charges, and kept out of all professional employment by widespread blacklisting practices. It comes as no surprise to those of us who have known how good American scientists have had to face vilification by political speechmakers in and out of Congress, and have been falsely prosecuted for perjury, and have been improperly denied passports, or have had their passports seized and invalidated without due process by the State Department, or

_____
* Originally published in the Science and Humanity Section of *Saturday Review*.

who have had their telephones tapped or their letters intercepted by government agents. . . .

I do not wish to seem boastful, and in this respect I would gladly change places with any of you, but I think that I have probably had a bigger dose of this kind of mistreatment than any of my fellow members of the American Physical Society. It began ten years ago last summer.

In that time I have had two full-scale loyalty hearings in the Department of Commerce, a full field investigation for the Atomic Energy Commission, which occupied the efforts of 300 FBI agents, and finally in 1954 had a hearing under the policies and procedures set up by this Administration. In all of these I received full clearance. All covered essentially the same ground, which was no ground at all. The House Committee on Un-American Activities made numerous attacks on me in 1947 and 1948 before its then chairman went off to serve a term in a Federal penitentiary. . . . Finally, this committee staged a political hearing on the same old stale and outworn material just before the 1952 elections.

During most of this period I kept on working to develop the scientific strength and stature of the National Bureau of Standards. Happily, this work is being carried on by my successor in spite of his having been summarily fired for a time by the present Secretary of Commerce who wanted the free play of the marketplace to take precedence over careful scientific experimentation.

Edward Teller told the last personnel security board hearing in April 1954 that the bureau's work on the hydrogen bomb which I organized advanced our achievement of that goal by many months, probably a year. If he is correct in the implication that without that work we would have been delayed by about a year, then the lack of that work would have made us come in second in the international rivalry for the hydrogen bomb.

Nevertheless, all the old stuff was rehashed once in 1952 and again in 1954. I was badgered all those years for having been interested in the American-Soviet Science Society, an organization which received a grant from the Rockefeller Foundation ten years ago to foster translation and wider distribution in this country of the Russian scientific literature. Now, a decade late, we read of crash programs to translate the Russian scientific literature. . . .

In July 1954 I was given complete security clearance by the Eastern Industrial Personnel Security Board. You might think now that I would be allowed to go back to work. Yet in October 1954, just before the elections, we find Nixon . . . boasting that he got the Secretary of the Navy to suspend my clearance, as was done on October 21.

It was arbitrarily suspended without any pretense that additional evidence needed to be considered. It was suspended by a Secretary of the Navy who admitted that he had not seen the record. I was told that I would have to go through the same old dreary business again. Three years ago I faced a very difficult decision—whether to continue to fight for the Government's honor, or whether to yield to the Administration's determination to disgrace itself. . . .

You might think that now I would be allowed to go back to work. I came East in January 1955 after giving my retiring presidential address to the American Association for the Advancement of Science and was offered the post of chairman of the department of physics in a leading university. In March the chancellor of that university told me that he could not follow through on the appointment because a high government official threatened one of the university trustees that if my appointment went through that university would lose all of its Federal funds.

In June 1955 I was asked to serve on a committee on a nonclassified problem of military importance—and then suddenly asked not to, just before the first meeting of that committee.

Incidentally, I *was* cleared from July 1954 to October 1954. During that period some Navy people came to see me with an urgent problem on the development of a radome for a guided missile. It was highly secret, but I was cleared for it. By the time we had the development models made my clearance had been suspended "pending further consideration," as Secretary [of the Navy] Thomas put it. Some of our cleared young men tried to deliver the radomes but found these Navy men in such a state of panic that they would not accept them! A few weeks later—all this was just about three years ago—they regained their courage and sheepishly asked to have the radomes. They were tested and found to be good and are now in production. Detail problems about them come up from time to time, but I am not allowed to help in their solution. . . .

Responsibilities of scientists in the atomic age

EUGENE RABINOWITCH
Bulletin of the Atomic Scientists, XV (January 1959), 2–7

Everybody has a responsibility to the society of which he is a part and, through this society, to mankind. In addition to the common responsibility of all citizens—such as to obey laws or to pay taxes—many individuals have additional responsibilities, arising from their belonging to special groups, endowed with special capacities, possessing special knowledge, or enjoying special power. The doctor, the teacher, the minister, the policeman, the soldier have such special responsibilities, often covering not only their work or service but their behavior in general. In our time, when science has become an important force, affecting both the life of the individual and the fate of society, scientists have acquired a peculiar responsibility, originating from their special knowledge and the power associated with it. What is it?

II

More clearly than anybody else, scientists see the senselessness and the tragedy of the present situation of mankind—the *reductio ad absurdum* by modern technology of the historical tradition of humanity divided into warring factions which threaten each other with armed might.

Despite this knowledge, scientists remain the weaponeers of hostile nations. They are caught in a vicious circle. If scientists of one country refuse to provide it with all the weapons science can invent, they may be responsible for putting their nation at the mercy of another, hostile one. This was the motivation which caused the greatest physicists of our time to urge upon the American government the development of the atom bomb at the beginning of the Second World War. Without the fear that Germany might be the first to threaten the world with an atom bomb, scientists in England and America would not have mustered up sufficient enthusiasm for the

job, and the feeling of urgency which made the atom bomb a reality
before the end of the war. After the war, it was apprehension—and
as it later transpired, a justified apprehension—that the Soviet
Union might be close to the production of a thermonuclear bomb,
that caused a number of American scientists to press for the development of the American H-bomb.

Some people (scientists as well as nonscientists) see the root of
the tragedy in wrong personal decisions of scientists. Max Born has
lamented that his former pupils and co-workers—Heisenberg, Oppenheimer, Fermi, Teller, among them—have not learned, as he
himself did, the wisdom of not lending their genius to the evil purposes of weaponeering. Robert Jungk, in his book *Brighter Than a
Thousand Suns,* presented the whole history of the atom and hydrogen bomb development [2] as one of the failures of scientists to
make the correct moral decision—to refuse to supply their governments with the terrible new weapons. These critics do not admit that
a conflict exists between two ethical imperatives with which a scientist is confronted in our divided world—the conflict between the
voice of scientific conscience, which counsels him against putting
his knowledge and skill in the service of destruction, and the counsel
of loyalty to his state and his society, which tells him that he is not
entitled to decide on his own whether this country and this society
should be left to face an enemy with inferior weapons—which is
likely to mean, in effect, with practically no weapons at all, except
moral strength, and consciousness of rectitude.

Some—a relatively small number—of scientists escape the conflict by becoming "conscientious objectors." This is the credo of the
Society for Social Responsibility of Scientists. Among its members
are some prominent scientists—Max Born, Kathleen Lonsdale. We
have been told—even if we do not know it for certain—that, in the
Soviet Union, Peter Kapitsa has refused to put his capacities in
the service of atom bomb development. It is, however, unlikely that,
in any one country, a majority of scientists will choose this path, and
thus effectively impose unilateral disarmament on their own nation.

III

Dr. Jungk suggests that it may have been only lack of communication that prevented an agreement between scientists on both sides

of World War II not to make an atom bomb, thus escaping the dilemma of unilateral disarmament. According to his story, leading German nuclear physicists consciously and consistently evaded working in this direction, and misled the German government as to the possibility of the development of the bomb. If only these German scientists had made a determined effort to let their American and English colleagues know of their decision! Then, Dr. Jungk suggests, Western scientists could have followed the example of their German colleagues, and the American A-bomb project would have bogged down, as the German one did.

I believe that the conspiracy of German scientists not to give the atomic bomb to Hitler, as described by Jungk, is a *post factum* rationalization of a vague uneasiness which caused German nuclear scientists to drag their feet, rather than to put into the atomic bomb work the same enthusiasm and urgency that animated their British and American colleagues. The German scientists, while not outright defeatists, had not the same fear of Hitler's defeat as the Western scientists had of a German victory. They grasped at evidence that the bomb could not be made in time for use in the war; and their a-scientific, if not anti-scientific, officialdom did little to urge them on.

IV

I believe that the basic cause of the predicament, into which the discovery of nuclear energy has brought the world, lies not in the inadequate ethical standards of scientists, or in the difficulties of communication between them. Rather, it lies in the low ethical standards of national governments, and difficulties of communication between them; and this, in turn, is the consequence of the stubborn survival of an obsolete organization of mankind, its division into separate sectors which require—and receive—full and exclusive loyalty from their members. Within such a world system, only a few individuals are likely to claim and assert the right to hold to their self-set standards of moral behavior, when this behavior—if emulated by a large part of their colleagues—could inflict fatal damage on the society to which they belong, and to which they owe their freedom and their living. Scientists as a profession are not likely to assume this attitude, any more than a whole class of American draftees is likely to turn one day into conscientious objectors. Scientists may be intellectually more advanced than the average population; but this intellectual level has nothing to do with attitudes in the face of this dilemma. While scientists see more clearly than can others the terrible consequences of the use of the weapons they are developing, they see with equal clarity also the possible consequences of their nation being left at the mercy of an enemy equipped with them; they are less likely to cherish the illusion that "old-fashioned" weapons could provide adequate defense against modern technological armaments, or that these armaments may not be brought to bear on the decision in a major future war.

The conflict between loyalty to his scientific ethics, and loyalty to his nation, weighs as heavily on the conscience of an atomic physicist as it does on that of a farmer, worker, or lawyer called into military service. It is not because of insufficient moral fiber, or indifference to human suffering, or high monetary rewards, that scientists do not walk out *en masse* from weapons laboratories. It is because they, like all other human beings in our time, are trapped in an obsolete structure of mankind, which our ancestors have bequeathed to us. They are part and parcel of a humanity divided into fractions, each of which enforces a certain moral code within it, but acknowledges (whatever its leaders may proclaim) no such code for its relations with other nations. Scientists cannot hope to change dramatically this situation through passive noncooperation of individuals, but they could—and, in my opinion, they should—contribute individually and collectively toward gradual reform of the world structure, ultimately to make possible a unified, harmonious humanity.

V

The political leaders of most nations understand that [3] the arms race cannot last indefinitely, and that, sooner or later, a form of international existence must be found which would permanently exclude war, and thus make competitive armaments to win this war unnecessary. However, they postpone acting for such a new world system until after the victory of their economic or political ideology, which they confidently expect to win. Western nations believe—and point to historical experience in support of this belief—that popular control of governments by free elections is the best guarantee against military adventures into which personal or ideological dictatorships are almost inevitably drawn. The Communist leadership—also quoting historical evidence—believes even more ardently that the capitalist economy, with its recurrent conflicts between unrestrictedly competing economic groups, inevitably leads to war, and that only world-wide acceptance of an economic system not motivated by profit, can put an end to them. Neither side is swayed by examples—some of them quite recent—which obviously contradict their generalizations. Both play for time, in the hope that the other side bears seeds of inner instability, and will sooner or later collapse.

But mankind cannot afford to wait. Each additional year of the arms race means an additional chance of nuclear catastrophe. However small these annual increments, the risks of subsequent years add up—and eventually they will become overwhelming.

As scientists, we should realize that at the time when the ideological lines which now separate the world into apparently irreconcilable camps were first drawn, the capacity of technology, founded on consequent application of science, to create wealth (by developing new sources of energy, by utilizing new raw materials instead of the scarce and unevenly distributed traditional ones, and by increasing productivity of labor through mechanization and automation) was much less obvious than it is now. We now know that with a well-developed science and technology (and given a sensible rate of population increase) enough goods can be produced to supply the basic needs of everybody, whether the economic system is the best one imaginable or not. Socialists believe, and will keep believing, that the most equitable distribution of the products of labor can be achieved under a fully planned socialist system, and that the increase in productivity will be fastest if it is not stifled by the requirements of profit earning; and they will quote chapter and verse for their belief. However, if we at all aspire to objectivity, as scientists must, none of us will deny that an economic system based on individual initiative and profit incentive has demonstrated, in America and elsewhere, a capacity to produce enough goods to achieve a fair standard of living for all. In the same way, the belief of many Americans that because of the absence of profit motive, socialist economy cannot achieve a high level of productivity, has been revealed as demonstrably wrong by the industrial development of the Soviet Union (and of the socialized segments of industry in Great Britain and other countries). In other words, while scientists may—and many will—maintain the conviction that one economic system is not only fairer, but also more efficient than the other, they will see the difference in quantitative and not in absolute terms.

VI

An important area affected by these considerations—an area in which (I believe) scientists of all countries have an abiding stake —is the economic advancement of educationally and industrially underdeveloped peoples. For these nations, the problems of political freedom and of the best economic system are overshadowed by the immediate and urgent need somehow to pull their masses out of the desperation in which want, undernourishment, and ignorance keep them. They need help from more advanced nations, through capital investment, through the spreading of education, and through the training of technical personnel, in order to be able to win the critical race between the increase in their agricultural and industrial productivity and the growth of their population.

Scientists of all countries must feel an obligation to help human progress win against blind forces of nature—not only for humanitarian reasons, but also because they are (or should be) aware that, in our age, peace and prosperity have become indivisible, worldwide problems; so that their own, at the present time more fortunate, nations cannot remain secure and prosperous as long as large parts of the world are not on the way to sound economic growth, and consequent stability. I believe that scientists of all countries should combine [4] efforts in this field, irrespective of their political allegiances and economic beliefs. They should urge their governments to join in providing such educational and technical help, leaving to the recipient nations the choice of economic and political forms in which to mold their aspirations. That such cooperation is possible, has been demonstrated by the International Atomic Energy Agency. I think scientists should explore together the possibilities of other creative international programs in technical, economic, and scientific areas.

VII

It is more difficult—but perhaps not impossible—to mitigate also the second ideological controversy which now divides the world: that between belief in individual freedom, and in centralized political, economic, and intellectual guidance by the state. We in the West believe that the greatest over-all human progress can be achieved if maximum scope is given to the thoughts and aspirations of the individual. True, we cannot fail to see that, in certain respects, society can be weakened or its progress slowed down by the clash and pull of contradictory ideas, desires, and impulses of different groups within it. However, in the last reckoning, we expect this weakness to be more than balanced by a greater wealth of new ideas, by the spur of competition, and by the greater enthusiasm with which people work when they are permitted to pursue their own ideas and aspirations. On the other side, the view prevails that more rapid progress can be achieved by restricting severely the play of contradictory ideas and forces, and making everyone work in a coordinated program, outlined by the ideological and political leadership of the nation.

Historical examples can be quoted in support of both views. Could we, as scientists, perhaps approach this controversy also in a quantitative, relative way, rather than as a matter of dogma? As scientists, we have a common experience—that, in science, free inquiry and untrammelled exploration by individuals are the ultimate sources of the most important progress. The greatest scientific discoveries have come through efforts of nonconformist individuals, who have asked heretical questions, and boldly doubted the validity of generally accepted conceptions—be it flatness of the earth, the necessity of continued application of force to keep a body moving, the universality of time, or the continuity of matter.

On the other hand, we have witnessed, in our time, impressive examples of organized application of science under central direction, and cannot gainsay that such efforts can produce the greatest practical results in the shortest possible time—be it an atomic bomb or a sputnik. These epoch-making feats, are, however, not the great scientific breakthroughs the public thinks them to be; rather, they are spectacular practical exploitations of scientific breakthroughs which had occurred earlier, and often unnoticed, in the quiet of fundamental laboratories, or at the desks of mathematicians or theoretical physicists.

Generalizing our experience as scientists, we may perhaps agree that society needs the free striving of individuals, as well as organized collective effort. We will disagree among ourselves as to how much scope should be given to these two forces to achieve the greatest progress of science and technology—not to speak of an attempt to extend the same approach to other areas of human endeavor, such as economic or political advancement of mankind. What we may, perhaps, agree on, is that the relative scope to be given, respectively, to the free, creative individual and to the organized collective should be considered as an empirical, experimental problem, without dogmatic prejudice.

VIII

I believe that the responsibility of scientists in our time is to bring into human affairs a little more of such skeptical rationality, a little less prejudice, a greater respect for facts and figures, a more critical attitude toward theories and dogmas, a greater consciousness of the limitation of our knowledge and consequent tolerance for different ideas, and readiness to submit them to the test of the experiment. These are the attitudes on which the progress of science has been founded in the past, and on which it remains based now. For scientists, there should be no final truths, no forbidden areas of exploration, no words that are taboo, no prescribed or proscribed ideas. Their common enemies are stubborn, preconceived ideas, prejudiced and close minds—forces whose triumph would mean the end of science.

It is this open-mindedness that makes fruitful the international gatherings of scientists, such as the atomic energy meetings at Geneva, and the numerous other, less glamorous scientific conferences. Many believe that this type of cooperation cannot extend beyond purely scientific or, at best, technical areas. Perhaps they are right, but the sequence of our meetings is dedicated to the hope that this is not the case. Our meetings suggest that with increased penetration of science into all areas of human life, an attempt to extend to new areas the approach that has permitted men of different creeds and political or economic attitudes to work successfully together in science, is at least worth making. The fact that we are meeting for the third time, and that those of us who were present at the first and second conference left them with a certain elation and a desire to return next time, is encouraging. True, we should not fool ourselves, or others. We are still only on the periphery of mutual understanding; we talk very cautiously, trying to respect the difficulties which our colleagues from different nations face in meeting with us. We try to talk mostly about our common beliefs, not to argue [5] out our differences. Ultimately, we will be justified in speaking about a real success of our endeavors only if we are able to explore together the whole situation of mankind, analyze both the things that divide and those that unite us, and find a common program of action —not in pretended ignorance, but in full consciousness of these differences. This cannot be achieved immediately. It will require time and patience; but to aim at less would mean soon to find our movement at a dead end.

IX

The first work in which scientists can and should combine their efforts, the first area of our common responsibility, is the education of peoples of the world and of their leaders to the understanding of the fundamental facts and implications of science for world affairs. The world must become aware of the essential irreversibility of scientific progress, of its dynamic character, of the impossibility of forcing it into pre-scientific patterns of national and international life. The leadership that will in future neglect to give to the sober facts of science priority over ideological concept, in the determination of its political conduct, as well as over established traditions or national passions, will do it not only to its own peril, but—unfortunately—also at the common peril of humanity.

A second common effort of scientists could be aimed at securing greater understanding of the importance not only of scientific fact, but also of scientific methods of solving problems, for the future fate of humanity. No scientist will be brash enough not to recognize the continuing and often decisive importance, for the behavior of nations, of irrational factors—of political and national animosities, established traditions; ideological, racial, and religious fanaticisms. Many people, skeptical of the scientists' intrusion into political areas, say that they are ignorant or wilfully neglectful of all these forces and that they naively presume that mankind can be promptly reorganized on a rational, scientific basis. This is not true; but, without underestimating the power of the irrational forces in shaping the relations between men and nations, scientists must, *first*, analyze these forces with as much objectivity and open-mindedness as they can possibly bring to bear on these matters; and *second*, try to find a reasonable compromise between these forces and the arguments of reason. In this way they help mankind to avoid the grave dangers of the dawning scientific age and to utilize fully its bright promises.

X

If, as scientists, we attempt to analyze the world situation, prognosticate on its future, and search for the best way to improve it, on a broader basis, including psychological, emotional, and traditional factors in addition to the scientific and technological ones, we will undoubtedly disagree violently among ourselves. Some will believe that they are in possession of fundamental principles and of a methodology, which can give them final answers to most if not all of the crucial questions. Others will bring into their attitudes a much greater skepticism if not agnosticism; still others, a religious or ethical attitude, based on belief in revealed truth. The one thing that could bring us together, and could entitle scientists to a certain degree of leadership, would be the demonstration of greater humility in the face of the unknown, greater tolerance of each other's points of view, and greater respect for mutual difficulties of nations and societies, than are commonly displayed in the political and ideological controversies. For us, all these disagreements and conflicts must be overshadowed by common knowledge of the great challenge which the progress of science and technology places before mankind, of the dilemma of nations either subordinating their political, ideological, and national aspirations to a common interest, or perishing together.

XI

One of our colleagues at Lac Beauport remarked after a few days of this meeting "I thought at first that we were wasting time. But now I see this is a different kind of conference. We have been accustomed to come together to call for a certain thing, or to proclaim a belief we have held in advance, and then to disband. This is a conference to which people come with doubts in their minds, to search together for truth. People must be made to understand this."

This, of course, means only that we come to discuss public affairs as scientists, and try to approach them in the same spirit in which we approach other problems in pure or applied science.

To the extent to which our scientific analysis does lead to definite conclusions, on which competent experts can agree, we can authoritatively address ourselves to the public. Our conclusions concerning the destructive possibilities of atomic warfare, the radiation dangers, or the nature and possibilities of scientific progress, belong in this category. On these matters, the clear and present responsibility of scientists is to educate the people and their leaders.

I believe, however, that this does not exhaust our responsibilities. Beyond spreading information on positively established scientific facts, it behooves us, as scientists, also to assist mankind in finding adequate answers to the many new problems of national and international life in the scientific age. This requires first of all, that we should study these problems in the spirit of scientific inquiry. It would be improper for scientists to try to advise others, without having first appraised the situation on their own, and acquired as much positive knowledge of the facts as possible. Our second responsibility, then, is, to *study* the impact of science on the affairs of man, and search for objectively adequate answers [6] to this challenge, as fearlessly and open-mindedly as we possibly can, accepting no ready-made answers from the outside—in the same way scientists would approach any other unexplored area of knowledge.

The continued Pugwash program should thus, I submit, have a twofold aim. One is to educate peoples and governments in things we know; the other, to expand our knowledge. In both directions, scientists from different backgrounds, with different political and national allegiances, should be able to work together.

Beyond these two responsibilities of *education* and *investigation,* some would suggest that scientists' responsibilities include also *action*—both individual action along the lines described at the beginning of this paper (refusal to work on military research, active participation in technical assistance programs, and similar constructive projects), and collective, concerted action, to stop the arms race and prevent the misuse of science for destructive aims.

I argued at the beginning of this paper against the belief that the crisis into which the discovery of atomic energy has brought mankind, could be prevented by the decision of individual scientists not to work on the new weapons. I am equally doubtful that similar individual decisions could now put an end to the arms race. It would be, however, something different if scientists of the world could agree on organized, collective action. However, this could occur only in an open world (for which Niels Bohr has called so eloquently in his well-known appeal to the U.N.). This world does not exist now, and is not likely to come into existence in the foreseeable future. In its absence, no common action of scientists throughout the world can be reasonably contemplated. However, the world changes before our eyes, more than ever in history. What looks impossible today may become a possibility in the next generation. In the meantime, perhaps, we should not be afraid of thinking—and even talking together—about this matter.

Exercises and theme topics

EXERCISE V. PROBLEMS OF TECHNIQUE: COHERENCE AND TRANSITION

To communicate effectively, the material of any expository article, including your own papers, must be arranged in a meaningful and logical (or dramatic) sequence providing *coherence* both within each paragraph and from paragraph to paragraph. As you know from Exercise I, any subject divides into certain organic parts. These may include the background of an event, the event itself, its consequences, the problems arising from those consequences, and proposed solutions to those problems. As you also know, however, a writer need not follow this simple, essentially chronological sequence but may impose upon the material an arbitrary arrangement in order to achieve some desired effect or emphasis. Like Eugene Rabinowitch, he may begin with a statement of his thesis and then turn to a discussion of background. Again, before he begins to develop his own idea, he may state the ideas of another group, as does Bronowski in his "The Real Responsibilities of the Scientist." Whatever order he gives to his material, he will keep in mind one basic principle: the reader must be able to follow easily his train of thought. He may rely upon such devices as chronological order, climactic order (moving from the least important to the most important point), classification, or comparison and contrast, to name a few.

The principle of *coherence* also applies within a paragraph. To achieve it, the writer will make use of parallelism, effective subordination, reference of pronoun, repetition for emphasis—all intended to show the exact relationship between his ideas.

No matter how carefully the writer works out his sequence of ideas, the relationships may not be easily followed unless he has employed devices to achieve effective *transition*. By means of transitional words and phrases he will tie his paper together; he will erect signposts to guide his readers. These signposts should connect both the sentences within a paragraph and the paragraphs themselves.

Skillful *transition* is not obvious; the author avoids such artificial phrasing as "let us now consider . . ."; "let us turn . . ."; "come with me, dear reader, while we view with alarm. . . ." Not only does he make use of subordinating and coordinating conjunctions, he also uses conjunctive adverbs (then, first, nevertheless, finally, subsequently) and correlative conjunctions (neither . . . nor, both . . . and, not only . . . but also). Then, too, he employs phrases which indicate logical relationships (on the other hand, in contrast, despite these factors). Occasionally he writes a brief paragraph that bridges some progression in his thought. He may sometimes use rhetorical questions or repeat key words, but with them he must be particularly careful, for they are the most difficult devices to work with. He will show his skill by *not* using the same device— the same conjunction or phrase, for example—over and over until it becomes noticeable. At all times he will remember that these transitional devices aid the reader to grasp the meaningful, coherent sequence of his paper.

Assignments

1. What method, or methods, does Chauncey D. Leake use to gain *coherence* in "What We Don't Know Hurts Us"?
2. What transitional devices does L. V. Heilbrunn use in "The Waste of Scientists"?
3. If you find an article, or parts of an article, in Part III in which the *coherence* and *transition* are not fully effective, suggest specific ways to improve upon them. (Do any rewriting you believe necessary.)
4. So far as *coherence* and *transition* are concerned, what is the most effective article in Part III? How does the author achieve this effectiveness?

EXERCISE VI. CLASSIFICATION AND ANALYSIS

Two of the most important forms of exposition are *classification* and *analysis*. Although at first glance you may think them virtually identical, they are not. *Classification* concerns itself with the systematic arrangement of objects and ideas into categories which can frequently be combined to form other, more general groups. (Biology provides an excellent example.) In this way it serves as the basic procedure of abstraction, because with it you may begin with an individual, physical object and move to a high level of abstraction. For example, beginning with your own car, you may progress through all makes of cars manufactured by that one company to all makes by all companies, to consumer goods, to all factory products, to industrial assets, to national assets. But normally you will be neither so concrete nor so abstract in your papers. Instead, you will deal with three or more *types* within a larger group: station wagon, sedan, convertible as American family cars; or winged-T, split-T, single-wing as football offenses. Instead of a formal, already existent *classification*, you may on occasion wish to make up a personal one. Whatever your subject, however, you will need to follow two principles. First, choose a category which will divide into three or more distinctly separate subgroups. (A division into two only would become a comparison and contrast rather than a *classification*.) Second, choose a single common denominator as the basis for your division, as in the examples above.

Whereas *classification* concerns itself with the description of types and the differentiation of one from another, *analysis* concerns itself with discovering the component parts of a single unit, as, for example, the parts of an automobile or the parts of a living cell. Most simply it lists, enumerates, these parts—1, 2, 3—and describes each one. Herman Finer's article, "Government and the Expert," illustrates this reliance upon enumeration. (Notice that in one instance at least he comments upon, evaluates, each item as soon as he presents it.) In this function, *analysis* closely resembles *classification* in that both are primarily descriptive.

Analysis goes beyond mere description, however, to deal with problem solving. It is in fact indispensable to problem solving and comes as a necessary preliminary (or accompaniment) to any judgment you may make. In all your college classes and examinations you will be called upon to make analyses: in literature, to analyze the structure and symbolism of Melville's *Moby Dick* or The Pearl Poet's *Sir Gawain and the Green Knight*; in history, the causes of the Civil War; in chemistry, a solution of unknowns. Outside the academic experience you face the same procedure whenever you make a choice: when you select a college or career; or when you select a location and design for your house. In Parts III and IV, "The Scientist and Modern Society" and "Science and Education," each writer presents a problem for the reader's consideration. But notice how differently they handle the essentially analytical situations. In "The Scientist in Society" Oppenheimer skims briefly over many phases of the problem in order to concentrate upon that which "bothers me especially" (p. 124). In "The Real Responsibilities of the Scientist," Bronowski pursues his thesis primarily by contrasting the roles of the scientist, the government, and the public. Although the theses are similar, notice how differently Rabinowitch develops "Responsibilities of Scientists in the Atomic Age." Other contrasts may be drawn from the articles on education in Part IV.

Yet however broad or narrow their perspective, however objective or personal their tone, these writers follow basically the same procedure. What is the nature of the problem? What factors (parts) contribute to it and why? Which of these factors is (are) most significant? Having answered these questions, they may then offer a solution, or solutions, but in doing that they move beyond the realm of *analysis*.

Assignments

1. How effectively does Warren Weaver develop his *analysis* in "Science and the Citizen"? What is the nature of the problem? What factors contribute to it? Which are most significant?
2. Compare the methods by which Bronowski and Rabinowitch develop their analyses referred to above. Are they equally effective? If they are not, what makes one more effective?
3. Did any one article, or part of an article, seem especially ineffective? Suggest the causes for this weakness. Make specific suggestions to improve it. (Do any rewriting you believe necessary.)
4. Of all the articles in Part III, which did you regard most effective? How did the author achieve that effectiveness?

THEME TOPICS

1. Write a critical summary of any one of the articles. What is the author's main idea? What are his supporting points? What illustrative evidence does he introduce? Is he effective in persuading you to his point of view? Does he maintain an objectivity toward his material, or does he show a bias? Does he

omit any phase, or phases, of the topic in order to strengthen his own conclusions?

2. What effect do the writers believe secrecy has had upon science and scientists, the government, the general public?

3. What do the writers regard as the essence of present problems involving science and society? Why? What solution(s) do they offer?

4. Define such a term as progress or responsibility as the different authors use it. Do they use it in a special sense?

5. Do the other authors support Bronowski's contention that "people hate scientists"? Is he justified—on the basis of the evidence he presents—in holding this view? If he is wrong, how does the American public view the scientist?

6. What view(s) of the general public do these writers hold? Does their position, or positions, seem justified?

7. What attitude(s) do these writers have toward the Renaissance? The eighteenth century? The nineteenth century? (Any one period may well provide the basis for your entire paper.)

8. Oppenheimer contends that science no longer affects culture and ideas, as it did during the Renaissance and succeeding periods. Attack or defend this assertion.

9. What picture of science in Germany under the Nazi regime do these writers give?

10. Defend or attack Heilbrunn's assertion that "to some extent Madison Avenue has moved" into scientific research.

part IV

SCIENCE AND EDUCATION

A crisis in science teaching

FLETCHER G. WATSON
Scientific American, 190 (February 1954), 27–29

Everyone knows about the shortage of scientific manpower. The need for scientists in industry, government and the military services is critical, and all indications are that it will become more critical in the coming years. The focal point of the problem is in the secondary schools, where the nation's youth take the decisions that shape our working force: what vocation to take up, whether to go to college, whether to enter engineering or the liberal arts or to major in a scientific field. Let us look at the situation there.

The U.S. has some 25,000 public and 3,300 private secondary schools, operated by nearly as many different school boards. The schools vary in size from a few score pupils to 5,000 or more. Half of the 6 million high school students attend schools which enroll less than 400.

So far as number goes, the secondary schools offer an immense and rapidly growing pool of human resources. In the past 80 years high school rosters have grown 18 times faster than the population. We now face an even sharper rise due to the soaring postwar birth rate. In the two years immediately after the war births jumped from 2.7 million to 3.7 million, and the trend is continuing: 1952 hit an all-time high. On the basis of these births and of a slowly rising percentage of teen-agers who go to high school, it can be predicted that high school enrollments will shoot to 9 million by 1960 and to over 11 million by 1966.

Where will the teachers be found to handle this increase? The 340,000 teachers in the high schools today are barely adequate to staff them. Within six years we shall need 418,000 teachers and by 1966 we shall need 520,000.

If we narrow this down to the specific case of science teachers, the picture becomes truly alarming. The requirement is expected to rise from 67,000 science teachers today to 84,000 by 1960 and

100,000 by 1966. Already some 7,000 new science teachers are needed each year. This demand, based upon replacements as well as new positions, will soon go to 10,000 a year. Altogether we shall require a total of 100,000 new science teachers between now and 1966.

In the face of this need the sources of teaching strength are drying up. College graduations have declined 30 per cent from the G.I. peak year of 1950. Because the colleges are still drawing from the low birth rates of the depression years, the current figure of 300,000 graduates [27] a year is not expected to increase appreciably in the next five years. Furthermore, the number of persons qualified to teach has fallen off more than the number of college graduates. In mathematics the decrease is 41 per cent, in the other sciences 48 per cent. Last year fewer than 5,000 potential science teachers were graduated, as against the need of 7,000. Moreover, many of these potential teachers were lost to industry or to the military services. A recent study in Minnesota showed that only 41 per cent of potential science teachers were actually employed as teachers in the year after their graduation. Of all subject areas, science had the lowest yield to the teaching profession.

Just as serious as the shortage of quantity is the shortage of quality. There is no yardstick for measuring the quality of teachers, but at a minimum we must expect the teacher to know the subject he is teaching. We find in the first place that the state requirements are far from exacting. In 29 states a person can be licensed to teach science on the basis of study in just one science subject. Thirteen other states have rather specific course requirements. Only five states require study in comprehensive fields such as the physical or biological sciences.

There has been no nationwide survey of the actual backgrounds of teachers engaged in teaching science, but a consistent picture emerged from studies made in eight states and from a nation-wide sampling of biology teachers. The states were Alabama, California, Massachusetts, Minnesota, Nebraska, Pennsylvania, Texas and Utah. A considerable number of the persons teaching science in secondary schools in those states were not certified to do so: about 20 per cent of all the high school teachers taught one or more science courses, but apparently only half of them were qualified in science.

Of those certified in science, many had only meager training in it. A fairly large proportion had prepared in just one science. Teachers of general science tended to have less training than those teaching special subjects. At the other extreme, many of the science teachers in those states had done graduate work in science and education. In general, science teachers in large schools tended to be better prepared than those in smaller ones.

How do teachers with so little equipment to teach science as some of these have get into the classroom? One loophole is the "life certificate," which allows old teachers licensed many years ago to teach subjects in which they have had no college instruction. The other is the general secondary school certificate granted in a number of states, which permits an individual to teach in any subject area irrespective of his training. Athletic coaches and physical-training instructors are commonly used as part-time science teachers, though they often have less than the minimum background. Such makeshifts have been increased by the shortage of new science teachers, which has forced many school administrators to shift teachers from social studies or English, where replacements are available, to science classes. Although many of these teachers are acutely aware of their deficiencies, they have no escape.

For want of a few thousand competent new science teachers each year, science instruction in our schools must either be curtailed or become such a caricature of teaching as to bore or repel promising students. It is clear that if the shortage of scientists and technically trained people in the U.S. is to be solved, the first requirement is a joint effort of all concerned to encourage and train competent young people to become science teachers.

Certain myths need to be dispelled. One of the commonest, carried over from our memories of college instruction, is that a high-school science teacher teaches only science or only one science subject. Actually only half of the people teaching science in secondary schools do so full time. The other half teach at least one course in some other area of learning. Philip A. Johnson, formerly of the U.S. Office of Education, wrote in 1950: "Fragmentation of science teaching by the assignment of several teachers, each serving only one or two science sections, often results in the read-about, talk-about type of science teaching deplored by school leaders and tolerated by the pupils. . . . The large number of part-time science teachers . . . suggests that division of responsibility may be the most serious weakness of our science teaching enterprise." As school enrollments rise, administrators will have increasing opportunity to correct this by scheduling science teaching as the full-time responsibility of a few well-trained teachers.

Most of the full-time science teachers today teach more than one science. A study in Illinois in 1946 showed that 61 per cent of biology teachers, 98 per cent of chemistry teachers and all physics teachers taught other subjects as well. Similarly, a study in New York found that 53 per cent of all science teachers [28] had three or more different science subjects to prepare each day. Similar results were reported in Minnesota and Utah. Furthermore, the subject assignments often changed from year to year.

This means that science teachers should have at least some preparation in each of the major sciences. The narrow specialization often required by colleges is especially undesirable in the preparation of science teachers. Breadth of study must be obtained even if it means sacrificing so-called depth. Fortunately a growing number of states require five years of preparation for high school teaching, and future teachers may be able to obtain both breadth and depth in one or more fields. Already some five states require this longer preparation for the high-school certificate.

Another myth is that teaching is an easy job. Besides the 23 to 25 hours a week they spend in classes, teachers have a multitude of other school duties, including work with individual pupils, grading papers, taking care of laboratory equipment, preparing new instructional material and keeping informed in their fields. Up to 40 per cent of science teachers work under the handicap of having no permanently assigned room, so that they must move their material from room to room. A National Education Association study showed that the average teacher puts in 48 hours a week on school work. Only 21 per cent of the sample interviewed reported less than 40 hours, while 22 per cent reported more than 55 hours per week.

Considering the meager rewards of teaching, either social or financial, one wonders why anyone chooses to become or remain a teacher. Last year the average income of all teachers in the U.S. was $3,530 per year. In 1938 teachers were in the top third of the income groups of the country: by 1948 they had dropped into the bottom third. To make ends meet many teachers must carry extra jobs during the school year and take unskilled or semi-skilled work during the summer.

Fortunately there are competent people who "just have to teach," whatever the rewards, and they form the backbone of our educational system. But that is not enough. Teaching in science has become increasingly important as our society has become more technical and more wealthy through the fruits of science. It will take serious, thoughtful and cooperative efforts by all concerned—educators, parents, industry and government—to meet the needs in science education.

Current problem in perspective

CHARLES DOLLARD
The Scientific Monthly, 83 (June 1956), 277–281

The problem that I am to discuss can be stated with relative simplicity. The United States has achieved an unexampled level of material prosperity, chiefly by exploiting its own scientific discoveries and those of other nations. There is a chicken in every pot and an electric stove to cook it on, a car in almost every garage, and a television aerial on every other roof. Science enables us to live longer, work less, dress more comfortably in all kinds of weather. We no longer have to leave the house to go to the movies. We can lunch in New York and dine in San Francisco on the same day, or spend the weekend in Paris without missing more than a day at the office. We are eating high off the hog, thanks to science and its handmaiden, technology.

We have not, indeed, achieved this prosperity without exciting envy and aggression in other, less prosperous nations. There is a considerable portion of the world's population that regards us with unfriendly eyes and that would be glad to see us one with Nineveh and Tyre. Here again our main dependence is on science. The enemy may outnumber us 10 to 1, but so long as we are confident that we have the edge on him in science and technology, we feel relatively secure. The very heart of our defense system is the relatively small corps of scientists who man our laboratories.

Here we are then in the midst of the 20th century, fat and prosperous, and for the moment, at least, relatively secure against aggression from abroad. The fly in the ointment is that we have become painfully aware that the army of science is not getting enough recruits. There is disagreement about the extent of the shortage in the ranks, but there seems to be no disagreement about the central fact. The annual demand for men trained in science and in engineering exceeds the annual output of our colleges and universities by a considerable margin. And the steady decline in enrollment in science courses in our high schools and colleges gives rise to the fear that the situation is getting worse rather than better. To add to our worries, word comes from the enemy's camp that his potential in science and technology, measured in terms of trained manpower, is growing apace and will soon exceed ours if indeed it does not already do so.

The relative decline in high-school enrollments in science and the undersupply of college graduates with good training in science and engineering are phenomena that can be measured. More frightening but less measurable is the possibility that science [277] in this country is no longer attracting to its ranks a fair share of the relatively small fraction of our population that is capable of first-rate intellectual work. The lack of well-trained technicians to man our expanding laboratories and drafting rooms is cause for alarm. The failure to recruit the much smaller number of men in each generation who are capable of the original and creative work that makes science a growing thing might easily be fatal. We cannot hope to maintain our industrial preeminence or our defenses against outside aggression merely by exploiting yesterday's scientific discoveries.

CRITICISMS AND REPLIES

When any group or nation is confronted with a problem that threatens its welfare, its first reaction is to look for a scapegoat. If something is wrong, someone is to blame. In this case, the search for the villain in the piece has been going on for several years. Recriminations are the order of the day. The scientists blame the public schools for drying up the pool of talent on which science depends by diluting the curriculum, by substituting the pablum of courses in social adjustment and citizenship for the good red meat of chemistry, Latin, and mathematics. Some of the more extreme critics of the public schools go so far as to allege a plot by which the teachers colleges of the country have degraded the high-school curriculum to conceal the incompetence of their own graduates. High-school programs nowadays, these extremists say, are determined by what the teacher is capable of teaching rather than by what the student should learn.

As might be expected, the teachers are ready with answers to their critics. Indeed, they have some indictments of their own to offer. They point out that, whereas in 1900 they had to serve only the top 10 percent of the population of high-school age, they now must accommodate 80 percent; and that this vast increment represents in large measure the children and grandchildren of foreign-born Americans. The public-school teachers remind us also that their share in our phenomenal prosperity has been a meager one and that they are, on the average, paid less well than railroad switch tenders or brick layers. In defense of their much abused curricular innovations, they protest that, especially in the cities, the public schools are now called upon to perform many of the youth-training functions once performed by the family and the church and that they have become the major instruments for preparing children with diverse family and ethnic backgrounds for life in a society much more complex and confusing and competitive than that which their fathers knew. They argue that if they are to be blamed for juvenile delinquency and gang warfare, they must be allowed to spend a fair share of the school day dealing with problems that give rise to these difficulties. If the curriculum has changed, they say, it is only in response to changes in the size and the diversity of the population that the school must serve.

The liberal arts colleges have also come in for their share of blame. Like the high schools, they are accused of offering a vast assortment of trivial courses that cater to the weak and tempt the strong to take the easy, rather than the hard, route to the baccalaureate degree. They are charged with loading the dice against programs of study that require real intellectual effort by offering alternative programs that, for the bright student, involve almost no effort at all.

The critics of the colleges also charge that these institutions share the blame for the decline in high-school standards by reason of their failure to motivate their best students to become teachers. To this the colleges reply that so long as their graduates can earn twice or three times as much in business or industry as they can earn in teaching, the situation is not likely to change markedly. Finally, the colleges complain with increasing bitterness that government and industry are making a bad situation worse by bidding away from the colleges the able young scientists who are so badly needed to train the next generation. How can we be expected to produce better crops, ask the colleges, if our seed corn is taken from us?

The Federal Government comes in for its share of blame too. It is accused of diverting our best teachers to defense research, either by awarding fat contracts to the universities or by offering individual teachers large inducements to move to government laboratories. And on all sides we hear the complaint that the government is using the power of the purse to divert effort from the basic research that keeps science on the march to developmental work that merely exploits last year's discoveries.

Each of these indictments has a large element of truth in it. By denying teachers as a group a fair share in our national prosperity, we *have* suffered a loss in the quality of teaching all along the line and especially at the secondary-school level. Industry and government *have* made it hard for the colleges to hold able men in their faculties by offering salaries that the colleges couldn't possibly afford to match. We *have,* indeed, been eating our seed corn. The teachers colleges *have* gone overboard [278] on method as against content. Many of our teachers, especially in the sciences, *are* badly trained. The high-school curriculum *is* less rigorous than it once was, and many of our colleges *are* offering a host of courses that have little intellectual content. We *have* undoubtedly burdened our public school system with a great many tasks that have little or nothing to do with training the mind.

STEPS TOWARD IMPROVEMENT

Now it would be quite misleading to imply that in this crisis all our energies have been devoted to a futile search for a whipping boy. On all sides we see encouraging and intelligent efforts to do something about the situation. The American Association for the Advancement of Science is now conducting a major study of ways and means to improve the teaching of science at all levels. The Ford Foundation has raised the flagging spirits of college teachers everywhere by its magnificent series of gifts for the improvement of faculty salaries. To an ever-increasing degree, industry is recognizing its responsibility by making unrestricted grants to colleges and

universities and by supporting scholarship programs designed to reduce the loss of talent which we now suffer by reason of the failure
of many of our brightest students to enter college. The Fund for the
Advancement of Education is supporting a variety of studies and
experiments looking toward the improvement of teacher training,
better utilization of our present supply of teachers, and the development of more challenging programs for the very bright high-school
students. The Federal Government is moving on various fronts too.

The aggregate effect of all these measures is bound to be good,
and we are justified in looking for some improvement all along the
line. The changes will not be dramatic or sudden. In attempting to
reverse the trend, we must pay the price of having a highly decen-
tralized educational system in which change must be accomplished
by example and persuasion rather than by fiat.

To me, one of the most heartening aspects of the situation is that
most of the remedial efforts on the educational front to which I have
referred recognize the fact that first-rate scientists are not wholly
the product of good training in science. To the best of my knowledge, no one has seriously proposed that we should attempt to solve
our present dilemma at the expense of neglecting other aspects of
the great tradition of liberal education, of which science is a part.
There seems to be a general awareness that the student who has not
been permitted and encouraged to cultivate a taste for the arts, for
literature, for philosophy, and for the social sciences is unlikely to
develop the breadth of mind and the habits of thought that distinguish the real scientist from the technician and the gadgeteer. There
seems to be general agreement that science will be best served not
by improvement in science teaching alone but by raising standards
of instruction across the board.

In the course of preparing this paper I was reminded of a speech
that the late Frederick Lewis Allen, long-time editor of *Harper's
Magazine*, delivered in New York some years ago. Allen recalled
that as an undergraduate he had been impressed by the determination of his roommate, Louis Zahner, to make his name ring down the
corridors of time by stating a law that should bear his name. In his
last term at Harvard, Zahner achieved his objective. Zahner's law,
as Allen pointed out, is in the great tradition. It admits of no exceptions. It can be tested empirically. It requires only ten words for its

statement. It runs as follows: "If you play with anything long enough, it will break."

Allen confessed that he was so jealous of his friend's achievement that he could not rest until he had matched it. Allen's law covers a wider range of phenomena than Zahner's, but it too is characterized by elegance and simplicity. It reads as follows: "Everything is more complicated than it seems to most people." Does Allen's law apply to the present situation?

WILL YOUNG PEOPLE CHOOSE SCIENCE?

Assume for the moment that our various efforts to toughen the curriculum and improve teaching [279] achieve a fair degree of success. Assume that at least the best of our high schools can be motivated and enabled to teach chemistry and physics and biology and mathematics as well as these subjects are now taught in the freshman year in the best of our colleges. Assume, finally, that our young people today are on the average as idealistic and no lazier than American boys and girls ever were. Does it follow that an adequate number of our most gifted young people will seek careers in science? Are there other factors to be defined and dealt with, more subtle than those already discussed, which are making science as a career less attractive to young people than it once was?

This question arises because, as one surveys the educational scene, one is impressed by the fact that our schools and colleges, with all their weaknesses and imperfections, are still managing to produce an adequate—or more than adequate—number of candidates for admission to other professional fields in which standards of training and performance are relatively rigorous. Our medical schools have at least 3 times as many qualified candidates as they can handle. Our law schools are overflowing. Graduate departments of psychology and economics are besieged with candidates for advanced training. Are students entering these disciplines rather than the basic sciences, not because they are lazy or because science is poorly taught, but because science no longer presents itself to the young as a field of human endeavor in which a man can achieve a full and free and useful life?

Before attempting an answer to this question, it might be well to consider for a moment the context in which young people in our society determine their life careers. As in other aspects of our culture, the doctrine of *laissez faire* holds. There are many influences but no directives, many suggestions but no commands. Parental ambitions play a part. So does admiration for gifted teachers, or for lawyers, doctors, clergymen, and other adults within the circle of the child's experience. Ours being a culture in which money is a very important value, the question of material rewards weighs heavily with the majority. The best evidence we have indicates that career choices tend to be made at about the ninth grade.

One factor that undoubtedly plays a part in leading young people, especially the more idealistic ones, in one direction or another is the public image of each profession or calling that is current at the time the choice of career is made. This public image, or stereotype, is a product of various forces and may have little basis in fact. Indeed, fiction plays a major part in its formation. I suspect, for example, that many young men born in Great Britain in the second half of the 19th century were diverted from careers at the bar by reading Charles Dickens' novels, which, as you will recall, pictured all lawyers as unprincipled, self-seeking charlatans with no concept of public service. Molnar served the doctors of his time in much the same fashion. Conversely, Kipling's romantic picture of the life of the British soldier in India undoubtedly helped to keep the Queen's armies abroad well supplied with recruits. In our own time, such novels as Maugham's *Of Human Bondage* and Thompson's *Not as a Stranger* have done much to make medicine appear to the young as a career at once exciting and socially useful.

The tide of events, national and international, plays its part too in the formation and alteration of these public images. Bankers lost caste during the dark days of the depression; at the same time the freshness and excitement of the New Deal attracted hundreds of able and idealistic young men to government service.

Has something happened in recent years to the public image of science and the scientists—some change that makes science less appealing to the most gifted and idealistic young people of our time than it was to earlier generations? To answer this question satisfactorily would take a great deal of research. We should have to know much more than we now do about factors that affect the career choices of young people. But even in the absence of such exact knowledge, I offer some speculations.

To the boys of my generation, science wore two faces. One was the face of a fictional character named Tom Swift. Tom Swift was a boy genius, who single-handedly produced a flow of marvelous devices and gadgets more spectacular than the combined output of Alexander Graham Bell, Thomas Edison, and the Wright brothers. Tom Swift made the life of the inventor appear to be at once the most exciting and the most profitable that a boy could possibly choose. I suspect that he drew a substantial number of my contemporaries to careers in engineering and science.

The other face was a composite of Ben Franklin, and Darwin, and Newton, and all the other great men of science whom we encountered in our history books and in our outside reading. This composite picture appealed to a much smaller number of my contemporaries. It suggested long years of hard work, and self-discipline, and short rations. But for the idealistic it opened up vistas of a life of great personal satisfaction and benefit to mankind, with the possibility of fame at the end of the road.

Now, different as they were, these two images had something in common. Both suggested unlimited opportunity to indulge one's curiosity, to [280] follow one's own nose, to work alone if one chose and at one's own pace. Although one route led to fortune and one, at best, to fame, both involved a journey full of excitement and both symbolized freedom in all its aspects.

Does my son's generation have the same image, or images, of science and technology? I wonder. I suspect that to our young people today the scientist appears as a man who works under wraps, on small segments of highly specialized problems defined by someone else—a man under pressure to get an assigned job done, hardly less subject to authority than an Army recruit. I suspect that the image of science as a life of freedom and high adventure may have been one of the major casualties of the last war.

At this point I must remind you that I am speaking of images rather than of realities, of how science looks from the outside rather than from the inside. I'm sure that the image of the scientist that I have recalled from my own high-school days is a most romantic and unrealistic one. I am equally sure that, in spite of security regulations and all the other heavy burdens that considerations of national defense impose on scientists, in spite of all the pressures toward programmatic research, in spite of vast, highly organized laboratories, science is still for the most part the land of the free. I'm sure, too, that the role of what James Conant aptly called the "uncommitted investigator" is no less important and challenging than it was in Newton's day. Nevertheless, I am convinced that the public image of the scientist is quite a different one.

POSSIBLE MEANS TO AN ANSWER

If misconceptions regarding the conditions under which scientists live and work are to a greater or less extent keeping young people out of science, what can we do to remedy the situation? I don't think there is any simple answer to this question. If there is, I'm not ready with it.

Undoubtedly some of the steps that have already been proposed will help. We know, for example, from such studies as that of Goodrich and Knapp that the gifted science teacher can make science appear to be the most interesting and rewarding of all professions. But there never has been and never will be enough such teachers to go around. It therefore behooves us to think of other means of giving young people a truer image of science.

In discussing this problem with teachers and others interested in science education, I have come upon one suggested experiment which I think might be worth conducting. The essential steps in this experiment are as follows. (i) Choose two communities of approximately 100,000, which so far as can be judged have high schools of about the same quality. (ii) Within these two communities identify all the ninth graders who appear to have the capacity to do well in college, whether in science or in any other field. (iii) Expose the selected children in one community to every possible experience that would help to give them a fair picture of what scientists do, how they work, and what their rewards are, leaving the children in the other community, so to speak, in the dark. When I say every possible means, I intend to include not merely printed materials or lectures but also visits to laboratories, opportunities to ask questions of working scientists, perhaps even actual employment in a laboratory for a brief time. The essential aim would be to enable youngsters to smell and feel science as well as read about it and hear it discussed. (iv) Without changing the course of study usually available to either group, or the teachers, determine how many students from each group choose science as a major when they enter college.

If the exposed group, to borrow a medical term, produced a significantly larger number of recruits for science than the unexposed, we would have at least a clue as to what part misconceptions about science as a career play in depleting its ranks.

I referred earlier to the fact that our concern over declining enrollments in science was increased by news from abroad. If the figures that we are now getting on the present and prospective production of scientists and engineers in the Soviet Union are reliable, we may fairly assume that the Communists are resorting either to bribery or to conscription. Since the Communist government now controls all the educational facilities within its borders, the problem of who shall study what is a simple one for them to solve.

Our value system commits us to a much more difficult program. We can undoubtedly increase the enrollment of our engineering schools measurably by increasing the salaries of engineers, and we undoubtedly will. But science as a creative activity must compete for talent against all the other exciting and socially useful professions and vocations which a great industrial nation offers to its young men and women. It will be given an advantage in this competition by all the steps now under discussion—by better teaching, better teaching facilities, better textbooks, better means of identification of the most gifted children and more attention to their needs. But in the last analysis, science cannot hold its own in this country unless we convince our young people that, as of old, the life of the scientist is a life of freedom, of adventure, and of self-fulfillment.

The plight of science education

HOWARD A. MEYERHOFF
Bulletin of the Atomic Scientists, XII (November 1956), 333–337

Continental drift has been the subject of heated debate among geologists in recent years. According to the theory, a closely knit supercontinent, centered upon what are now the Arctic and Atlantic basins, has been fractured and the parts have "drifted" away from each other, tending to converge upon, and to narrow, the huge Pacific basin. With obvious qualifications, the theory of continental drift has its counterpart in astronomy, where the expanding universe presents a somewhat similar picture of the disruption of a relatively compact whole, the segments of which are now heading at breakneck speed for parts unknown.

The validity of these theories need not concern us here, but the concept of disruption, drift, and virtually explosive dispersal has metaphorical application to the current relation existing between science and technology, on the one hand, and between society and education, on the other. The situation is the more paradoxical because the structure of our society now has more technology than anthropology built into it. Indeed, it is the anthropological hangover that thwarts the unity science and technology could bring to society were the processes of education and communication more effective.

Unlike the drift of the continents or the expansion of the universe, the defection of science from education can be traced historically, step by step. Starting as natural philosophy, science became fragmented into astronomy, biology, chemistry, geology, and physics as the body of knowledge regarding the heavens, the earth, and life grew beyond the comprehension of any one natural philosopher. Then, as the study of life progressed, biologists found specialization forced upon them, and each ultimately took more pride in being a phytologist, an entomologist, a physiologist, a microbiologist, an endocrinologist, or an embryologist than in being a biologist.

The American Chemical Society needs twenty-one divisions to encompass its specialists, holding them in a single society, in effect, by keeping them apart, each to speak the language of his own specialty.

CONFUSION COMPOUNDED

To be sure, we have the Old Testament's word for it (*Gen.* 11:9) that God frowned upon human efforts [333] toward unity and brought about the confusion of tongues at Babel; but specialization in the fields of learning—generally described under the misnomer *scholarship*—has compounded the confusion. To it humanists, linguists, and social scientists have contributed as liberally as have the scientists, until now, apart and distinct from language, we have a new discipline called *communication*, which is still struggling in ineffectual infancy.

To a degree, the Babel of scientific jargon can be justified. The systematist in biology needs binomial nomenclature to differentiate the rich variety among biological species, living and extinct. The specialist in any field requires a technological shorthand to communicate accurately with his co-workers with minimum loss of time and space, and with maximum comprehension. Tragically, however, too little effort has been expended in retaining a common language, until there is not even a Lowell-Cabot-God sequence in any major field. Unless geneticists are talking to geneticists, or petrologists to petrologists, they can talk only to God.

Within the broad educational discipline known as science, the dispersal resulting from the explosive expansion of specialized knowledge is seriously hampering scientific progress. Perhaps the frontiers in each of the sciences are "endless," but further advance lies in large part in reintegration. In the earth sciences, for example, a most fertile and promising field of research is proceeding at a pedestrian pace, and will continue to do so until geologists and geophysicists learn not merely to speak each other's language, but also acquire understanding of, and respect for, each other's knowledge of, and experience with, earth phenomena. Team research is a helpful device in breaking down interdisciplinary barriers, but its utility is limited to the participants in, and by the scope of, each individual project. Its function is specific; it plays no part in reintegrating science or education.

THE FRAGMENTATION OF KNOWLEDGE

The expansion and fragmentation of knowledge have thus reached the point of diminishing returns in science, and new advances will be accelerated as rapidly as communication effects reintegration of the parts, or specialties. The process of reassemblage, however, will be piecemeal, and it will not restore the natural philosophic content that once made science an accepted and essential part of every scholar's training. Science has, moreover, come under suspicion among humanists, linguists, and social scientists for other reasons that make them wonder whether it still deserves a place in our system of higher education.

No one can deny that science has lost much of its alleged "purity" and has become increasingly vocational. Thirty years ago scarcely one scientist in ten entered industry. Science was a cultural, ivory-tower subject and profession, plied in the classroom, the university laboratory, or the museum. The curriculum in each field was designed accordingly, and it had a strong natural philosophic and scholastic flavor. The scientist vigorously differentiated himself from the engineer, whose vocational training prepared him for industrial employment rather than scholarship.

SCIENCE BECOMES VOCATIONAL

In the year 1956—one generation later—nearly 50 per cent of the practicing scientists, whether bachelors, masters, or doctors, are employed in industry. In many schools the curriculum has been shaded or modified, the better to prepare the science major or the graduate student for an industrial career. The graduate thesis, as often as not, is some facet of a government project or industrial contract upon which the thesis director is working and for which he is being paid. Inevitably, the Greek and Shakespearean scholars and the historians and sociologists on the faculty look with mingled feelings of dismay, contempt, and jealousy upon the vocational cast of scientific training; the larger enrollments in science fostered by the lure of scholarships, fellowships, and highly remunerative employment following graduation; the auxiliary income of the science staff; the superior equipment of science departments; and the abandonment of pure, or scholarly, research in favor of applied research.

In view of these trends, there is an only too human tendency on the part of German and English and art professors on faculties to unite against the scientists, and to reduce the science requirements or to limit the kinds of courses that will meet the broad cultural objectives for graduation. Several factors aid and abet them in this procedure. The poor preparation of entering students has compelled colleges to relax entrance requirements and to broaden the freshman-sophomore curriculum to cope with a lower common denominator of precollege training. Mathematics and science have followed Greek and Latin, first as electives, and then as discards, among the courses our educationists deem essential in the so-called life-adjustment programs in many secondary school systems. To solve the problem of nonpreparation of entering freshmen, and in the hope of reculturizing required science, colleges have tended to imitate the example of the secondary schools, where "general science" has displaced physics, chemistry, and earth science. Today the college freshman ordinarily finds himself with a choice—or a requirement—of introductory physical science or introductory biology, in which he is exposed to scientific principles but is rarely trained in the rigorous methodology and precision that comprise the essence of science.

ENTER GENERAL SCIENCE

Science faculties initially resisted the introduction of general courses, which brought them few majors and [334] little pedagogical satisfaction. The resistance has waned—in the liberal arts colleges because the general science course is a simple device to get the poorly prepared student out of the way, and in the larger schools because the staff is far more interested in the training of graduates than in struggling with undergraduates. A great deal has been made of the recent discovery that the small liberal arts colleges produce a much larger proportion of the nation's scientists than the undergraduate schools of large universities, but little attention has been paid to the significance of this fact: Institutions with large graduate schools commonly attach no importance to undergraduate training and provide, at best, mediocre and uninspired instruction at the college level.

During the chaotic war years, the question of college science seemed academic, and after the war, with classes bulging, the science departments were not interested in measures that would add to their enrollments. Since 1950, however, the tide has turned, and only the impending population increase promises to stem ebbing college interest in science and mathematics. The beach at ebb tide is not entirely a thing of beauty, but it brings the viewer face to face with some of life's (and death's) homely realities. By analogy this is the time to take stock of some of the realities in the situation confronting science and scientists.

In the field of education, science, as we have seen, has lost stature through the many concessions to vocationalism. The acute shortage of physicists and mathematicians, and the need for still more chemists and geologists than our schools are training, have placed our science departments under pressures that are novel in academic circles. The most insistent demand for more and better specialists comes from industry, which annually deploys recruiting teams over the academic world, and does not always stop with the recruitment of students. The most vocal clamor for more scientists and engineers is now coming from the Congress, which has awakened to the fact that science and technology are the bone and sinew of national security and economy.

LACK OF WELL-ROUNDED SCIENCE TEACHERS

A demand from nonacademic sources for scientists in nonacademic fields of activity has had at least one disastrous consequence, with others imminent. College and university staffs have grossly neglected the training of well-rounded, cultured scholars whose sole or primary interest lies in teaching and/or in pure (i.e., nonapplied) research. The result of this neglect is now rearing its ugly head in the secondary schools. Since 1950 the number of college students training for careers in teaching science and mathematics has dropped 50 per cent, and half this dwindling supply is lured into industry. Forty per cent or more of the secondary school vacancies that must be filled in so basic a subject as mathematics are being filled by teachers who lack the qualifications to teach it. This is the situation despite the fact that modern educational theory has reduced the need for mathematics instructors by turning from solid instruction in a few fundamental subjects to mass education by way of a bewildering assortment of electives, many of extremely dubious value for any purpose. Under this theory, only one quarter of our high school students are taking two years of algebra, and fewer than 10 per cent manage to acquire the mathematical background that qualifies them for college work in science and engineering. Low salaries and unsatisfactory working conditions in the public schools further complicate the problem created by scientists' neglect of their source of student supply and by the "life-adjustment" theory of mass education. In prospect, therefore, it is by no means certain that science and engineering will get their proportionate share of the large post-depression crop of students.

Soon the pinch for gifted teachers will be felt at the college level. In one sense it is already being felt, because, as noted above, few of the larger institutions of learning place any premium on good teaching. In fact, it is heavily penalized, and assigning a staff member to undergraduate instruction is equivalent to transferring a policeman to a beat on the city's outskirts. The result is a matter of record: The ratio of scientists coming from the big schools is small, out of all proportion to the size of their student enrollments, the reputation of their faculties, and the amount of their investment in plant and facilities. In fact, one wonders whether they might not serve the professional manpower and general educational needs of the nation better by liquidating their undergraduate activities. The only alternative is a drastic change in attitude toward the role of teaching versus the role of research. When the faculty itself is not hostile to the objective of good teaching, the administration often is, although it is hoped that few administrations carry things to the extreme of the dean in a well-known institution who keeps a record of the number of lines published by each member of his faculty, to minimize unfair advantages resulting from variations in article length and in page size. Apparently the caliber of the research carries no weight in his otherwise meticulous record.

The widespread indifference in our universities toward producing and rewarding good teachers is puzzling. Ninety per cent of our young people are influenced by their elders in the choice of careers, and, as a guess, 75 per cent of the time a teacher casts the deciding vote. In engineering the hour of decision generally comes in high school. For science and the teaching profession it may be deferred until the college sophomore year, provided no crucial omissions are made in earlier years. In view of this elementary fact, the scientists' indifference toward brilliant teaching, and their neglect of the teaching profession, are suicidal acts which, under existing circumstances, are contrary to the national interest. [335]

The temptation to vocationalize undergraduate and graduate training is no less ill-advised, because virtually every employer not only expects, but prefers, to train recruits for the specialized work to be done in his laboratories. The historical fact is, industrialists have done far more to discover and develop the technological potential of America's human resources than educators. At the more advanced educational levels, industry prefers highly trained and well-informed mentality to efficiently drilled technological competence. Thus, without serving industry, the drift toward vocationalism in our colleges and universities is curbing the normal advance of science, drying up the wellsprings of recruitment and supply, and prostituting the cultural values of science as one of the four basic ingredients of a liberal education.

LACK OF PUBLIC APPRECIATION OF SCIENCE

Except in the field of biology, scientific educators are now in a minority. In 1953, for example, industry hired 85 per cent as many Ph.D. chemists as were graduated from our universities in June of that year. In biology, the figure was only 11.3 per cent. Yet the educators, not the industrial scientists, control the future of science, not alone in our national security and economy, but also in our culture. To date, under the successive pressures of war, postwar adjustment, and industrial demand, they have abdicated their control to the dictates of circumstance. In spite of the efforts of a devoted corps of science writers, who have received little help from the profession in their efforts to compete with sensational "human interest" stories, there is little public appreciation of science and technology. To the man in the street, they are represented by the atom bomb and the "magic" of television which, like the telephone, the airplane, aluminum, and plastics, are destined to become as humdrum a part of life as orange juice and fresh eggs for breakfast. In short, while trying to meet the research needs of the moment, scientists have fallen down on their most elemental obligation—communication—which, if effective, is the *sine qua non* of education.

There is something strangely familiar about the problem confronting science. Just as the American people found themselves unprepared to assume the role of leadership thrust upon them during and after World War II, so with the scientists. Hailed and damned for the release of atomic energy, they are doing too little too late to publicize the vital role it can play in promoting social welfare and progress. With the national security and economy virtually in their hands, they have made belated protests against the waste of scarce scientific and engineering brainpower and have left the power of decision entirely in the hands of uninformed legislators and government administrators who seek guidance on this moot subject as avidly as they seek votes. With the key to modern civilization and to future progress in their formulas and instruments, scientists have stood idly by while educators have trimmed science and technology to a bare minimum in school curricula that are supposed to "adjust" young people to life in an age of science and technology. And now, when their birthright in the field of education is threatened, they remain passive, although the creative imagination of scientists who gave us the principles of evolution and genetics, the law of gravitation, and the periodic table must be ranked with the inspired contributions of Shakespeare, Goethe, Beethoven, Kant, and Herodotus to our culture.

POORLY PREPARED FRESHMEN

Although the remedy for these deficiencies and outright failures lies in education, education cannot begin without communication. At present communication seems to end, instead of begin, in the classroom. In most of our state and large private universities, the instruction of teachers is scorned. The task is left to the ill-equipped and underfinanced teachers' colleges. Yet scientists are loudest in their condemnation of the school systems that deliver to them poorly prepared freshmen. They too often consign these beginning college students to the tender but unseasoned care of a young instructor not far enough away from the technical minutiae of his dissertation, or to an overworked graduate student in training for his orals. Most beginning students acquire a quick and lasting immunity to the mental DDT contained in this kind of instruction, and to the subject matter of the course; whereas the few who are affected become the same kind of scientists as their instructors. Yet here is the place to present an inspiring canvas of earth history, or evolution, or nuclear energy; to stimulate the thirst for more, equally inspiring knowledge in the same or related fields; to encourage the dissemination of the knowledge gained, in other classrooms, in the press, or in the lecture hall. Specialization, when it comes, should be relegated to its proper place in the field and should be kept in perspective. And it should never be permitted to destroy or impair the art of communication.

THE ROOT EVIL—SPECIALIZATION

Like many extinct species from the geologic past, science exhibits the symptomatic effects of orthogenetic evolution. Unless it is bred with new strains it will grow progressively more impotent at a time when it can—and should—become the most potent of factors in world progress and unity. The prime orthogenetic factor is specialization. With specialization, the tempo of research is being maintained chiefly by the artificial respiration of team or operations research; but this is not communicated, hence has only a negligible influence in reintegrating the sciences, or even the specialties within each discipline. Specialized science moves farther away from the public and from that stream of public consciousness on which it ultimately depends for its existence. Only through a handful of interpreters does it maintain communication [336] with the rest of the world. Its lack of concern about communication is already evident in the diminishing supply of teachers, and this will be followed by a shrinking pool of students, in a descending spiral leading toward technical competence but to cultural extinction.

"RESTORATION OF LEARNING" NEEDED

It is easy to rant about the defects of a system but difficult to prescribe correctives. In a recent book dealing with the secondary school problem, Arthur Bestor describes the corrective as "the restoration of learning." No better label could be devised for the needs of the moment and of the future, but the situation in the sciences is more involved than Bestor recognizes. The Congress and the Administration are aroused to the dire need for more scientists and engineers if we are to maintain our national security and economy at their present relative level. Industry, in general, is so absorbed in meeting its contractual obligations that it still lacks a conscious concern—or a conscience—about the future source of trained personnel. (Witness the case of the aircraft company that, last summer, hired six of the eight physicists from the faculty of a small engineering school, thus wrecking the physics curriculum for the entire student body.) With a few noteworthy exceptions, our science faculties have yielded to the pressures of industrial demand for their product and to student demand for good jobs and high salaries, and have vocationalized their instruction.

Here is an aggregate of forces that need not necessarily be countered. On the contrary, it appears feasible to organize and direct them into the one essential goal that is being neglected—that of self-preservation. Nature's chief concern is reproduction, and it must be made a primary objective among scientists. Reproduction takes place at every level of instruction, and only through instruction. It demands, first, good teaching, which can come only from broadly trained scholars in our universities and colleges. This good teaching must be employed, among other objectives, to inspire more students to enter the teaching profession, particularly at the secondary school level. It should also be directed toward effective communication that will reach the public and impart a knowledge of science, its aims, its methods, its achievements, to every segment of a nation that has risen to greatness through science and the applications of science. Self-preservation does, indeed, require the restoration of learning, the resurrection of scholarship, the reentry of science into education.

Science—the endless adventure

LEE A. DU BRIDGE

Bulletin of the Atomic Scientists, XIII (March 1957), 74–79

Much has been written in recent years about science as the hope of man's future and also about science as the instrument of man's destruction. You have read of the possible glories of tomorrow's world of technology when people won't have to work—but only push buttons—and can spend endless hours of leisure speeding across the country in radar-guided, air-conditioned, pink Cadillacs at 120 miles an hour or more. And you have also read of the utter ruin which civilization would face in case of an all-out war using all the modern techniques of destruction.

You have heard of many such things which are probably true. Advancing technology is going to bring about great changes in our methods of living—changes in the next fifty years as great as those in the last fifty. But it is also perfectly possible that an all-out nuclear catastrophe will intervene.

You have also read other things that are untrue or improbable. I think the imminence and practicality of space travel by humans (not to mention its desirability) have been grossly exaggerated. Cheap and abundant atomic energy is still a long way off—though in some parts of the world (not in America) it will soon be cheaper than other sources they have available. Still other promises you have heard violate basic laws of physics or would be fantastically expensive.

I cannot say whether these extraordinary things that technology is going to bring us are good or bad. In fact, no one can say—for *anything* can be *either* good or bad, depending on how it is used, whether it's a stick of wood or a stick of dynamite. *Things* aren't bad; only *people* are bad. And as to whether people are going to be bad or not there is no argument; some of them certainly will be. But whether they are or not, these new *things* are going to come anyway—*for no force on earth can stop men from thinking,* from inventing, from exploring.

The things men invent will arise from new things they learn, from new understanding they acquire about the world. On the foundation of new ideas, men create great new technologies, new industries, new machines, new ways of doing things.

I propose to examine not the superstructure that men have erected on the foundation of knowledge, but the foundation itself. I am not going to explore the glittering upper rooms and towering pinnacles of technology—I propose to go to the basement and examine the foundations of science on which all technology is based.

And I propose to discuss first about science not in the light of the new technology to which it may lead, but to talk about science for its own sake—science as a method of thinking, science as a method of acquiring new knowledge, science as the key to understanding, the road to comprehension of the physical world. I am going to discuss science, the endless adventure.

From the day that man first acquired consciousness he began to observe the things about him—the nature of fire, of water, of the winds, the sea, the stars. And as he observed, he remembered and reflected. He noted the regularities of nature. Fire could nearly always be produced in a certain way and extinguished in certain ways. The sun marched regularly across the sky—though more careful observation showed that its path changed almost imperceptibly from day to day, from week to week, and at the same time the weather became warmer, [74] then cooler, then warmer again. When these invariable regularities of nature are reduced to their simplest form, we call them the "laws of nature."

THE MANY NUMBERS

At a very early time man must have been conscious of numbers—the number of his children, the number of his wives! How many animals he killed, how many enemies he had. Primitive men had words for only three numbers—one, two and *many*. Gradually the "many" became sorted out—3, 4, 5, 10. Curiously enough, it was a very long time before men discovered the number "zero" and learned to use it.

At this juncture I should like to pause a moment and reflect upon the importance of numbers—and upon the science of mathematics which has been built upon them. How many of us realize how utterly impossible our modern way of living would be without a number system and without our science of mathematics. Suppose we had not yet invented numbers above 10. Suppose even we had to add and multiply with Roman numerals. For example, how do you multiply XVI by MCMXL?

Suppose we were unable to deal with numbers higher than a million, or even a billion. That might have a salutary effect on government budgets, of course, but there are quite a few large corporations whose gross income is above one billion dollars too.

But, if we come to think of it, how many people *do* know what a billion really means—or even a million? Counting as fast as you can—say 3 per second—it would take you 3 days, 24 hours a day, to count to a million—over 8 years to count to a billion.

Is it any wonder that we find it difficult to realize what it means when we say that a modern hydrogen bomb has an explosive energy 20 million times as great as a 1-ton TNT bomb? That is a big bang indeed. But we should not be misled the other way either. For the radius of destruction of a bomb depends on about the cube root of its explosive energy. And that means a 20-megaton bomb has a radius of damage only the cube root of 20 million—270 times as big as for a 1-ton bomb. That's still a damage radius of 10 miles or more. But a Los Angeles paper recently published a letter expressing fear that Los Angeles people might be hurt by the Bikini tests—3,000 miles away! To do that would take the power of 27 million 20-megaton bombs!

Now I am not trying to confuse you or scare you. I am only giving some spectacular illustrations of being able to think in quantitative terms. Why do we still teach arithmetic as though numbers bigger than 100 or 1,000 were too complicated to grasp? A million is 10^6, a billion is 10^9, a million squared is 10^{12}, and $10^6 \times 10^5$ is 10^{11}. It's very simple! Even a little experience with exponents would give youngsters a lot of fun—and would make it possible for them, out of their own experience, to deal with millions and billions in a more meaningful way.

I noted just the other day a curious example of this inability to deal with numbers larger than a billion. A science story in a weekly news magazine contained the statement that in a certain volume of air there were "billions of molecules." Now of course that is perfectly true, but it is about as significant a statement as though we said that on the earth there live dozens of people. There are, of course, many dozens of people on the earth; in fact, there are about a half a billion dozen. Similarly, there are many billions of molecules in a cubic centimeter of air; in fact, there are 30 billion *billion* molecules. We feel sorry for primitive men who were unable to distinguish numbers higher than 3 and referred to everything else as "many." Some day in the future, people will think of us twentieth-century humans as being rather primitive because we were unable to think in terms larger than a billion.

Our whole modern civilization is built on mathematics! Not a street can be laid, a foundation dug, or a building constructed, without the use of algebra, geometry, and trigonometry. Not a machine can be designed, an engine's performance predicted, an electric power plant constructed, without mathematics through calculus. And the design of an airplane, a ship, a guided missile, or an electronic computer requires a profound knowledge of higher mathematics. No one, in short, from a grocer's clerk to the nuclear physicist can do without mathematics—and the study of mathematics can be a great adventure in the methods of quantitative thinking which will provide a lifetime of better understanding of a technological world.

A CLIMB TO THE SUN

But let us turn now to adventures in the world of physical science rather than mathematics. I should like to start the adventure with a journey to the sun. Adventurers who climb Mt. Everest are pikers; we are going to explore (in our minds at least) what we would find at the center of the sun.

Now the first thing we notice about the sun is that it is hot. It is very hot, in fact. The surface temperature is about 11,000° F. That is higher than any temperature ever observed on earth except in the burst of an atomic bomb. That is far above the melting point of any material we are familiar with; it is far above the boiling point of most materials. Therefore, the sun is very much like a ball of hot gas.

But the surface of the sun is its coolest part. It is easy for an astrophysicist to prove that, because the sun is so massive and the gravitational forces are therefore so enormous, the sun would promptly collapse into a very much smaller object unless the central part of the sun is at a very high pressure and temperature. In fact, the central temperature is probably about 23,000,000° F. [75] The pressure is so great that the central portion has a density 10 times the density of lead—though it is still a gas!

The age-old question about the sun, of course, is what keeps it so hot. We know that the earth has been at roughly its present temperature for 4 billion years or so. The sun must have been at about its present temperature equally long. Where does all that energy come from?

Up until just before World War II—very recently you see—not even the beginnings of a satisfactory answer had been found. We know now that the only source of energy possible is the transmutation of matter—specifically, in the case of the sun, the transmutation of hydrogen into helium. The sun, in other words, is a big continuously operating hydrogen bomb. It would, in fact, explode just like a bomb except that the gravitational forces are so enormous that it is all held together in a very nice balance.

Fortunately, there is a lot of hydrogen still left in the sun—enough to last for another few billion years in fact. Some day, however, it will be gone. What then? Will the sun collapse and cool off? No, strangely enough, it will collapse and get hotter! The gravitational energy developed in contracting generates still more heat, so the interior will get hotter as the sun gets smaller.

And then? Eventually the internal temperature will rise to about 200,000,000° F. at which point something new will happen. The helium which was formed by the conversion of hydrogen will now be at a temperature where it can begin to "burn." Three atoms of helium can join to make one atom of carbon; four atoms of helium can make one atom of oxygen. In both cases energy is again released so that this source of heat will maintain the internal temperature of the sun at 200,000,000° F. until the helium in turn is all used up.

At this stage the sun will start to collapse again; the internal temperature will rise still higher until the point is reached at which the carbon and oxygen atoms will begin to combine to form still heavier atoms, building up eventually to elements in the neighborhood of iron. By this time, the temperature of the center may have reached several billion degrees F.

During these various processes, there are intervals of possible instability and the possibility of an explosion arises. We do not know precisely the conditions under which an explosion might take place, but explosions of distant stars have been observed in the heavens. They are known as supernovae. But at this point our knowledge gets very vague indeed. In fact, it is only in recent months that a detailed quantitative picture of the evolutionary history of the stars and of the process of atom building has been worked out by combining the knowledge of astronomy with knowledge recently acquired in the laboratories of nuclear physics. Again the problems and techniques of mathematics play an important role. Just recently, Dr. Fred Hoyle of Cambridge has evolved a project for making detailed computations of the evolutionary history of the stars, a project which will require five years to complete on one of the fastest of modern computing machines.

This, I claim, is one of the greatest of all adventures in science— the most daring, the most intricate. The sun is only one of a billion stars in our galaxy. And there are millions of other galaxies equally large scattered through space. The faintest that can be seen on plates of the great 200-inch telescope at Palomar are 2 billion light years away. Yet we know that the same elements—the same kinds of atoms and molecules—occur in these distant stars as in our own sun. The same laws of physics apply—the same sources of energy must exist. No doubt there are some stars which are fairly young—are just beginning to "burn" their hydrogen. Others are probably old and hot. Some stars have gone through the explosive phase. Some supernovae are still glowing after many years; some appear to be "decaying" with a half-life of two months or so, like a radioactive element. Indeed, there is evidence, recently noted by Fowler, Burbidge, and Hoyle at Cal Tech, that possibly the great explosion did produce a vast quantity of radioactive material—just as does the explosion of a thermonuclear bomb.

This is one of the most exciting aspects of the great adventure of modern astronomy—the intimate way in which it brings together the sciences of spectroscopy, of nuclear physics, of electronics, of cosmology, of quantum mechanics—each one helping to fit in some piece of the vast jigsaw puzzle.

Why do I tell you all this? Because I think students in high school and college ought to be introduced to this great adventure. Just as the youngsters of 100 years ago were excited about pushing back America's western frontiers, so the children (and adults too) of today can reap equally great rewards from hearing about the frontiers of 1957—the frontiers of science.

RADIO WAVES FROM THE STARS

There are other exciting developments in astronomy. Many years ago a radio physicist named Jansky was tracing down some of the sources of noise in a sensitive radio receiver. There were faint hissing sounds which he could not trace to electric motors, spark plugs, thunderstorms, or the usual sources of "static." He eventually found that these flickering radio waves were coming from the sun! So began the science of radio astronomy.

It was not until 1946, however, that electronic techniques had been developed to allow radio observations to be made consistently and exactly. But today we know of hundreds of objects in the sky which are sources of radio waves. Some are stars like the sun; [76] some are distant galaxies. Possibly the most interesting source is the great cloud of hydrogen gas which exists in the Milky Way galaxy and which gives off radio waves of a frequency of 1420 megacycles —a wave length of 21 centimeters, about 8 inches.

Radio waves from the stars! Who would have thought it possible a few years ago? Who would have thought too that obscure studies at Columbia University on the energy levels in hydrogen could have led a couple of physicists at Harvard to guess that hydrogen in space could emit 21-centimeter radio waves—then to look for such waves and find them! Today great radio antennas, radio telescopes—far larger than the 200-inch, but less expensive—are being built all over the world to explore further the nature of the stars as revealed by the radio waves which the racing electrons in their outer atmosphere emit. Since radio waves penetrate air and haze and clouds with ease, a radio observatory does not have to be located in a clear climate—like Southern California—or on a mountain top. The flat plains of Belgium and the clouded moors of England and of Australia have been primary locations for radio work. They have there detected waves from sources which are so distant that for their waves to be detected here they must have been projected from a source as strong as a 50-kilowatt broadcasting station—multiplied a *million billion billion billion* times over! The power production is the inconceivably large figure of 10^{33} kilowatts. That's as much energy as the total energy from a hundred billion suns. That, in fact, is just about the number of stars in that particular galaxy. There is thus more radio energy coming from that galaxy than light energy. It is lucky indeed that the galaxy is so far away. If it were much closer, the earth would be so blanketed by radio "static" that radio and television broadcasting would be completely impossible. It is possible that radio telescopes may be detecting objects that are so far away that they cannot be seen or photographed at all—even with the Palomar telescope.

We see then that astronomy, though it is one of the oldest sciences, is being rejuvenated even today. New telescopes have made our distance measurements more accurate; new electronic techniques are extending the power of both optical and radio telescopes; new knowledge of nuclear physics is helping us understand how the energy of stars is produced, how all the different chemical elements are built up from primordial hydrogen, how the stars evolve, how some blow up, condense again and begin a new existence.

I am told that back in the fifteenth century so few people could read that there were millions of young people who were contemporaries of Columbus, Magellan, and the other early explorers but who never heard of their explorations—never knew that the new world had been discovered or that a ship had sailed clear 'round the earth.

THE LANGUAGE OF SCIENCE

Today we run the danger that because our school children are unable to "read" the language of modern science, they too will miss knowing about the great explorations of this generation—the intellectual examination of the frontiers of space. It is true that some day people may travel out into space beyond the earth. But such excursions will be limited indeed. We could conceivably reach the moon in one day of travel at 10 times the speed of sound. We could reach Mars in 6 months. But to come into the vicinity of even the nearest star would require 100,000 years. Even at 100 times the speed of sound it would take 10,000 years. Hence, the only experience that human beings will have with the far reaches of space will be through the messages brought by light and radio waves. And even these, the fastest of all messengers, have been on the way for millions or billions of years.

So let us make it possible for our new generation to have the fun of understanding these marvelous adventure stories. Just a little familiarity with mathematics and science will help a lot.

The adventures of science are by no means confined to outer space. And the chief practical reason for learning the language of science may not be to understand about distant galaxies, but to understand what is going on right here on earth. There are adventures in each day's routine.

You arise in the morning to the ring of an alarm clock—an electric clock, no doubt, synchronized within seconds to millions of other clocks all over the country, all over the world. Synchronization is achieved by the miracle of alternating current in our power lines, connected in a network extending hundreds of miles, and connected by radio to other networks far away. Adventures? Just follow those alternating current impulses back along the wires to a transformer on a pole in the street, to higher voltage lines leading to a substation, to still higher voltage lines strung across the countryside to a power station by a dam in the mountains.

Or maybe the power station burns coal or oil—where man's most primitive discovery, fire, is producing his most modern carrier of energy, electricity. Think of the inventors, engineers, scientists— back through the generations, the centuries—who made that possible. Think of Michael Faraday in a little laboratory thrusting a magnet into a coil of wire and noting that a current was produced; pulling it out, the current was reversed—an alternating current!

OUR DAILY ADVENTURE

And so, even before we awake in the morning of each day, our adventure has begun. We get out of bed, put on nylon hose, a dacron shirt or an orlon sweater—fabrics made of coal and air and water. Shades of the alchemists who tried to make gold from lead! They [77] would have been far better off if they had made nylon from air! And as you dress be glad you are not a silk producer of Japan or a wool grower of Australia whose very livelihood is being threatened by synthetic fibers made in America. Yes, adventures in science have their tragedies too.

Your breakfast is another kind of adventure—food brought to you from the far corners of the earth, prepared over a flame which burns gas piped from Texas. And as you eat you read of world events only a few hours old—long stories, and even pictures, which have been flashed with the speed of light from London, or Calcutta, or Cairo. Only a few years ago—less than 100—a famous British physicist, Lord Kelvin, slaved away years of his life supervising the laying of a cable across the Atlantic through which feeble electric impulses could be slowly pushed—dot, dash, dot—so slowly, but thousands of times speedier than the fastest ship.

After breakfast you step then into a real miracle—your car. You seldom look under the hood to witness the bewildering array of examples of the laws of thermodynamics, of mechanics, of electricity, of metallurgy—of almost every science and technology. All we care is that this device converts a gallon of gasoline into many miles of travel—at speeds much faster than we ought to drive.

As your day passes, you will skirt the edge of many adventures: a jet plane will streak above you; you will read that Congress is arguing about guided missiles, about satellites which leave the earth, and you wonder if the Congressmen know what they are talking about.

You read that a group of scientists visited Russia—and that they found themselves in full agreement with the Russian physicists on the neutron capture cross-sections of nuclei and also on the best design for a synchrotron. You were not interested of course—but you should have been. It was another example of the fact that adventures in science are international. All countries agree on the laws of physics. We may fight over the writings of Karl Marx—but not over those of Isaac Newton or Albert Einstein. Not even in a dictatorship was it possible to suppress for long the findings of science. A fake genetics promulgated by a certain Lysenko was given official state sanction in Russia for a time. But Lysenkoism is now dead; politics cannot for long suppress the facts of nature. We have tried it here too. We thought that nuclear physics could be kept secret; we forgot that scientists in other countries can ask questions of nature too—and get the same answers that we do. We also learned that secrecy in science is very expensive, for secrecy impedes the advance of science and also the advance of technology.

But your day's adventures have only begun. You drive past a TB sanitorium that is being closed—for lack of business. You pass a hospital where once fatal illnesses are cured in a few days. You may see some youngsters getting polio shots and know that another dread disease is on its way to extinction.

INSIDE A LIVING CELL

If the adventures in the stars or the atomic nuclei do not interest you, what about adventures inside a living cell? In recent years giant strides have been made in unraveling the chemistry of living things. The structure of protein molecules has been worked out. And now it is found that viruses, too, are complex molecules built in the form of multiple helices. These virus molecules can be crystallized and kept on a shelf for years, like any other chemical. But when they are given a chance to enter a living cell, they begin the miraculous process of sorting out the substances in that cell and building up a new molecule just like themselves. These molecules can reproduce themselves; they possess one of the essential features of living things.

The properties and behaviors of viruses can be studied now with all the modern techniques of physics and chemistry—not solely by trial and error, but by systematic analytical methods. One by one the different harmful viruses will be isolated, bred, and studied until methods of destroying or controlling them are evolved. Beneficial viruses—those that kill harmful bacteria—will also be studied and used in the control of other diseases. The days of bacterial and virus diseases are numbered. It may be years and there will be some exhausting struggles. But these elementary substances now can be understood and controlled.

These then are a few of the thrilling adventures of today's science: the understanding of genes and nuclei and stars; the unraveling of the laws of atomic physics and cosmology and chemical biology. There are also adventures in the application of this understanding to new things to make people healthier, more comfortable, and to improve their way of life.

These adventures are daily getting more exciting. And they are adventures that more and more people will eventually participate in. The fraction of the United States working force engaged professionally in scientific and engineering pursuits has multiplied by 5 in the past 50 years. It can't multiply by 5 again else it would be getting up to 100 per cent. But it may well double. The need is great and the opportunities are endless. The great challenge of our school system is to help every child with potential talents to develop them to the utmost.

But men and women without professional interests in science may still enjoy these adventures of science. The language of the atom can be learned. After all, people enjoy music who do not perform. People enjoy literature who do not write. People enjoy adventure stories who cannot walk. Lawyers and businessmen and English teachers have learned to enjoy science.

For the exciting adventures of science have a great [78] immediacy. From morning alarm to evening TV program we are living in a world which has resulted from adventures in science. Just as the great adventure of Columbus opened a new continent, so the inspired adventures of many scientists—from Galileo to Einstein; from Newton to Bohr; from Faraday to Edison to the thousands of trained men and women working today in laboratories throughout the world—have created on this new continent a new kind of civilization. There are certain things about this civilization that we are not satisfied with. It is far from perfect. But the defects will be fixed by those who understand the nature of the world in which we live. The world will be made better by knowledge, not by ignorance.

A NEW ILLITERACY

But the adventures in science are not only fun; they are an essential part of our everyday intelligent living. I have referred to Congressmen who vote on vast technical projects which they cannot possibly understand. But men and women in everyday life, in business, in law, in politics, are experiencing and making decisions on things which they too cannot understand. We spent strenuous efforts in this country to reduce illiteracy, to make it possible for every man, woman, and child to read and write. We succeeded—but we face a new type of illiteracy today in which citizens are unable to read and understand the things about which they must make decisions, all the way from spending billions on nuclear energy to investing a few thousand dollars in a new chemical company; decisions as to what to do about smog; about putting fluorine in drinking water; about paying higher salaries to teachers of science. The ability to understand the adventures in science has a real practical value in addition.

And what, you may ask, does all this have to do with you, the school teachers of America? I think it is clear that it has everything to do with you. The making of a future scientist or the making of the future intelligent citizen begins in the fifth grade or before and continues at all levels through the university graduate school. Except for a very few unusual individuals, scientists and engineers are made, not born. Interest and facility in mathematics and science are created by fine teaching; by intelligent, sympathetic interest in the individual; by the uncovering and stimulating of exceptional talent; by making the subject matter exciting rather than dull.

But there are certain illusions about science and mathematics that must be eliminated before the adventures of science can be appreciated and advanced more rapidly in America.

The first illusion is that mathematics is too hard for young minds to grasp. That is false. Properly presented and properly taught mathematics is an exciting adventure—especially for youngsters. What has made it seem hard is the endless procession of dull and useless problems which are normally taught—"How many square rods in 19½ acres?" or "If A has 3 apples and B has twice as many as A and C together . . . ?"—you know the kind. Why crush the glorious excitement of the great principles of algebra, geometry, trigonometry—yes, and calculus—with an avalanche of useless detail? I suggest that to prepare a really first-class series of 7th- to 12th-grade texts on mathematics that really arrest a youngster's imagination, challenge his curiosity, and develop his quantitative reasoning would be the greatest project that a teachers' group could undertake.

The second illusion that must be eliminated is that mathematics can be taught by teachers who don't know any math—or are only a chapter ahead of the student. As long as teachers of math must take

16 hours of education and only 3 hours of math, mathematics will be badly taught. For it is a subject which becomes really alive only with years of study and can be conveyed in simple and exciting ways to students only by those who have themselves caught its true spirit. In this respect, it is like most other subjects of real intellectual content—it will certainly be taught badly by those who know nothing about it, no matter how much methodology they have learned.

A third illusion that needs crushing is that mathematics and science are narrow, technical, or vocational subjects and that only humanities and social science are "liberal" and "broadening" and teach one how to get along with human beings. Nonsense! Mathematics and science are great intellectual adventures that have enlarged and broadened men's intellectual horizons, freed the human spirit from ignorance and fear, and elevated him above a primitive existence. They are a proper part of every liberal education. And if our country is to continue to make material progress in evolving the material tools necessary to insure attaining economic, political, and moral goals which we seek, then we as a nation had better re-examine the adequacy of our school curricula in preparing young people to talk the language and understand the problems of *tomorrow*.

For if we are cheating our children of the opportunity of enjoying the adventures in science, we are also cheating our country of the benefits of profiting and prospering from the talents of its people.

American education and the sciences

EDITORIAL FROM *THE NEW REPUBLIC*
The New Republic, November 25, 1957, pp. 4–5

The President recognized, at Oklahoma City, the importance of "two longer term problems: strengthening our scientific education and our basic research." "According to my scientific advisers," he said, the first of these "is for the American people the most critical problem of all."

The fact has begun to sink in that when a Russian graduates from high school he has completed 10 years of mathematics, five years of physics and biology, one year of astronomy, and five years of a foreign language.

The fact that the Soviet Union is graduating twice as many scientists and engineers as the U.S. and all the NATO countries combined is beginning to penetrate too—and along with it the realization of what this means to the future growth of Soviet technology.

As a result, even the most economy-minded members of Congress will, we are ready to bet, be prepared to support a considerable expansion of federal assistance to scientific training when the new session begins. The climate will be favorable to all the specific ideas the President mentioned for speeding the production of scientists:

a system of nationwide testing of high school students; a system of incentives for high-aptitude students to pursue scientific or professional studies; a program to stimulate good quality teaching of mathematics and sciences; provision of more laboratory facilities, and measures, including fellowships, to increase the output of qualified teachers.

Congress and the public will also be inclined to agree with the President that we need "even greater concentration on basic research—that is the kind that unlocks the secrets of nature and prepares the way for such breakthroughs as atomic fission, electronics and anti-biotics." And with even moderate coaxing from the White

House, Congress will probably support steps to catch up with the immediate level of Soviet scientific education and basic research. Our regret is that the President's speech shows so little understanding of what it will take to do more than that. We hope, therefore, that before the President sends Congress his list of what it should do in these fields he will read and reread the recent speeches and reports of the two experts in his Administration—the Secretary of Health, Education and Welfare, Marion Folsom, and the Director of the National Science Foundation, Dr. Alan Waterman. Both have been making uncommon sense. If what we are concerned with is where this country will stand in scientific achievement 10 to 20 years from now, they tell us, it will not be enough to undertake a "crash" program to mass produce mathematicians, scientists and engineers or simply to increase the proportion of basic research carried on in government laboratories. (Seventy percent of all funds for research are spent by industry and private organizations.)

The first thing is to realize, as Dr. Waterman recently reminded us, that "we cannot train scientists and engineers in a vacuum. We must have a strong educational system with adequate facilities and competent teachers in all subjects from the elementary grades on up." It will take a broad federal aid-to-education program to bring this about—far more than the $1.3 billion school construction program which Congress failed to pass this year, when the President withdrew his support from Secretary Folsom at a critical time in the Congressional battle.

Then, with reference to the special problem of adequate emphasis on science, Mr. Folsom argues that,

If there is to be a greater appreciation of the broad base needed for scientific and engineering education in America, we will have to reassert a pair of elementary truths, sometimes obscured. One is that we must try to give each American more understanding of science. We must teach more and better science in our schools and colleges, not just to those who plan a career in science and engineering, but to all. And secondly, we have to educate professional scientists and engineers in such a way that they have a broad concept of the relationship between their technical interests and their responsibilities as citizens.

A "crash program" would do the opposite and

tend to isolate science from the broad community of educational interests and, ultimately, from the whole community on which it depends for moral and material support. For better or for worse, the future of scientific and engineering education is fused with the future of every other valid element in our educational structure.

That structure will need a great deal of repair and expansion if it is to accommodate double the present student population in 10 years time—the number expected to apply for college entrance. Getting and keeping properly trained college faculties is the objective which should have first priority. If every one of those now receiving doctoral degrees in all subjects were to enter teaching, that would not even replace those with such degrees leaving teaching each year. Obviously, more fellowships should be offered those who will enter college teaching. But it won't do much good to train college teachers if, as Mr. Folsom says, "what lies beyond graduate school is social and economic disappointment"—low salaries and lack of respect for the profession.

We need to get better students, as well as better teachers into all fields, not just science. One third of the top quarter of high school graduates don't go on to college now. Every other major nation except the United States offers national scholarships to such students. [4]

Colleges and universities will have to construct more new facilities in the next 10 years than in the past century. One item, the amazingly expensive equipment needed for modern science, is out of the financial reach of most institutions. The federal government will have to share in the cost if time is not to be lost.

Obviously the dollar cost of all this will be immense, and beyond the resources of all but the wealthiest of our 1,800 institutions of higher learning. But "there can be no question that this richest of all peoples in the world can afford to grasp the opportunities ahead in education," Mr. Folsom says. "It is conceivable that we may have to get along with a little less chrome and perhaps a few less country clubs in order to have more classrooms and better paid teachers." What he means is that we will have to pay higher taxes, but even this brave Modern Republican avoids those horrible words!

The path we should follow in "strengthening our basic research" is equally clear.

Out of an estimated total of $5.5 billion spent in this country for research and development in 1953 [Dr. Waterman tells us], less than $500 million, or 8 percent, was spent for basic research in the sciences. When we realize that this sum represents less than 1/10 of one percent of the gross national product, we can appreciate what a small proportion of our national effort goes for research at the frontiers of knowledge.

What should we do?

It is becoming increasingly obvious that the proper support of basic research is indeed a public responsibility. Investigators who are pursuing research unconnected with specific problems, or unrelated to the missions of specific agencies, find it more and more difficult to obtain support for such research. Often the time and energy of able research scientists are consumed with the difficult and distasteful task of seeking sufficient funds to enable them to continue their research during the ensuing year. Such a situation is wasteful of valuable talent and generally unproductive. It is unrealistic to suppose that industry can make up the deficit by extending greater support to basic research. Industry is already being called upon to contribute to general education; and to add the demands of basic research is, in effect, to compete with general education for the same dollars. Even if industry doubled its present research support to universities, this would be merely a drop in the bucket.

Then, too, we must face the fact that the tools required for modern research are more and more beyond the resources of private enterprise. Such instruments as nuclear reactors, nuclear accelerators, large-scale telescopes (both optical and radio telescopes), electronic computers, and other research equipment are beyond the means of a single university, or even groups of universities. That is why the National Science Foundation has undertaken to support, within the limits of its resources, the new radio astronomy observatory, being built and operated at Green Bank, West Virginia, by Associated Universities, Inc.; the National Astronomical Observatory, to be located somewhere in Southwestern United States; and has helped to finance computers, accelerators, and reactors for use in basic research and training. I believe we must accept the fact that this constitutes the pattern for the future.

Certainly, as the President said in Oklahoma, there is "much more to security than money." For one thing there is the quality of the scientific work performed. And the conditions which have surrounded research in the last 10 years have not been such as to assure that another J. Robert Oppenheimer will appear in the next 10. That is a subject on which Mr. Eisenhower did not dwell.

The President might have gone on to add, also, that just as there is more to security than money, there is much more to education than to science. (He did concede that we need Washingtons and Emersons as well as Einsteins.) We need a general educational revival, not merely an accelerated race with the Russians to see who can produce the greatest number of technicians in the next generation. But we find no note in Mr. Eisenhower's first two lectures or in the budget comments made by his Cabinet that suggests he will ask Congress for the added billions in taxes such a revival would require.

What kind of science teaching program?

LAETITIA BOLTON
Science, April 25, 1958, pp. 948–951

Herbert Hoover's indictment of the American high-school system as "one of the major causes" of our failure to produce enough scientists and engineers is typical of one kind of widespread public reaction to Sputnik's assault on our national self-esteem. Scientific authorities and politicians have been telling us that we should not have been surprised by this revelation of the Russians' superiority in space science. In an atmosphere ringing with echoes of "We told you so," it is hard for any of us to escape a conviction that we have made a massive, collective blunder, and it is natural for us to cast reproach on the people we hold responsible for it. First on the list are the educators, who are now hard put to answer the accusing question, "Why aren't we producing more scientists?"

Before making a scapegoat of education we should recognize that, by and large, it is an instrument of national policy rather than a prime mover. Teachers who have been struggling to carry out the national mandate to educate all our children for a democratic way of life should not be held too strictly to account for a program dictated primarily by school boards, which are more or less [948] responsive to students and their parents, and by the national economy.

WHY IS SCIENCE UNPOPULAR?

Of course it is shocking that only about one-fourth of all our high-school students study physics, only a third take chemistry or geometry, and only two-fifths take intermediate algebra. Yet we cannot agree with Mr. Hoover that the failure of students to go in for science or mathematics stems primarily from their wish to escape hard work. Science is unpopular partly because of cultural pressures, because of our heritage of anti-intellectualism, which makes young people suspect that a scientist is a queer duck, not quite human and probably not very happy. Science also fails to attract many students for the simple reason that they have had little opportunity to become interested in the subject. At the elementary level, for the most part, science is either not taught at all or is presented in a way that discourages enthusiasm.

Children who are exposed to a stimulating science experience are much less subject to adverse cultural pressures. They are not so likely to be frightened by what they hear about the destructive aspects of science, and they are less awed by popular misconceptions of what scientists are like. Those who have experienced personally the joys of search and discovery that are the scientist's rewards are far better able to appreciate his achievements and enter into his world. Because they have found science exciting, they are eager to continue studying it.

SHOULD WE COPY THE RUSSIANS?

Most intelligent Americans would agree with Wernher von Braun that science education in the United States needs the kind of "powerful boost" he hopes that Sputnik may provide. But where should the pressure be applied? Is more required science in high school the answer, as Mr. Hoover suggests? Or should we adopt a crash program modeled on Russian methods, impose a rigid "ten-year schedule" on carefully selected children in order to assure the production of an aristocracy of scientists and technologists? Responsible American educators, and most scientists working in this country, do not believe that this kind of program would be either workable or desirable for us. Whatever course we adopt must be contained within the democratic structure of our society.

Moreover, the kind of science teaching we provide must be different from the Russians', and differently motivated, because our overall aims are not the same. Here is where the educators come in. It is their responsibility not merely to train more scientists but to foster understanding of science. They must undertake to create more enlightened citizens, capable of integrating knowledge and appreciation of scientific aims and achievements into our general culture. As Edward Teller said in his appearance on "See It Now" last December, "we need more science fans." James R. Killian has pointed out that "the liberal arts of our time cannot be liberal if they reject or disdain science and technology," and that, conversely, "science and technology cannot fulfill their responsibilities if our scientists and engineers lack the humanistic quality which has been ascribed to the Athenians—the art of making gentle the life of mankind." This integration, which should be basic to our whole science education program, cannot be carried out successfully if it is left until college or even high-school age. We must start by making science intelligible and interesting to children while they are still young enough to incorporate it into their scheme of values as well as their core of knowledge.

SUCCESSFUL TEACHING PRODUCES RESULTS

The Ethical Culture Schools of New York City, where science is introduced in nursery school, afford an excellent example of the fact that children who enjoy a satisfactory science experience at an early age are likely to acquire a lasting interest in the subject and a sympathetic attitude towards scientific problems (1). Most of the students attending the Fieldston School—the Ethical Culture high school—come from the two elementary schools in this group, the Midtown School and the Fieldston Lower School, which offer well-planned science programs. The science faculty believes that this preparation accounts for the fact that about 70 percent of Fieldston students, boys and girls, choose to take more science than is required for graduation or for college entrance. Over the past five years, half the boys and about 6 percent of the girls have taken all three sciences—chemistry, physics, and biology—offered in the upper school. These subjects are elected by the students from a rich curriculum, which includes classical and modern languages, many arts courses, and a full athletic program for all students, in addition to other basic subjects commonly offered in high schools (2).

About one-fifth of all Fieldston students choose an accelerated mathematics program leading to a year of college mathematics in their senior year. A high proportion of graduates also qualify for advanced placement in college chemistry and physics. This outstanding record is not due to pushing or cramming. Every effort is made to avoid overloading students or increasing tensions caused by anxiety over college admissions. For each student the science or mathematics course is kept to what he can absorb and enjoy.

Conservation, also introduced in the elementary schools, is taught at the high-school level as an integral part of social studies and biology. An extensive, laboratory-based science program in the seventh and eighth grades makes unnecessary the conventional ninth-grade "general science" course.

This interest is reflected in the fact that, in a recent survey of Fieldston graduates, more than a fourth of the careers reported were in the fields of science, medicine, or science teaching. This is a significant number for a school which offers a general college preparatory course with no special emphasis on any one area of learning.

WHAT KIND OF PROGRAM?

To produce this degree of voluntary involvement, an elementary program must be based on the premise that every child is a potential scientist. The small child's natural, unbounded curiosity about his world—about animals and plants, wind and weather, sunrise and sunset—is the most powerful tool he and his teacher can use to investigate this world and its forces. Anyone who has watched children absorbed by the wonders of Chicago's Museum of Science and Industry, New York's Museum of Natural History, the Hayden Planetarium, or "Mr. Wizard's" television program on NBC, can see with what delight children latch onto this kind of presentation. But their introduction to science need not be even so formal as this and is more effective if it is an integral part of their daily life at school. A science program for children should grow out of their constantly expanding interests, should satisfy their curiosity and stimulate it to further discovery. [949]

HOW YOUNG CAN THEY START?

It is interesting to note that even advocates of elementary science education do not always realize at what an early age science can become a part of children's lives. Senator Margaret Chase Smith, in a recent plea for teaching science in grade school, said: "Obviously we can't start teaching science to 6- and 7-year-olds in the first grade." Yet schools which gear their teaching to the experience and interests of children themselves find that even in nursery school children can acquire some understanding of and appreciation for science. At the Fieldston Lower School, for example, last winter's first snowfall triggered off a month-long investigation of the effects of temperature by a group of five-year-olds who wanted to know why the snow melted when they brought it indoors. They tried refreezing it and went on to find out something about how snow differs from ice and how refrigerators work. To discover some of the effects of heat, they baked cakes in an oven, checking time and temperature. This is a typical example of how an imaginative teacher can utilize the common experiences of everyday life to introduce young children to the joys of scientific discovery and the fundamentals of research.

Last February, Governor Harriman signed a bill making science teaching mandatory in New York State from the first grade through the eighth, beginning in September 1958. The state's recommended curriculum, already adopted by many New York elementary schools, is built around ten topics: "kinds of living things, keeping healthy, using electricity, common chemical and physical changes, lifting and moving things, energy from the sun, the atmosphere, earth and sky, rocks and soil, survival of living things."

This is an interesting list which should prove suggestive to teachers, but much of the success of the new program will depend on how these topics are approached. Cornelius Denslow, science teacher at the Midtown School, has pointed out, for example, that "information per se is not understood or retained unless the child is ready to receive it. Only when it satisfies a genuine curiosity is it truly assimilated" (3). Let us hope that in our zeal for science education we do not make the mistake of trying to "cover" prescribed subject matter at the cost of discouraging real interest in young people. "Science is not a mere matter of information," says Randolph Smith, director of the Little Red School House in New York City. "Keeping children's natural curiosities alive and fostering the essence of the scientist's avid search for knowing in every nook and cranny of his world is the nub of the job." There are all sorts of ways in which this can be done. At the Little Red School House, as at the Ethical Culture Schools, the earliest science experience is often focused on the care of animals and their young. A rabbit, a snake, a mouse, or a skunk may be not only a treasured classroom pet but also, for city children especially, an open-sesame to a new world of living things. This leads by degrees into a study of biology and human physiology.

A seven-year-old group at the City and Country School, another independent elementary school in New York City, recently did some research on hydraulics in order to install a water system for their building-block reconstruction of Manhattan. When an over-enthusiastic "engineer" poured too much water in the sand-pile reservoir, the class began investigating the effects of soil erosion.

At the Little Red School House, a dying jack-o'-lantern that developed mold once inspired a month-long exploration of molds (including penicillin)—where they come from, how they grow, and what they are good for.

Science experiences often grow out of other classroom work or school activities. The eight-year-olds who run the school post office at the City and Country School recently solved a complicated electrical problem when they found that the "special delivery bell" they had installed, to be operated from the school office, did not work. With the help of the science teacher they did some careful testing and found that the steel wire they had used provided too much resistance to carry electricity from their small battery source. In copper wire they found the answer to their problem.

With no sacrifice of its importance, science may be closely integrated with social studies. For example, the nine-year-olds who run the school supply store at the City and Country School study the products they sell. This usually involves a visit to a paper factory, with an introduction to chemistry through the process of making their own paper in the science laboratory.

The city itself becomes a laboratory as children investigate how fires are extinguished and how garbage is disposed of. In the course of constructing and lighting a model of their city, students at the Little Red School House discover the underworld of subways, cables, and conduits that lie beneath its streets. They find out how power is produced, how pumps work, how gravity and friction affect the operation of all these utilities.

An unusual workshop-laboratory such as that which the Walden

School maintains for nine-, ten-, eleven-, and twelve-year-olds may help to provide, for city children, a substitute for the kind of opportunity offered by a rural attic or suburban junk-pile—a chance to take things apart and put them together; to handle, feel, discover for themselves how things work. From old radio parts, old telephones, clocks, or vacuum cleaners these youngsters sometimes derive as much scientific understanding as from the more formal laboratory equipment which the school also supplies. One boy, for example, made out of three old radio rheostats an apparatus to regulate the lighting for a school play. An old motor was repaired and used to spin colored disks, which led to a study of light and color by children of different age groups working together.

In all these schools, photography serves as an exciting introduction to chemistry and physics, as children learn to develop and print their own pictures. A child who is fascinated by glass blowing may go on to make his own thermometer or hourglass. At the Midtown School, more formal instruction may include carefully supervised chemistry experiments—making ink, freeing oxygen, crystallizing chemicals from solutions, separating mercury from mercurous oxide. At Walden, children do some dissecting of earthworms, crayfish, frogs, fish, and chickens. An eighth-grade study of ecology climaxes the science course at the City and Country School.

TECHNIQUE AND EQUIPMENT

In all these schools children become familiar with equipment and learn to handle it efficiently and safely. All except the Little Red School House have a full-time science teacher and a well-equipped science room which is used by the older children for classes and "free period" science work. These are important assets, but the equipment for an elementary school laboratory need not be elaborate or costly.

Techniques, Denslow feels, are best taught in response to "children's natural desire to learn better ways of doing things." Katharine Reichenbach of the [950] Walden School finds that techniques often improve when a child becomes so fascinated by an experiment that he does it over and over again.

MUST WE SCRAP DEMOCRACY?

I have suggested only a few of the ways in which early science experience can be made a vital part of every child's education. I hope that these examples may suggest the kind of elementary science teaching which should be an important part of our answer to Sputnik. One of the immediate reactions to its launching was to lay the blame for our tardiness on democratic society. "Too much gabbing has been going on these days," Max Ascoli wrote in *The Reporter* last fall, "about the prospects—if not, indeed, the actual evidence—of the superior capacity a slave society has over a free one in getting things done." John R. Dunning, dean of Columbia University's School of Engineering, reminded us in an excellent article in the *New York Times Magazine* that "we should not be deluded into thinking that dictatorship is necessarily more efficient than liberty. . . . The voluntary principle is the very thing we are defending in the cold war."

If we reject, as most of us do, the notion of drafting scientists, we must find some better means of increasing our supply. Most of the current clamor for reform has been aimed at the upper levels of education. But high schools complain that students are not interested in science; colleges find them ill prepared. The widespread introduction in American schools of science teaching, democratically motivated by the interest and curiosity of younger children, would seem a made-to-order method for raising the level not only of our science education but of our culture as well.

Notes

1. An issue of the Ethical Culture Schools' publication, *School and Home,* for March 1930 reveals that at that time science had long been an important subject at all levels in these schools.
2. The students' choice does not appear to be motivated by parental interests, since Fieldston families represent a wide range of occupations and cultural backgrounds. Since a majority of the students are admitted in the primary or preprimary grades, where no intelligence tests are made, the factor of exceptionally high IQ ratings does not apply.
3. *Sci. Teacher* (December 1956).

Liberal education in a scientific age

BENTLEY GLASS

Bulletin of the Atomic Scientists, XIV (November 1958), 346–353*

As our eminent American historian, Carl Becker, humorously pointed out over twenty years ago, the paramount difference between Pithecanthropus and us is that somehow, in the interim of about a half-million years, we have acquired sufficient power to be able to put the old fellow, were we to meet him on University Avenue, rather expeditiously into the zoo. Progress may be defined in terms of power, the augmentation of which was very slow in prehistoric times, developed rapidly after the advent of sword and pen, even more rapidly after the introduction of gunpowder and printing, and today, in the age of atomic energy and satellites, is accelerating exponentially into outer space. This augmentation of power is the principal theme of history—indeed, it may be essential to history.

However that may be, this vast increase in power is wholly dependent upon a transmission of knowledge from one generation to another, a transmission that is a peculiarly human attribute. Heredity determines the characteristics of each and every animal species, including its capacity to learn. But even those animals that learn reasonably well transmit little or nothing of their experience and knowledge to their young, beyond the nature of the enemy. The young learn by imitation; the old protect and defend, but do not actively teach. We do not know whether Pithecanthropus could do more, for education presupposes language. Neanderthal man, however, passed on his painfully acquired knowledge of how to chip a flint so as to get a sharp edge. Already man had begun not only to transmit his knowledge and skill; he had begun to think about his place in the universe.

* Originally given as a Davis Washington Mitchell Lecture at Tulane University, this essay then appeared in *Science and Liberal Education,* Louisiana State University Press, pp. 54–86. The essay appears here in the condensed version which was printed in *Bulletin of the Atomic Scientists.*

These, in short, have been the two primary functions of education from the beginning: the one, to transmit from each generation to the next the knowledge requisite to power and to the extension of power; the other, to enlarge the comprehension by man of his place in the universe. The first of these may be called the technical aspect of education; the second, the philosophical. Both are necessary.

In the last 350 years these two developments of human thought and education have fused in the growth of modern science. The functions of science in society may thus be said to parallel those of education, as already stated. On the one hand, science is concerned with the development of increasingly adequate concepts about man and man's place in the order of the universe. On the other, science has acquired the function of enlarging man's command over nature (including his own nature) by means of new knowledge acquired through systematic, accurate observation and controlled experimentation. The two aspects are not independent. New knowledge gained by observation and experiment forces a continual revision of inadequate concepts and theories; while the measure of the adequacy of concepts and theories is their success as a basis of accurate prediction and their fruitfulness in suggesting additional observations and experiments.

The freedom of the mind enlarged by these two aspects of education and science is, nevertheless, somewhat different in the two cases. The conceptual side of science and education has brought about a freedom from fear of the supernatural, from superstition and magic. It has widened our vision immeasurably, if leaving us lonely and ultimately impotent in the immensity of the galactic universes. In Carl Becker's unforgettable words: [346]

At some moment, relatively early, in the 150,000 million years which is the sun's span of life, we note that certain bits of matter on the surface of the earth, by virtue of temperatures not elsewhere obtaining, assume unusually complicated forms and behave in unusually unstable ways. We understand that certain of these bits of animated dust distinguish themselves from others, dignify themselves with the name of Man, and take credit for a unique quality which they call intelligence. They are not aware that intelligence is no merit; the reverse rather, since it is only an inferior form of energy which Nature has given them in partial compensation for the extreme rapidity with which the law of entropy (dS/dt is always positive) degrades their vitality. So long as the sun maintains on earth the necessary temperature, these bits of animated matter will no doubt continue to manifest a perceptible movement, a measurable although diminishing energy. But their activities, however long continued, are infinitesimal in extent and impotent in effect, of no consequence to the universe, or in the end to them either, since within a brief moment of eternal time the light of the sun will inevitably wane, the earth will grow cold, and all of man's alleged imperishable monuments and immortal deeds will be as if they had never been, nor will anything that then is be either better or worse because of anything that man has ever done or ever wished to do.

So a cosmic intelligence might estimate human progress, so it might answer the questions: What is the significance of man? What is the meaning of existence? But then what is this cosmic intelligence that thus asks and answers? It is after all the intelligence of man himself. Apart from man, the cosmos merely is; it does not ask or answer questions. The significance of man is that he is that part of the universe that asks the question, What is the significance of man? He alone can stand apart imaginatively and, regarding himself and the universe in their eternal aspects, pronounce a judgment: The significance of man is that he is insignificant and is aware of it. Man, says Pascal, has this superiority: He knows that the universe can with a breath destroy him, yet at the moment of death he knows that he dies, and knows also the advantage which the universe thereby has over him; but of all that the universe knows nothing.

Of all that, the universe knows nothing. Apart from man, the universe knows nothing at all—nothing of itself or of infinite spaces, nothing of man or of his frustrated aspirations, nothing of beginnings or endings, of progress or retrogression, of life or death, of good or evil fortune. The cosmic view of the universe of infinite spaces, and of man's ultimate fate within it, is man's achievement—the farthest point yet reached in the progressive expansion of human intelligence and power. It is not rightly to be taken as a description of events that are relevant to man's purposes, but rather as an ideal result of those purposes—the manifestation of his insatiable curiosity, his indefeasible determination to know. As such it is less an objective world of fact than man's creation of the world in his own image. It is in truth man's most ingenious invention, his supreme work of art.[1]

[1] Carl Becker, *Progress and Power* (Stanford University Press, 1935), pp. 98–102.

The enlargement of freedom by the technical, empirical, side of science is, on the other hand, an enlargement through the extension of choice and opportunity. Man, to paraphrase Lyman Bryson, is not free to choose what he has never heard of or what doesn't exist. Prior to writing and printing, he could not choose to read a book; and prior to the invention of television he was not free to choose between reading a book and watching a television program. Nor can he choose wisely what he has never been free to think about, whence derives the importance of freedom of the mind in the truly liberal education.

The thought may be made even more explicit. Science is the one most powerful means devised by the mind of man for arriving at truth in respect to the world of matter and energy, and indeed also the realm of mind and behavior. Science is the greatest force in human life making for change in ways of living, through increased power to alter and control the environment. Science is the great liberating, liberalizing force in human thought. It is obvious that in the modern world the strength of a nation, whether in war or in peace, resides in its science. The future solutions of the most critical problems of society—the problems of uncontrolled population increase and insufficient food and water, sources of energy and supplies of raw materials, and the imperative task of the mobilization of skills—lie in the applications of science.

Education, which transmits from each generation to the next the heritage of the past and the seeds of new powers yet to be, ought then to reflect the central reality of modern life. If we agree with the pragmatist that "life adjustment" is the goal of education, then paramount in such adjustment must be the reckoning with science and the technology which is based upon it, as the sources of continual change in the conditions of life. If we agree with the proponents of a liberal education, we must equally recognize that science is inescapably the core of a truly liberal education.

THE PRESENT DIVORCE OF SCIENCES AND HUMANITIES

It is a basic fault of our present theory and practice of education in the United States that the natural sciences stand apart from the social and humanistic studies, as if they were a fearsome body of technical facts and mathematical concepts, and that only. If the natural sciences are to become indeed the core of the curriculum, they must unquestionably sacrifice something of their forbidding character. Much effort must be expended to develop science courses that will avoid unnecessary jargon and that will aim not so much at the training of the technical expert as at the liberal education of the citizen. As to the scientific spirit, there is little of that in either the conventional textbook or lecture. One meets it better in *Arrowsmith* or the *Life of Pasteur*. It is born by contagion; its home is the laboratory, the observatory, or the field, wherever the inexperienced person can observe experience, and the novitiate partake of the zest of discovery.

In teaching science we must not forget, in other words, that it is simultaneously social study and creative [347] art, a history of ideas, a philosophy, and a supreme product of esthetic ingenuity. The graduate who has missed this experience, whether science major or nonmajor, has missed the basis for a rational judgment of today's crucial problems. He has likewise lost a revelation of deep meaning and unending beauty.

To say, however, that science must become the core of the modern curriculum is not at all to say that students must study science and little else.

There is a most unfortunate educational connotation about the phrase "the core of the curriculum" which implies that certain studies should be emphasized to the exclusion or detriment of others. This is by no means what I intend. The core of the apple is certainly not the whole apple—not even the most beautiful or most delicious part of the apple. Yet the core gives the rest of the apple meaning—here lie the seeds without which, in a state of nature, there would be no more apple trees and no more apples. A coreless apple might be just as attractive to behold and even more luscious to eat, but it would be a biological monstrosity. Permit me another biological analogy, if you will. The skeleton is not the most beautiful part of the human body, except perhaps to an anatomist. Few would concede it superior to brain or heart or muscle in importance. But lacking a skeleton, the body would collapse into a flabby sack of viscera with rubbery limbs. Its form, proportion, support, and power of locomotion, indeed the very beauty of the human form, inhere in the skeleton hidden within it.

These analogies, within the limitations that circumscribe all analogies, express what I contend to be the place of the natural sciences in the curriculum. We have reached a point in human history where the structure of our civilization and its staggering technology depend vitally on the sciences for support (the skeleton) and for new ideas and concepts (the seeds of progress). Education, to reflect modern life, to prepare for life, to adjust to life, must reckon with this clear reality.

A friend of mine, Dr. Warren Weaver of the Rockefeller Foundation, argues with me that he does not "want to see science as the central core, with the arts, letters, philosophy, and ethics, and all the rest relegated to a less central, less dominant, less significant position. I want," he continues, "to see science in a full partnership with other approaches to the order and beauty and meaning of life. Science (to me) contributes *most* to our understanding of 'order,' a good deal to 'beauty' (largely via order), and still less to 'meaning.' The humane arts start with the middle one of these three words, contribute chiefly at that point, and spill over in each direction. Moral philosophy starts with the third, and diffuses back to the second and the first. If I had to assign priorities, it would be to moral philosophy."

This is an admirable statement, and one with which I could scarcely disagree. But the argument misses my point. I have no wish to assign priorities, but rather to emphasize the essentiality of the sciences to modern man's concepts of beauty and meaning no less than to those of order. Alfred North Whitehead touched on the former when he wrote: "In his youth, the born poet often wavers between science and literature [he had mentioned Shelley]; and his choice is determined by the chance attraction of one or other of the alternative modes of expressing his imaginative joy in nature. It is essential to keep in mind, that science and poetry have the same root in human nature."[2] Carl Becker, in the passage already quoted, has dealt expressly with "meaning."

[2] Alfred North Whitehead. "Science in General Education" (1921).

One more thing must be said. Beauty and meaning—ecstasy and apprehension of truth—may as always in the past be grasped intuitively. More and more, however, as science occupies a larger place in human life and as it transforms the conditions of our existence, the area of beauty and meaning which scientific understanding reveals becomes magnified relative to the intuitive. One example may make this apparent. It requires no scientific understanding to take delight in the green of woods and meadows and the rustle of leaves in spring. But the deeper insight into the significance of green leaves which the scientific understanding of leaf structure, photosynthesis, and the ecological interdependence of living things can generate in the mind detracts not at all from intuitive appreciation while it adds immeasurably to it.

INFUSING THE CURRICULUM WITH SCIENCE

To say, then, that science must become the core of the modern curriculum is to state only that the remainder of the curriculum must be more fully and more consciously related to the place of science in human life. This sense of relationship cannot be deferred until the college years if it is to develop properly. In the secondary schools, and indeed most of all in the elementary school years, science must be taught as an integral part of modern life, and the distinction as well as the limitation of its methods made apparent. It is my conviction that the increasing need of this nation for scientifically trained people, and the alarming shortage of such persons at the present time cannot be met by measures at the college and university level. A large majority of college entrants have already chosen some career, or at least have already developed marked preferences for one kind of study rather than another. An enthusiasm for science is most easily engendered in the child and young adolescent; and the dearth of able candidates for careers in science, mathematics, and engineering simply reflects the lack of able, enthusiastic teachers of science in secondary schools and elementary schools—of teachers, that is, who can teach science not as an authoritative body of facts, principles, and concepts, but instead as [348] an imaginative way of systematically exploring the unknown aspects of nature, a way of integrating experience and developing a workable philosophy of life, based on an appreciation of one's participation in a great social enterprise, and pervaded by beauty.

It thus seems to me that while the amount of science now taken by students in the elementary and secondary school years is rather inadequate, and while I would regard the sciences as something that should be taken every year by each student, like English or the social studies, nevertheless, the amount of science taken is not so important as the way it is taught and the qualifications of the teacher. Particularly in the elementary and secondary schools, where the breadth of subject matter taught is necessarily wider than at the college level, we have far too many teachers of science who are ill-prepared for their tasks. There are many reasons for this. One of course is that our college training in the sciences tends to be far too narrow and too specialized. It turns out technicians of extremely circumscribed vision. Another reason is the poor social recompense of teachers for their labor and the more remunerative possibilities in other types of work. These circumstances draw away many of the most promising prospective science teachers, and cause even a number of the abler persons already teaching to forsake the trying task of inspiring and educating young minds. Yet another reason is the overwhelming emphasis in the traditional training of American teachers on the value of courses in education, instead of on the attainment of the requisite breadth and mastery of knowledge of subject matter. Not at all that I object to worthwhile courses in education, but it is my experience that teachers of science who are inadequately prepared in their subject matter and have great gaps in their knowledge of it tend to teach by the book. This is one thing that should be anathema in the sciences, which if anything at all have endeavored to dispossess authoritarianism and to substitute for it direct, confirmable observation. Yet legions of our science textbooks serve up to hapless students a crystallized, anonymous science that seems to have descended perfect, like the divine city out of heaven, straight from unquestionable authority. How can we make of any science such a travesty as to teach it upon the word of authority?

Politically it has been demonstrated that a house divided against itself cannot stand. I affirm that it must also be true that a nation of a microscopically few scientists molding and altering people's lives, and a populace uncomprehending, superstitious, and resistant to the novel ideas of the scientist while blandly accepting the technological fruits of those very ideas, likewise cannot endure. Somehow, and soon, mankind must become truly scientific in spirit and in endeavor. Otherwise we face oligarchy, and eventual collapse of our form of civilization, our way of life.

The problem, then, is to integrate the teaching of the sciences with the rest of the liberal studies. Much is to be done in the reformation of our science-teaching and the preparation of our science teachers. But even more is to be done in the remainder of the curriculum of liberal education.

INFUSING ENGLISH COURSES WITH SCIENCE

A basic problem in science is communication. The very jargon of which scientists are accused, so often rightly, is the outgrowth of an effort to communicate to their fellow-scientists with utmost accuracy the fruits of their observations and experiments; and of course new concepts, such as quanta, cosmic rays, or genes, must be expressed in new words that for a time are unfamiliar elements of general language. Nevertheless, clarity is paramount in scientific as in all other forms of communication. The ability to express one's self clearly is also a part of the ability to think clearly. Mastery of one's native language is thus primary in all education, but perhaps insufficient attention is given in teaching it to the rules of clear thinking. In our own schools, the emphasis on English grammar and spelling might well be supplemented with a much greater consideration of logic and the nature of deductive and inductive thinking. The relation of logic to mathematics and of mathematics to logic should be pointed out very early. In learning to write, surely clear exposition should take precedence over purely descriptive, narrative, or "creative" writing. Yet all of these play some part in scientific writing, and in the study of literature occasional examples of scientific writing at its best can be included. There are excellent anthologies that will be of use here, for example, *The Book of Naturalists*, edited by William Beebe, and *A Treasury of Science*, edited by Harlow Shapley. Such fine examples of exposition as Rachel Carson's *The Sea Around Us*, or of description so full of natural beauty as W. H. Hudson's *Naturalist in LaPlata* or *Long Ago and Far Away*, of gripping narration such as Sinclair Lewis' novel *Arrowsmith* and Dexter Master's *The Accident,* and of the acceptance of scientific conceptual thought in poems such as Tennyson's *In Memoriam* may well serve to relate science more closely to the study of English. There should be no undue constraint in this, no monopolizing of the limelight by the emphasis on the sciences. Let it be fitted naturally and germanely into context. How this may be done can be brought out particularly well in connection with poetry. The point to be made has been well expressed by Douglas Bush in his book *Science and English Poetry:*

> The modern poetic revolt against scientific positivism has some obvious similarities to the romantic revolt against Newtonian mechanism, but modern poets have recognized the inadequacy of romanticism partly through being deprived by science of some elements of the romantic faith. All modern [349] poetry has been conditioned by science, even those areas that seem farthest removed from it. And though modern poets have been united in revolt against the positivistic and mechanistic habit of mind and the world it has created, they have of course revolted in very different ways and directions.[3]

LANGUAGE STUDY

Science by its very nature knows no national boundaries, and the communication between scientists of different tongues is an obstacle of enormous magnitude. How unfortunate that the effort to utilize Latin as a truly international scientific language, still widespread during the eighteenth century, foundered on the inelasticity of the ancient language when faced with a flood of new scientific phenomena and concepts. There seems little hope in the near future for a truly international scientific language to secure wide adoption. Meanwhile, we may note that Latin and Greek are even more important roots of scientific language than they are of the everyday languages of the Western world. It is also helpful that even in the Slavic and Oriental languages the scientific words for the same phenomena, species, or concepts are nearly always the same, so that if the differences in alphabets and characters can be overcome, scientific

---

[3] Douglas Bush, *Science and English Poetry* (New York: Oxford University Press, 1950), p. 151.

articles constitute the easiest of materials to translate, and can be used far more widely than now in language study among students who are acquainted with the sciences involved.

Russian and Japanese will certainly need to be more widely studied than at present, and other Oriental languages, too, in all probability. Meanwhile we may expect the study of the Romance languages and of German to continue for some time to be the most available and most commonly chosen, not alone because they represent the nations of Western Europe and Latin America with which we have most ready access for travel, greatest trade and economic relations, and closest cultural and historic ties, but also because, together with English, they are the great languages of science in the past. Emphasis upon the historical growth of science through the "case study" approach advocated by Conant and others makes the importance of study in these languages far greater than if the study of science is naively considered to be no more than the absorption of the latest fashion in concepts or theories, or a knowledge of the latest new experimental findings. Perhaps I will be pardoned if I relate an experience of my own to illustrate this point.

As a geneticist, I have long wondered about the failure of his contemporaries to appreciate the discoveries of Gregor Mendel, discoveries which had to wait for thirty-five years, and a long time after Mendel's death, before their rediscovery and confirmation in 1900. How frequent is such a lag in scientific advancement because of the blindness of scientists unready for a complete reorientation of thought? If frequent, it is surely important to find ways and means of minimizing such lapses. When studying the history of the evolution theory and the ideas of various precursors of Darwin, I came upon some essays written long ago (1904–11) by the philosopher Arthur O. Lovejoy. Among eighteenth-century evolutionists there was mentioned a French scientist named Pierre Louis Moreau de Maupertuis, about whose remarkable views Professor Lovejoy wrote so stimulatingly that I felt nothing less than a visit to the original would satisfy me that a man writing over a hundred years before the time of the *Origin of Species* could indeed have anticipated so fully the role of natural selection and of hereditary variations in the production of new races and species. Obviously, had I not been able to follow with moderate ease the courtly eighteenth-century

French style of M. de Maupertuis, I could not have read, as I did, his *Venus Physique* and *Systéme de la Nature*. What I there found, to my amazement, was that Maupertuis had in many points anticipated not only Darwin, but also Mendel. Over a century before the great revolutions of biological thought associated with those two giants of science, this unknown man had developed a particulate theory of heredity—as we would now say, a theory of genes—paired in each offspring because derived one of each sort from the father and the other of each sort from the mother, and occasionally becoming lost or present in excess or permanently changed so as to account for defects in the development of the embryo, or for the appearance of extra structures, or for what we would nowadays call mutations. Upon the basis of these hereditary changes, acted upon by natural selection and isolated in different geographic regions, new races and species might in time appear, adapted to the particular circumstances of their environments. Most remarkable of all was that this man could well have claimed to be the first scientific human geneticist, for he based his ideas on the studies he made of the inheritance of polydactyly in a Berlin family, and tried to confirm them by breeding experiments with dogs and other animals. Why, then, was Maupertuis virtually unknown in the annals of biological science, and especially in the history of evolutionary and hereditary concepts?

The answer is most interesting. In his own time Maupertuis was a notable figure, a scientist of renown. He introduced Newtonian theory to the Continent. He conducted an expedition to Lapland to measure accurately a degree of latitude in the far north and to compare its length with one measured near the Equator, and so to prove the flattening of the earth at the poles, as predicted by Newtonian theory. He was a philosopher, mathematician, and physicist of some fame. For many years he had been a friend of Voltaire, who had praised him in the most extravagant terms. [350] After both Maupertuis and Voltaire had been called to Berlin by Frederick the Great—Maupertuis as head of the Berlin Academy of Sciences which Frederick hoped would outshine the Académie des Sciences in Paris, a strange episode occurred. A young man named Koenig accused Maupertuis of plagiarism in having derived, without acknowledgment, his most famous scientific contribution, the Principle of Least Action, from an unpublished work of Leibniz. Maupertuis used his position to eject the young man from scientific society, and justly, it must appear, for it is extremely doubtful that Maupertuis had ever seen this production of Leibniz, and even if he had, his own Principle of Least Action was as far beyond Leibniz' formulation as the later formulations of Euler, Lagrange, and Hamilton were to surpass in mathematical refinement the formulation made by Maupertuis. Voltaire, however, thought he saw youth and innocence suppressed by arrogance and high position. He sprang to the defense. In pamphlet after pamphlet he directed his most scurrilous abuse and vindictive satire at Maupertuis, especially at his ridiculous biological ideas of hereditary particles. In spite of Frederick's half-hearted effort to keep peace between his prima donnas, Voltaire succeeded in so humiliating Maupertuis that the latter soon retired from active life and died in shame and disgrace not many years afterwards.

My pursuit of this story even led me to a minor literary discovery. One of Voltaire's better-known works of this period is called *Micromégas* (1752). It is a satire in the style of *Gulliver's Travels*, holding up to scorn the foibles of humankind, especially the idiosyncrasies of philosophers and scientists, as seen by giant and supergiant visitors to our planet from Saturn and Sirius. It is a book with which I had been moderately familiar since my own graduate days, when I found it mentioned in Raymond Pearl's witty discussion of books every young biologist should know, *To Begin With*. What no one, not even Maupertuis' most scholarly biographer, Pierre Brunet, seems to have perceived is that *Micromégas* is clearly among the satires and lampoons directed at Maupertuis. The shipwrecked expedition the giant Saturnian and the super-giant Sirian were supposed to have discovered and conversed with was undoubtedly meant for Maupertuis' Lapland expedition, which in fact did suffer shipwreck during its return; and Maupertuis and the little Lap sweetheart he brought back to Germany with him—I wonder if she wasn't really a Finn, anthropology not being too advanced in those days—were made the butt of Voltaire's nastiest, most unquotable witticisms!

This story has no profound moral. I tell it only to indicate how the pursuit of science in its historical aspects may lead one into a foreign literature, and how one may stumble upon an explanation of a literary work that would probably never occur to anyone but the probing scientist. To me, this experience epitomizes the meaning of a liberal education.

SCIENCE AND THE TEACHING OF HISTORY

It is perhaps when we come to the teaching of history that the greatest changes will be needed if science is to be recognized as the core of the curriculum in modern schools. History gives us perspective in time, but human history is only an infinitesimal portion of the history of life on the earth, even though that bit is of most concern to us. A better perspective might be gained by treating the prehistory of man as a natural culmination of the long record of animal evolution. Archeology fits naturally onto paleo-anthropology, just as the latter fits naturally onto paleontology. Scientific methods of dating by carbon-14 or fluorine content, and the determination of chronological sequences from clay varves, tree-rings, and microstrata have vastly amplified in recent years the possibilities of making the prehistoric cultures of man historic, even in the absence of written records.

It is the sequence of cultures and the development of technology that is most significant, rather than the records of military conquests or even the rise and fall of empires, except as these lead to the intermixture of cultures, to changing ways of life, and to advances in control over natural forces—to "progress and power." Conventional political history and economic history become relatively less important as one focuses on the ascent of man from the half-ape to the tamer of lightning and [351] thunder—the new Prometheus of atomic fission, hydrogen fusion, and space travel. The history of invention and technology looms more and more important, and the expansion of human ideas from the seed of Adam to that "cosmic intelligence" that asks and answers and creates the world in its own image—this becomes most meaningful, the most liberating study of all. In any such treatment of modern history, the growth of science and the development of scientific concepts are forced to the center of the stage.

Political economy, sociology, and political science, among the social studies, must likewise submit to a change of emphasis. Classical systems of economy have less and less relevance in a world which is overnight thrown into a tailspin by scientific developments. The monetary basis of national economy becomes less significant than the sources of power, the supplies of raw material, the abundance of food, and the relations of each of these to the growth of population.

Science creates problems in these fields which cannot be ignored. Can science help to solve them? Are the behavioral sciences, especially psychology, sufficiently advanced to give us real hope? Or can we strengthen the behavioral sciences so as to gain scientifically sound solutions to our bitter social and political problems?

SCIENCE AND THE FINE ARTS

I must pass more quickly over the fine arts and music. Is it not evident that the representative arts spring from nature, and that the study of nature is basic to art? One of many possible approaches may be found in a discussion by Paul Weiss entitled "Beauty and the Beast: Life and the Rule of Order."[4]

Many others, scientists and nonscientists alike, have found beauty in the order of nature. As good an example as any is found in the great work *On Growth and Form*, by that remarkable combination of classical scholar and naturalist, D'Arcy Wentworth Thompson. I refer especially to the chapter on "The Equiangular Spiral," with its remarkable treatment of the mathematical aspects of the shells of Nautilus and other mollusks.

To be sure, beauty is not limited to the appreciation of order. One may, however, agree with Northrop that "any art functions in two ways, either in and for itself, or as the means to an end defined by some other subject or science."[5] He goes on to say that poetry, as an example of art—and what he says is true of all the arts—has as its primary task to "keep men continuously aware of the freshness and ineffable beauty and richness of the immediately apprehended." Lost in the worries of everyday living or too engrossed in the ab-

---

[4] *Scientific Monthly*, **81** (1955), 286–99.
[5] F. S. C. Northrop, *The Logic of the Sciences and the Humanities* (New York: Macmillan, 1948), p. 169 ff.

stractions of our theories of cosmology or of photosynthesis, we may fail to see the stars and the green woods and fields before our eyes. "Unless we are protected by poetry and the other arts functioning purely in and for themselves, reality in its theoretical aspect is sought at the cost of losing its equally real aesthetic component, and the mind of man becomes overstimulated while his spirit dies." In this sense art is a corrective—but implicit in any corrective is an opposite extreme. The artist must therefore comprehend what it is that he wishes to correct, oppose, or defy. As Douglas Bush said of the poets, in the quotation already given, "All modern poetry has been conditioned by science, even those areas that seem farthest removed from it."

But there is also the second function of art, according to Northrop, that of "the instrument or handmaid for metaphorically and analogically conveying a theoretical doctrine, the truth of which can be determined only outside of art by some other subject or science." What he means is that art cannot support its own doctrine, for it has within itself no capacity to distinguish the true from the false. Truth may be beauty, but beauty need not be truth. "This is the reason," he declares, "why a society becomes demoralized when it tries, as the recent modern world has done, to base its theory of the good life upon the arts and the humanities, rather than upon the sciences and a scientifically determined philosophy. There is no criterion within the arts or the humanities to determine whether one theory rather than another of the theoretic component or reality which an artist may convey analogically is the correct one." It follows that art "in its second function must follow, not precede, or assume the role of science and philosophy." Northrop's language is somewhat labored, but his thought here is clear and forthright. Whether art plays the role of rebel or handmaiden, or savior or servant, she cannot exist alone, apart from science and philosophy. To be sought through education is the true and intimate union in each mind of these polarities in the apprehension of the universe.

SCIENCE AND MUSIC

As for music, it is audible mathematics. It is not chance coincidence that nearly all the scientists I know are extremely musical in taste. Mathematics, a logical form adopted by the sciences and essential to their progress, might well be taught more effectively at the elementary levels if it were related more closely on the one hand to music, and on the other to the sciences. It should arouse in the child a sense of beauty as well as a recognition of practicality. Much of the mathematics still taught in elementary and secondary schools is less suited to that end than other aspects of mathematics. From the standpoint of many of the sciences the introduction of the calculus and the study of probability and statistical interpretation could be taught much earlier [352] than now. Neither branch is inherently more difficult than much that is taught, and the scientific and social values are far greater. The testing of the significance of differences could certainly be included in high-school mathematics, where it would be an invaluable adjunct to the use of the experimental method in science and the interpretation of data.

SCIENCE AND PHILOSOPHY

Finally, philosophy. The philosophy of science is already a well-recognized, fundamental part of philosophy, and mathematical logic is another bridge between the sciences and philosophy. But what is most important is that every man, if he is to avoid confusion of spirit, must create for himself an integrated view of himself and his world. This is the function of philosophy, and in carrying out that function it must work within the framework of scientific knowledge and concepts.

At the beginning of the era of modern science, the discoveries of Galileo and Newton led John Locke to a philosophy which was, in Northrop's words, "not merely an idea of the good for the state and for culture but also a philosophy of the experimentally verified for nature." This moral philosophy, scientifically based, in turn went into the foundation of British and American democracy quite as fully as the philosophy of Marx entered into the basic assumptions of the Communist nations. The American Declaration of Independence and Constitution were framed in the spirit of Locke, who asserted the primary importance of the individual. For Marx, on the other hand, the individual signifies almost nothing, society everything. And society is conceived in terms of historical process based in Darwinian evolution with natural selection as its agent. To the good Marxist the philosophy of the Democratic West is antiquated, because based on views of physical nature and human nature which have been replaced in science by thermodynamics and evolution. But there are abundant signs that Marxist dialectical materialism is no better at adapting itself to the changing nature of scientific fact and theory than was the empirical philosophy of Locke and Hume. It painfully avoids coming to grips with quantum theory and relativity, with the mathematical theory of probability and Mendelian genetics, with the psychology of the subconscious.

What we sadly need today is a philosophy that will embrace the rights and the needs of the individual and also the welfare of society, as the Judeo-Christian outlook so successfully did for many centuries. At the same time, however, the new must be a dynamic philosophy, changing with the basic shifts in man's scientific understanding of himself and his world, working toward a higher synthesis and not irrevocably tied to Newton or Einstein, Pavlov or Freud, Darwin or Mendel. For all of these, however great, have seen through a glass darkly. The whole of nature is far beyond man's present comprehension, the edifice of science and philosophy a mere foundation, and not the completed structure it will some day be. For we hope to build of our ideas and conceptions a cathedral, vast and beautiful, time-tested, wherein the human spirit may find strength and courage, peace and wisdom.

SCIENCE AND VALUES

For this task, science has limitations as well as powers. It tells us much, but hardly everything. It can deal with matter and energy, space and form and time. It scarcely measures values; it is thwarted by intangibles. Science reveals truths, but perhaps never the whole of truth. Its grandest conceptual schemes and theories may fail and have to be replaced. It is objective, not subjective, and the inner life of man is, and must always remain, subjective. Science is the product of the human mind, but what the mind is we do not know.

Science, as Bertrand Russell has said, can enhance among men two great evils, war and tyranny. For the powers of science can be used for evil as well as good ends. How ironical that what I have declared to be the greatest force in liberating the mind might be turned to enslave man and destroy him! Yet this is true of all power. As man with previously unimagined physical and biological powers in his grasp, stands lonely and afraid in the universe, it is of himself that he is afraid, of the choice he must make between good and evil.

Science, in ever greater measure, must therefore permeate the study and teaching of each of the arts, humanities, and social studies. These, on their side, must mollify, enrich, protect the sciences.

ALDOUS HUXLEY

Brave New World Revisited. New York: Harper & Brothers, 1958, pp. 119–133*

Education for freedom must begin by stating facts and enunciating values, and must go on to develop appropriate techniques for realizing the values and for combating those who, for whatever reason, choose to ignore the facts or deny the values.

In an earlier chapter I have discussed the Social Ethic, in terms of which the evils resulting from over-organization and over-population are justified and made to seem good. Is such a system of values consonant with what we know about human physique and temperament? The Social Ethic assumes that nurture is all-important in determining human behavior and that nature—the psychophysical equipment with which individuals are born—is a negligible factor. But is this true? Is it true that human beings are nothing but the products of their social [119] environment? And if it is not true, what justification can there be for maintaining that the individual is less important than the group of which he is a member?

All the available evidence points to the conclusion that in the life of individuals and societies heredity is no less significant than culture. Every individual is biologically unique and unlike all other individuals. Freedom is therefore a great good, tolerance a great virtue and regimentation a great misfortune. For practical or theoretical reasons, dictators, organization men and certain scientists are anxious to reduce the maddening diversity of men's natures to some kind of manageable uniformity. In the first flush of his Behavioristic fervor, J. B. Watson roundly declared that he could find "no support for hereditary patterns of behavior, nor for special abilities (musical, art, etc.) which are supposed to run in families." And even today we find a distinguished psychologist, Professor B. F. Skinner of Harvard, insisting that, "as scientific explanation becomes more and more comprehensive, the contribution which may be claimed by the individual himself appears to approach zero. Man's vaunted creative powers, his achievements in art, science and morals, his capacity to choose and our right to hold him responsible for the consequences of his choice—none of these is conspicuous in the new scientific self-portrait." In a word, Shakespeare's plays were not written by Shakespeare, nor even by Bacon or the Earl of Oxford; they were written by Elizabethan England. [120]

More than sixty years ago William James wrote an essay on "Great Men and Their Environment," in which he set out to defend the outstanding individual against the assaults of Herbert Spencer. Spencer had proclaimed that "Science" (that wonderfully convenient personification of the opinions, at a given date, of Professors X, Y and Z) had completely abolished the Great Man. "The great man," he had written, "must be classed with all other phenomena in the society that gave him birth, as a product of its antecedents." The great man may be (or seem to be) "the proximate initiator of changes. . . . But if there is to be anything like a real explanation of these changes, it must be sought in that aggregate of conditions out of which both he and they have arisen." This is one of those empty profundities to which no operational meaning can possibly be attached. What our philosopher is saying is that we must know everything before we can fully understand anything. No doubt. But in fact we shall never know everything. We must therefore be content with partial understanding and proximate causes— including the influence of great men. "If anything is humanly certain," writes William James, "it is that the great man's society, properly so called, does not make him before he can remake it. Physiological forces, with which the social, political, geographical and to a great extent anthropological conditions have just as much and just as little to do as the crater of Vesuvius has to do with the flickering of this gas by which I write, are what make him. Can it [121] be that Mr. Spencer holds the convergence of sociological pressures to have so impinged upon Stratford-upon-Avon about the twenty-sixth of April, 1564, that a W. Shakespeare, with all his mental peculiarities, had to be born there? . . . And does he mean to say that if the aforesaid W. Shakespeare had died of cholera infantum, another mother at Stratford-upon-Avon would need have engendered a duplicate copy of him, to restore the sociologic equilibrium?"

Professor Skinner is an experimental psychologist, and his treatise on "Science and Human Behavior" is solidly based upon facts. But unfortunately the facts belong to so limited a class that when at last he ventures upon a generalization, his conclusions are as sweepingly unrealistic as those of the Victorian theorizer. Inevitably so; for Professor Skinner's indifference to what James calls the "physiological forces" is almost as complete as Herbert Spencer's. The genetic factors determining human behavior are dismissed by him in less than a page. There is no reference in his book to the findings of constitutional medicine, nor any hint of that constitutional psychology, in terms of which (and in terms of which alone, so far as I can judge) it might be possible to write a complete and realistic biography of an individual in relation to the relevant facts of his existence—his body, his temperament, his intellectual endowments, his immediate environment from moment to moment, his time, place and culture. A [122] science of human behavior is like a science of motion in the abstract—necessary, but, by itself, wholly inadequate to the facts. Consider a dragonfly, a rocket and a breaking wave. All three of them illustrate the same fundamental laws of motion; but they illustrate these laws in different ways, and the differences are at least as important as the identities. By itself, a study of motion can tell us almost nothing about that which, in any given instance, is being moved. Similarly a study of behavior can, by itself, tell us almost nothing about the individual mind-body that, in any particular instance, is exhibiting the behavior. But to us who are mind-bodies, a knowledge of mind-bodies is of paramount importance. Moreover, we know by observation and experience that the differences between individual mind-bodies are enormously great, and that some mind-bodies can and do profoundly affect their social environment. On this last point Mr. Bertrand Russell is in full agreement with William James—and with practically everyone, I would add, except the proponents of Spencerian or Behavioristic scientism. In Russell's view the causes of historical change are of three kinds—economic change, political theory and important individuals. "I do not believe," says Mr. Russell, "that any of these can be ignored, or wholly explained away as the effect of causes of another kind." Thus, if Bismarck and Lenin had died in infancy, our world would be very different from what, thanks in part to Bismarck and Lenin, it [123] now is. "History is not yet a science, and can only be made to seem scientific by falsifications and omissions." In real life, life as it is lived from day to day, the individual can never be explained away. It is only in theory that his contributions appear to approach zero; in practice they are all-important. When a piece of work gets done in the world, who actually does it? Whose eyes and ears do the perceiving, whose cortex does the thinking, who has the feelings that motivate, the will that overcomes obstacles? Certainly not the social environment; for a group is not an organism, but only a blind unconscious organization. Everything that is done within a society is done by individuals. These individuals are, of course, profoundly influenced by the local culture, the taboos and moralities, the information and misinformation handed down from the past and preserved in a body of spoken traditions or written literature; but whatever each individual takes from society (or, to be more accurate, whatever he takes from other individuals associated in groups, or from the symbolic records compiled by other individuals, living or dead) will be used by him in his own unique way—with *his* special senses, *his* biochemical makeup, *his* physique and temperament, and nobody else's. No amount of scientific explanation, however comprehensive, can explain away these self-evident facts. And let us remember that Professor Skinner's scientific portrait of man as the product of the social environment is not the only scientific portrait. There [124] are other, more realistic likenesses. Consider, for example, Professor Roger Williams' portrait. What he paints is not behavior in the abstract, but mind-bodies behaving— mind-bodies that are the products partly of the environment they share with other mind-bodies, partly of their own private heredity. In *The Human Frontier* and *Free but Unequal* Professor Williams has expatiated, with a wealth of detailed evidence, on those innate differences between individuals, for which Dr. Watson could find no support and whose importance, in Professor Skinner's eyes, approaches zero. Among animals, biological variability within a given species becomes more and more conspicuous as we move up the evolutionary scale. This biological variability is highest in man, and human beings display a greater degree of biochemical, structural and temperamental diversity than do the members of any other species. This is a plain observable fact. But what I have called the Will to Order, the desire to impose a comprehensible uniformity upon the bewildering manifoldness of things and events, has led many people to ignore this fact. They have minimized biological uniqueness and have concentrated all their attention upon the simpler and, in the present state of knowledge, more understandable environmental factors involved in human behavior. "As a result of this environmentally centered thinking and investigation," writes Professor Williams, "the doctrine of the essential uniformity of human infants has been widely [125] accepted and is held by a great body of social psychologists, sociologists, social anthropologists, and many others, including historians, economists, educationalists, legal scholars and men in public life. This doctrine has been incorporated into the prevailing mode of thought of many who have had to do with shaping educational and governmental policies and is often accepted unquestioningly by those who do little critical thinking of their own."

An ethical system that is based upon a fairly realistic appraisal of the data of experience is likely to do more good than harm. But many ethical systems have been based upon an appraisal of experience, a view of the nature of things, that is hopelessly unrealistic. Such an ethic is likely to do more harm than good. Thus, until quite recent times, it was universally believed that bad weather, diseases of cattle and sexual impotence could be, and in many cases actually were, caused by the malevolent operations of magicians. To catch and kill magicians was therefore a duty—and this duty, moreover, had been divinely ordained in the second Book of Moses: "Thou shalt not suffer a witch to live." The systems of ethics and law that were based upon this erroneous view of the nature of things were the cause (during the centuries, when they were taken most seriously by men in authority) of the most appalling evils. The orgy of spying, lynching and judicial murder, which these wrong views about magic made logical and mandatory, was not matched until our [126] own days, when the Communist ethic, based upon erroneous views about economics, and the Nazi ethic, based upon erroneous views about race, commanded and justified atrocities on an even greater scale. Consequences hardly less undesirable are likely to follow the general adoption of a Social Ethic, based upon the erroneous view that ours is a fully social species, that human infants are born uniform and that individuals are the product of conditioning by and within the collective environment. If these views were correct, if human beings were in fact the members of a truly social species, and if their individual differences were trifling and could be completely ironed out by appropriate conditioning, then, obviously, there would be no need for liberty and the State would be justified in persecuting the heretics who demanded it. For the individual termite, service to the termitary is perfect freedom. But human beings are not completely social; they are only moderately gregarious. Their societies are not organisms, like the hive or the anthill; they are organizations, in other words *ad hoc* machines for collective living. Moreover, the differences between individuals are so great that, in spite of the most intensive cultural ironing, an extreme endomorph (to use W. H. Sheldon's terminology) will retain his sociable viscerotonic characteristics, an extreme mesomorph will remain energetically somatotonic through thick and thin and an extreme ectomorph will always be cerebrotonic, introverted and over-sensitive. [127] In the Brave New World of my fable socially desirable behavior was insured by a double process of genetic manipulation and postnatal conditioning. Babies were cultivated in bottles and a high degree of uniformity in the human product was assured by using ova from a limited number of mothers and by treating each ovum in such a way that it would split and split again, producing identical twins in batches of a hundred or more. In this way it was possible to produce standardized machine-minders for standardized machines. And the standardization of the machine-minders was perfected, after birth, by infant conditioning, hypnopaedia and chemically induced euphoria as a substitute for the satisfaction of feeling oneself free and creative. In the world we live in, as has been pointed out in earlier chapters, vast impersonal forces are making for the centralization of power and a regimented society. The genetic standardization of individuals is still impossible; but Big Government and Big Business already possess, or will very soon possess, all the techniques for mind-manipulation described in *Brave New World*, along with others of which I was too unimaginative to dream. Lacking the ability to impose genetic uniformity upon embryos, the rulers of tomorrow's over-populated and over-organized world will try to impose social and cultural uniformity upon adults and their children. To achieve this end, they will (unless prevented) make use of all the mind-manipulating techniques at their disposal and [128] will not hesitate to reinforce these methods of non-rational persuasion by economic coercion and threats of physical violence. If this kind of tyranny is to be avoided, we must begin without delay to educate ourselves and our children for freedom and self-government.

Such an education for freedom should be, as I have said, an education first of all in facts and in values—the facts of individual diversity and genetic uniqueness and the values of freedom, tolerance and mutual charity which are the ethical corollaries of these facts. But unfortunately correct knowledge and sound principles are not enough. An unexciting truth may be eclipsed by a thrilling falsehood. A skilful appeal to passion is often too strong for the best of good resolutions. The effects of false and pernicious propaganda cannot be neutralized except by a thorough training in the art of analyzing its techniques and seeing through its sophistries. Language has made possible man's progress from animality to civilization. But language has also inspired that sustained folly and that systematic, that genuinely diabolic wickedness which are no less characteristic of human behavior than are the language-inspired virtues of systematic forethought and sustained angelic benevolence. Language permits its users to pay attention to things, persons and events, even when the things and persons are absent and the events are not taking place. Language gives definition to our memories and, by translating experiences into symbols, converts [129] the immediacy of craving or abhorrence, of hatred or love, into fixed principles of feeling and conduct. In some way of which we are wholly unconscious, the reticular system of the brain selects from a countless host of stimuli those few experiences which are of practical importance to us. From these unconsciously selected experiences we more or less consciously select and abstract a smaller number, which we label with words from our vocabulary and then classify within a system at once metaphysical, scientific and ethical, made up of other words on a higher level of abstraction. In cases where the selecting and abstracting have been dictated by a system that is not too erroneous as a view of the nature of things, and where the verbal labels have been intelligently chosen and their symbolic nature clearly understood, our behavior is apt to be realistic and tolerably decent. But under the influence of badly chosen words, applied, without any understanding of their merely symbolic character, to experiences that have been selected and abstracted in the light of a system of erroneous ideas, we are apt to behave with a fiendishness and an organized stupidity, of which dumb animals (precisely because they *are* dumb and cannot speak) are blessedly incapable.

In their anti-rational propaganda the enemies of freedom systematically pervert the resources of language in order to wheedle or stampede their victims into thinking, feeling and acting as they, the mind-manipulators, want them to think, feel and act. [130] An education for freedom (and for the love and intelligence which are at once the conditions and the results of freedom) must be, among other things, an education in the proper uses of language. For the last two or three generations philosophers have devoted a great deal of time and thought to the analysis of symbols and the meaning of meaning. How are the words and sentences which we speak related to the things, persons and events, with which we have to deal in our day-to-day living? To discuss this problem would take too long and lead us too far afield. Suffice it to say that all the intellectual materials for a sound education in the proper use of language—an education on every level from the kindergarten to the postgraduate school—are now available. Such an education in the art of distinguishing between the proper and the improper use of symbols could be inaugurated immediately. Indeed it might have been inaugurated at any time during the last thirty or forty years. And yet children are nowhere taught, in any systematic way, to distinguish true from false, or meaningful from meaningless, statements. Why is this so? Because their elders, even in the democratic countries, do not want them to be given this kind of education. In this context the brief, sad history of the Institute for Propaganda Analysis is highly significant. The Institute was founded in 1937, when Nazi propaganda was at its noisiest and most effective, by Mr. Filene, the New England philanthropist. Under its auspices analyses of non-rational

[131] propaganda were made and several texts for the instruction of high school and university students were prepared. Then came the war—a total war on all the fronts, the mental no less than the physical. With all the Allied governments engaging in "psychological warfare," an insistence upon the desirability of analyzing propaganda seemed a bit tactless. The Institute was closed in 1941. But even before the outbreak of hostilities, there were many persons to whom its activities seemed profoundly objectionable. Certain educators, for example, disapproved of the teaching of propaganda analysis on the grounds that it would make adolescents unduly cynical. Nor was it welcomed by the military authorities, who were afraid that recruits might start to analyze the utterances of drill sergeants. And then there were the clergymen and the advertisers. The clergymen were against propaganda analysis as tending to undermine belief and diminish churchgoing; the advertisers objected on the grounds that it might undermine brand loyalty and reduce sales.

These fears and dislikes were not unfounded. Too searching a scrutiny by too many of the common folk of what is said by their pastors and masters might prove to be profoundly subversive. In its present form, the social order depends for its continued existence on the acceptance, without too many embarrassing questions, of the propaganda put forth by those in authority and the propaganda hallowed by the local traditions. The problem, once more is to find the happy mean. Individuals must be suggestible [132] enough to be willing and able to make their society work, but not so suggestible as to fall helplessly under the spell of professional mind-manipulators. Similarly, they should be taught enough about propaganda analysis to preserve them from an uncritical belief in sheer nonsense, but not so much as to make them reject outright the not always rational outpourings of the well-meaning guardians of tradition. Probably the happy mean between gullibility and a total skepticism can never be discovered and maintained by analysis alone. This rather negative approach to the problem will have to be supplemented by something more positive—the enunciation of a set of generally acceptable values based upon a solid foundation of facts. The value, first of all, of individual freedom, based upon the facts of human diversity and genetic uniqueness; the value of charity and compassion, based upon the old familiar fact, lately rediscovered by modern psychiatry—the fact that, whatever their mental and physical diversity, love is as necessary to human beings as food and shelter; and finally the value of intelligence, without which love is impotent and freedom unattainable. This set of values will provide us with a criterion by which propaganda may be judged. The propaganda that is found to be both nonsensical and immoral may be rejected out of hand. That which is merely irrational, but compatible with love and freedom, and not on principle opposed to the exercise of intelligence, may be provisionally accepted for what it is worth.

Exercises and theme topics

EXERCISE VII. PROBLEMS OF TECHNIQUE: THE INTRODUCTION AND THE CONCLUSION

A classic story in publishing circles tells of the editor of a popular magazine who rejected any article or story whose first two hundred words did not gain his interest. While such an attitude is undoubtedly extreme, it does stress the importance of the opening paragraph(s) of any selection, including your own papers. In expository writing the *introduction* performs a dual function. First, it must attract the reader; second, it must anticipate the nature and scope of the whole article. In short, it is effective only insofar as it prepares for, and makes the reader want to read, the body of the paper, in which the writer will develop his main thesis. The methods of achieving these ends range from the statement of purpose and sketch of an attitude of the reading public, as in Lee DuBridge's "Science—The Endless Adventure," to the attention-catching anecdote, as in Bentley Glass's "Liberal Education in a Scientific Age," and the striking historical incident, as in Warren Weaver's "Science and the Citizen." No one method can be called *the* best method of introduction; rather, the nature of the material to be presented will suggest an appropriate opening which is concise and relevant to the main purpose of the paper.

Similarly, the *conclusion* becomes of paramount importance, for it provides the writer with his last opportunity to make his point. Again, no one method is always effective because each has its own strengths and weaknesses. Perhaps the most frequently employed method, particularly in longer articles, is the summary paragraph or summary statement, as in Laetitia Bolton's "What Kind of Science Teaching Program?" Equally effective if presented correctly is the rhetorical question which will lead the reader to consider the consequences of what has been said, or the statement, sometimes ironical in tone, which broadens the implications of what has been said, as in *The New Republic* editorial or Lee DuBridge's article. Again, a single illustration that in a sense dramatizes the author's thesis and conclusions may prove a potent ending. These suggestions do not by any means exhaust the possibilities, but they do represent popular methods. Whatever method is used, the *conclusion* provides the author with his last opportunity to make certain that the reader will remember what has been said.

Assignments

1. How do the writers in Parts III and IV open their articles? Which one held your interest most? Why?
2. How do the writers in Parts III and IV end their articles? Which one did you think was most forceful? Why?
3. Write a new *introduction* to any one of the articles in Part IV. What method(s) did you employ? Why?
4. Write a new *conclusion* to any one of the articles in Part IV. What method(s) did you employ? Why?

EXERCISE VIII. PROBLEMS OF TECHNIQUE: POINT OF VIEW

In expository writing, as in any writing, one of your most troublesome problems may involve your choice of an effective *point of view* toward your material. Throughout your paper you must maintain an appropriate and consistent attitude toward your topic in order to be fully effective. This means, most simply, that you must choose among the first, second, and third person *points of view.* Each has its advantages. The first person (I, we) emphasizes the author's participation in an event and his personal reactions to any situation or concept. It gives authority and authenticity to his account, particularly when he presents information unique to his own experience. Because it is personal, the first person gives an immediacy and vividness to what the author says. The second person (you) establishes an easy familiarity between author and reader and creates a feeling of participation on the part of the reader. Its use often identifies a paper which has been presented originally as a speech. The third person (he, she, it, one, they) is the most impersonal *point of view* and perhaps assumes that the significance of the material will sustain the interest of the reader. It is, of course, the most formal and objective of the three and is typically the *point of view* of the research paper. Perhaps your final decision will de-

pend upon the degree of formality or informality, objectivity or subjectivity, that you wish to attain.

Notice that with the exception of Turner in his "Is There a Scientific Method?" and Bronowski in his "The Real Responsibilities of
the Scientist" and an occasional sentence in other articles in which
(*you*) is the implied subject—"Consider a dragonfly, a rocket and a
breaking wave." (Huxley, p. 123); "Ask any working biologist
about how money is now spent. . . ." (Heilbrunn, p. 427)—the
writers do not employ the second person *point of view*. Nor does any
one of them rely exclusively on the first or third person throughout
his article. Instead of using a single *point of view* exclusively, they
combine the first and third persons. Although certain writers make
fairly extensive use of the first person, as do Aldous Huxley, Conant,
Lear, and Weaver, notice that for the most part the majority employ
only an occasional editorial *we*. They do this in an attempt to achieve
a familiar relationship between author and reader by creating the
impression of a group to which both the author and reader belong.
(This device may identify the article originally presented as a
speech.)

In informal writing, at least, such a shift in *point of view* is per-
missible—if only by long-established practice. Nevertheless, any
shift from one person to another can create a problem. If you do
not maintain a consistent and appropriate role throughout your
paper, you may reduce the effectiveness of your material. By using
the second person, you may give the impression of talking down to
your readers. By using the first person in a research paper, you
may distort the evidence and give the impression that your conclusions are based upon personal opinion alone. By using the third
person to relate a personal experience, you may destroy the immediacy and vividness of the event. In making your choice of an
appropriate *point of view*, you should be guided by the degree of informality or formality, subjectivity or objectivity, demanded by
the nature of your material.

Assignments

1. What effect does the second person contribute to Turner's "Is There a
   Scientific Method?" and Bronowski's "The Real Responsibilities of the

Scientist"? Will any other *point of view* present the material more effectively? Rewrite any part of the articles which you believe can be improved.

2. What use of the first person do the writers make in Conant's "Science and Technology in the Last Decade," Fred Hoyle's "The Religious Impulse in Man," Weaver's "Science and the Citizen" and "A Scientist Ponders Faith," and Compton's "Science and Man's Freedom"? In which article(s) is the first person used most effectively? Why? Rewrite any part of an article which you believe can be improved.

3. Change the *point of view* in any one of the other articles in Part V which makes only an occasional use of the editorial we. Does the consistent use of the first person or the third person make this article more effective? Why?

THEME TOPICS

1. Does your own experience and that of your friends support the contention of the several writers that American students are receiving inadequate training in science?

2. What course in high school or college has given you your most valuable and enjoyable contact with science? How do you explain its success? And/or: Have you had a course which made science particularly unattractive? How do you explain its lack of success?

3. What do the writers in Part IV regard as the chief problems facing American education? What are their causes? What solutions do the authors suggest? If there is a difference of opinion, can these differences be reconciled? How?

4. Defend or attack Bentley Glass's assertion that the liberal arts curriculum should emphasize, perhaps even center around, science.

5. To what degree do the authors blame specialization for the present plight of science education? What do they propose as a solution?

6. What does Huxley want education to accomplish? Do the other writers agree or disagree with his views?

7. What role do these writers believe language and communication should play in present-day education?

part V   SCIENCE, PHILOSOPHY, AND RELIGION

The changing scientific scene 1900–1950

JAMES B. CONANT

Modern Science and Modern Man. New York: Columbia University Press, 1952, pp. 50–57*

Just what does the new outlook mean for those interested in constructing a total picture of the universe? Professor Bridgman has said, in considering the philosophical implications of physics:

"Finally, I come to what it seems to me may well be from the long range point of view the most revolutionary of the insights to be derived from our recent experiences in physics, more revolutionary than the insights afforded by the discoveries of Galileo and Newton, or of Darwin. This is the insight that it is impossible to transcend the human reference point.

. . . The new insight comes from a realization that the structure of nature may eventually be such that our processes of thought do not correspond to it sufficiently to permit us to think about it all. We have already had an intimation of this in the behavior [50] of very small things in the quantum domain . . . there can be no difference of opinion with regard to the dilemma that now confronts us in the direction of the very small. We are now approaching a bound beyond which we are forever estopped from pushing our inquiries, not by the construction of the world, but by the construction of ourselves. The world fades out and eludes us because it becomes meaningless. We cannot even express this in the way we would like. We cannot say that there exists a world beyond any knowledge possible to us because of the nature of knowledge. The very concept of existence becomes meaningless. It is literally true that the only way of reacting to this is to shut up. We are confronted with something truly ineffable. We have reached the limit of the vision of the great pioneers of science, the vision, namely that we live in a sympathetic world, in that it is comprehensible by our minds."[3]

Professor Dingle of London has written, "The men who carried on the scientific tradition established in the seventeenth century did so truly and faithfully, but thinking all the time that they were doing something else. The revolution that came in the twentieth century was simply the overthrow of the false notion of what science was and is; science itself has pursued the same undeviating course from Galileo through Newton and Einstein to our own time."[4] [51]

"What the mid-nineteenth century scientists thought they were doing," Dingle goes on to say, was looking out "upon a real external substantial world of material bodies whose content was measured by its mass or weight. . . . The information thus provided gave clues—often very indirect—to the eternal and unchanging principles that were firmly believed to underlie the behaviour of the world. . . . The world was thus regarded as exhibiting, with the passage of time, a succession of states, each connected with its predecessor and successor by what were regarded as unbreakable links of absolute necessity. This was referred to as the principle of cause and effect. . . .

"In general terms we may say that the Victorians looked on the progress of science as a process of accumulation. . . . Our view today is very different . . . the picture of the whole which we form in our attempt to express its interrelations undergoes unceasing transformations. . . . We can no longer say, The World is like this, or the World is like that. We can only say, Our experience up to the present is best represented by a world of this character; I do not know what model will best represent the world of tomorrow, but I do know that it will coordinate a greater range of experience than that of today."[5]

According to this interpretation of the history of science, what nineteenth-century physicists thought they were doing was discovering the causal laws that governed the world of material substance;

[3] P. W. Bridgman, "Philosophical Implications of Physics," in American Academy of Arts and Sciences, *Bulletin*, Vol. III, No. 5 (February, 1950).

[4] Herbert Dingle, "The Scientific Outlook in 1851 and in 1951," *British Journal for the Philosophy of Science*, II (1951), 86.

[5] *Ibid.*, pp. 89, 98–99.

actually, to use Professor Dingle's words, "They were at little more than the beginning [52] of their task of understanding the world of experience." Yet in contrasting the present with the past, it is important to note that not all nineteenth-century scientists were of one mind as to the nature of their task. One need only mention the name of Ernst Mach, whose point of view in our own time has led to the doctrines of the logical empiricists, to indicate that there were some skeptics in regard to the possibilities of determining once and for all the nature of the material universe. P. G. Tait in 1876 in his lectures on "Some Recent Advances in Physical Science" stated that "nothing is more preposterously unscientific than to assert (as is constantly done by the quasi-scientific writers of the present day) that with the utmost strides attempted by science we should necessarily be sensibly nearer to a conception of the ultimate nature of matter." Even as orthodox a physicist as J. J. Thomson reflected the same view when, in the introductory paragraphs to his little book *The Corpuscular Theory of Matter*, published in 1907, he stated that his new theory was not to be regarded as "an ultimate one; its object is physical," he said, "rather than metaphysical." And he added these significant words, "From the point of view of the physicist, a theory of matter is a policy rather than a creed; its object is to connect or coordinate apparently diverse phenomena and above all to suggest, stimulate, and direct experiment."

If I tried to sum up in a sentence what seems to me the philosophic implications of the new physics, I should be inclined to paraphrase Sir J. J. Thomson. A mass of experimental evidence in the twentieth century has provided [53] powerful ammunition to those who look upon a scientific theory as a policy and has made untenable at least one theory regarded as a creed. A policy suggests always a guide to action, and of the various interpretations of science that are current today, those seem to me to be the most useful that emphasize the dynamic nature of science. There are philosophers, I realize, who draw a sharp line between knowing and doing and look askance at all philosophizing that seems to tie the search for truth in any way to practical undertakings. But for me, at least, any analysis of the process of testing a statement made in a scientific context leads at once to a series of actions. Therefore, I venture to define science as a series of interconnected concepts and conceptual schemes arising from experiment and observation and fruitful of further experiments and observations. The test of a scientific theory is, I suggest, its fruitfulness—in the words of Sir J. J. Thomson, its ability "to suggest, stimulate, and direct experiment."

The fallacy underlying what some might call the eighteenth- and nineteenth-century misconceptions of the nature of scientific investigations seems to lie in a mistaken analogy. Those who said they were investigating the structure of the universe imagined themselves as the equivalent of the early explorers and map makers. The explorers of the fifteenth and sixteenth centuries had opened up new worlds with the aid of imperfect maps; in their accounts of distant lands, there had been some false and many ambiguous statements. But by the time everyone came to believe the world was round, the maps [54] of distant continents were beginning to assume a fairly consistent pattern. By the seventeenth century, methods of measuring space and time had laid the foundations for an accurate geography. The increased success of empirical procedures in improving the work of artisans was already improving men's accuracy of observation. Therefore, by a series of successive approximations, so to speak, maps and descriptions of distant lands were becoming closer and closer to accurate accounts of reality. Why would not the labors of those who worked in laboratories have the same outcome? No one doubted that there were real rivers, mountains, trees, bays with tides, rainfall, snowfall, glaciers; one could doubt any particular map or description, of course, but given time and patience, it was assumed the truth would be ascertained. By the same token there must be a truth about the nature of heat, light, and matter.

To be sure, the map makers had been observing gross objects like rocks and trees, rivers and mountains, while, as science progressed, the force of gravity and atoms and waves in the ether became the preoccupation of the physicist. Still, tentative ideas played a similar part in both enterprises; working hypotheses as to the nature of a river valley, the source of a lake, or the frontier of a mountain range seemed to be the equivalent of the caloric fluid or the early corpuscular theory of light. The early geographers' methods of identification were essentially those of common sense. Any given set of observations might be in error. Yet even erroneous assumptions might serve, at times, a useful purpose. To have assumed the existence [55] of a lake beyond a certain mountain range might prove fortunate; as a "working hypothesis," even if false, it might lead an explorer to important goals.

Of course, the possibility of error exists in all surveys. Indeed, one can image a situation where even in geography no final certainty is possible. Assume an island surrounded by reefs that make direct access out of the question except with special equipment, and assume an explorer without such equipment. He must content himself for the time being with telescopic observations from several angles; he can thus construct a map but with many uncertainties. For example, are those highly colored areas due to rocks or to vegetation? On his return with adequate equipment, he can land, go to the colored areas and directly determine their composition. If before he returns, the island disappears below the surface of the ocean, that makes no difference as to the validity of his methods. We are all sure that in principle he could have returned and determined the accuracy of his suppositions about the nature of the terrain.

This use of the "in principle" argument, I have already pointed out, was the basis for the nineteenth-century physicist's confidence in his picture of a gas with its rapidly moving particles. Those who still hold today with the idea that the universe has a structure which, like the geography of an island, can be discovered by successive approximations, must cling to the "in principle" argument. Confront them with the phlogiston theory, the caloric fluid, the luminiferous ether—all now obsolete (except for pedagogic purposes)—and they will say, [56] "Yes, the first maps were imperfect, but in principle it is possible to find out what really is the structure of the universe."

On this basic issue there is far from complete agreement among philosophers of science today. You can, each of you, choose your side and find highly distinguished advocates for the point of view you have selected. However, in view of the revolution in physics, anyone who now asserts that science is an exploration of the universe must be prepared to shoulder a heavy burden of proof. To my mind, the analogy between the map maker and the scientist is false. A scientific theory is not even the first approximation to a map; it is not a creed; it is a policy—an economical and fruitful guide to action by scientific investigators.

From classical to modern physics:
philosophical implications of the discoveries of physics

G. O. JONES, J. ROTBLAT, AND C. J. WHITROW

Atoms and the Universe. New York: Charles Scribner's Sons, 1956, pp. 157–159*

It is tempting to say simply that there are no philosophical implications to be attached to the matters which have been discussed here, but this would be to ignore the fact that violent controversies of a philosophical character have existed in physics at least since the time of Aristotle. At any rate, the tendency among physicists is now to consider that the real content of a statement in physics lies in the statement itself, and that to speak of its philosophical implication to some extent reduces the force of what is said. Let us try to illustrate this by some examples.

One of the most important scientific controversies was that between the followers of Aristotle and Ptolemy, who said that the sun and stars travelled around the earth, which was thus the centre of the universe, and the followers of Copernicus and Galileo, who insisted that the earth travelled around the sun. These opposite views would naturally be thought to have philosophical implications. Indeed, the Copernican hypothesis was attacked on religious grounds because it was asserted that Copernicus had removed an obstacle to the idea, opposed by the Church, that the universe might be infinite. It was unthinkable that stars travelling around the earth could move with infinite velocities, as some must in an infinite universe, if all revolved around the earth.

Now what Copernicus had found was that if he assumed the earth to be a planet, like the other planets, and that all moved around the sun, a great mathematical simplification occurred. He could then account for the seasons and for many other features of the planetary motion. So he asserted that the earth moved around the sun. This idea was at the time a great scientific advance. But with our present knowledge of astronomy we know also that the sun is moving around the centre of the stellar system; when an astronomer studies distant nebulae the situation is still further complicated. So how is the earth really moving? Surely the real truth is that which is contained in the sum of all detailed assertions about relative motions. For practical purposes any suitable hypothesis may be used: a cyclist who wished to know what was lighting-up time would find the Ptolemaic system adequate.

This old controversy carries its lesson even today. Anyone [157] brought up in the Aristotelian tradition would resist strongly any suggestion that the earth was rotating on its own axis and revolving around the sun at enormous speed. All the evidence of the senses would persuade him that this must be a fantastic invention. Eventually, after calmer reflection, he would realize that it was really a very reasonable idea because it explained all the complex planetary motions—relative to the earth—as being also quite simple revolutions around the sun. Finally, he might arrive at the more empirical view, suggested above, that the real truth was the sum of knowledge about relative motions.

Nowadays, the ideas of relativity and quantum theory appear strange. But when they have been thoroughly assimilated future students of present-day writings on their philosophical implications may wonder what all the fuss was about! If a theory leads to a simplification or greater ordering of ideas then it is useful. The physicist does not argue as to whether it is *right*. In particular, he does not worry if he cannot explain the new postulates made. We have deceived ourselves if we think that anything can be *explained*— in the mystical, absolute sense usually attached to this word. It is only because of our extreme familiarity, almost from birth, with some of the ideas of classical physics that modern physics is so puzzling. For example, the indestructibility of matter seems so obvious from all our experience that the statement that matter can be converted into energy is difficult to accept. Also, we have rather firm ideas about the meanings of such words as 'force' and 'cause,' because we know how to exert forces (with our muscles, say) and we

can also cause events to occur. It is disturbing to be told that force
has to be redefined in order to carry through the development of relativity theory, or that force can be transmitted without the interven-
tion of a medium, or that certain physical events appear to occur
without cause—a feature of quantum theory.

It becomes less difficult to accept such changes when it is realized
that the concept of force is in itself empirical and somewhat synthetic. When Newton's second law is objectively analysed we come
to realize that what it does is to define force only if mass and accel-
eration have previously been defined. In relativity the definition of
force is slightly altered and the question [158] naturally arises as
to whether such a thing as *force* really exists. The answer is that
force is what we have now decided it shall be, and we have chosen
the present definition because it leads to an *all-round* simplification
of the laws of nature in their mathematical formulation. That is,
force, as now defined, enters simply into many other physical laws
besides Newton's second law.

It is useful when considering any statement about the philosophical implications of science to apply two tests. First: is the statement
framed with the same care as scientific statements usually are; do
the words used convey a precise meaning, and the same meaning
to everyone concerned in the discussion? At this point it is only being insisted that the same rigour in argument be employed as is required by modern philosophers—who have, as a matter of fact,
been as fundamentally influenced by the objectivity and empiricism
of science as by the exact reasoning of modern mathematics. But
very many of the assertions which have been made about the philosophical implications of science would fall to the ground when analysed in this way. Secondly: is that which is implied really contained
in that established by the scientific experiment? This requirement
seems so obvious that it is surprising to find how many philosophical assertions are made which fail to meet it. For example, it is often said that because of the element of uncertainty introduced into
quantum theory by wave mechanics there is an ultimate limit to human knowledge. Even this statement can be challenged, but it will
often be added that it implies that man is an imperfect creature who
should not presume to probe too deeply into scientific problems. Or
it may be said that, because the concept of causality seems to dis-

appear in certain quantum phenomena, man does have the power of making his own decisions. These arguments will hardly bear examination. At the very least it should be emphasized that the first part of each assertion is about electrons or nucleons; the second part is about man.

The scientific attitude is to avoid assertions containing terms which have not been objectively defined, and to regard each assertion about scientific fact as meaning precisely what it means and as containing precisely what it contains, neither more nor less.

FRED HOYLE

Man and Materialism. New York: Harper & Brothers, 1956, pp. 150–161*

Language is a phenomenally clever medium for expressing the activity that goes on in our brains, the activity that we describe as "thinking." Words are labels that we attach to concepts and ideas. When we speak or write we show the labels corresponding to our "thoughts" to each other. Yet ingenious and indispensable as the processes of language are, no one who has tried to express himself precisely (as we say) can remain unaware of the difficulties and shortcomings of language. The play of our thoughts cannot be communicated to others in their full vividness. All we can do is to hold up to each other a set of labels which may or may not be suitably matched to our ideas. One of the difficulties of putting a new idea across is that in its nature a new idea may be indescribable in terms of old labels. New labels, new words, have to be invented and have to be conveyed successfully to others. Almost always the delay in the acceptance of a new idea comes from the delay in the invention of suitable new labels and in their promulgation. Often enough an idea that seems utterly obscure to one generation seems quite obvious to the next generation. The [150] reason is that suitable new labels have had time to become widely diffused. It is in this matter of the labeling of ideas that the real Babel lies, not in differences of language. Languages differ only in the sense that the labels are associated with different sounds, not in the system of labeling. Notice how quickly it happens that when a new label has been invented in one language, essentially the same label spreads into other languages.

There is perhaps no section of human affairs in which this matter of labeling causes the confusion that it does in discussions of religion. Even the meaning that we attach to the word "religion" is open to misunderstandings, disagreements, and confusion. The same may be said of a host of other labels "God," "faith," "material," "spiritual," "blasphemy," and so on. What I propose to do in this chapter is to try to indicate what I mean when I use these labels.

Much of the difficulty in discussing religious questions arises from the penchant of those who claim to be religious for displacing a question. Consider the following sequence of questions and answers.

Q. What does religion consist of?
A. A belief in the power of God.
Q. What is God?
A. The eternal, the almighty.
Q. What is "eternal," what is "almighty"?

At each stage here the questioner is asking for an explanation of the concept underlying a particular label, and by way of [151] answer he only receives other equally unintelligible labels. It seems to me that this sort of discussion gets one nowhere at all.

Religion if it has any sensible meaning does not consist, or more properly should not consist, in holding beliefs by "faith" that are denied by rational thought. For instance I do not regard a belief that Jesus was born of a virgin as evidence of a religious turn of mind. A denial of rational thought in favor of beliefs of this sort that contradict the very fabric of the world is to negate the faculty that separates Man from the beasts of the fields and forests. Religion, if it is not to be pernicious nonsense, must be based on rational thinking.

Instead of considering religion by way of conventional beliefs let us approach the subject from an unexpected direction. In the last three chapters we have discussed three problems, each of great importance to mankind. There remains a fourth problem, perhaps still more important and certainly more difficult than the other three. This we may call the "problem of purpose." Imagine that you have all the things that you would like, and that you have achieved all your ambitions. What then? A very dull life indeed. The word "happiness" is one of the most difficult of all labels. Certainly happiness does not lie in a state of dreamy contemplation, it is not Nirvana. Happiness is a dynamic state of mind, associated with the active fulfillment of our desires. Once fulfillment is over happiness is lost. A man with a vast fortune often attains all his ambitions and wants, thereby using up his store of happiness. He becomes blasé and sophisticated, to use two more labels. It is clear then that an "end" in life, or better still many such "ends," are important to the individual. [152]

By and large this matter of "end" and "purpose" is most frequently satisfied in the rearing of a family; especially is it so in the case of women. But there are many other "aims" that a man or woman can have—success in a career, the solving of a scientific problem, achievement in one or other of the arts, playing a musical instrument, writing a book, climbing a mountain. It is the possession of one or several of these aims by the majority of individuals that keeps our modern communities in a more or less sane condition.

Yet this is not all. The sense of purpose in the life of an individual seems incomplete unless the whole community in which he lives possesses a common sense of purpose. A community with a clear-cut aim will be an enthusiastic, lively body—and if the aim should be achieved, for a time a happy body. Stagnation, fossilization, produces the contrary effect, leaving the individual with a sense of frustration, even if he should himself be possessed of an adequate stock of personal ambitions.

Today the communist countries are the ones with the clearest aims. Both Russia and China, the latter particularly, are backward economically and have a great deal of leeway to make up before the condition of their peoples becomes comparable with that of the Western countries. It is the sense of purpose arising from a tackling of their economic problems that gives the communists their ebullient confidence. The champagne-like quality of their sense of national purpose is so strong that the Chinese and Russian people have been willing to give up a large measure of personal liberty in order to achieve it. This would be all very well if the communists did [153] not go on to conclude in their enthusiasm that what may possibly be good for them is good for the rest of the world. This is not so. The United States is not backward economically and the American people do not need to give up any personal liberties.

The present enthusiasm of Russia and China cannot in any case be permanent. It represents an expansion phase no different in its economic roots to the U.S. expansion of the nineteenth and early twentieth centuries, no different indeed from the expansion phases of a hundred and one communities that can be traced in the historical record. We have mentioned several times the expansion phase that precedes fossilization. Such expansions are in their nature temporary and therefore do not supply humanity with a permanent sense of purpose.

A similar situation applies I think to the three problems discussed in the last three chapters. Here we have problems that can very well give us a sense of purpose, but of a temporary nature only. Once the problems of population, of fossilization, and of the single-power world have been conquered, humanity will be very much like the wealthy individual bored with life because he has gratified all his whims. What then? Where does the ultimate purpose, or aim if you like, of the human species lie? What is the point of the species reproducing itself generation by generation? Why are we journeying? It is in the propounding of questions such as these, and in attempting to answer them that (I would say) the religious impulse lies.

There are no easy answers to these questions, as is clear from the multitude of contradictory religious beliefs that have been held in the world. Yet an examination of the origins of the [154] major religions will show that in spite of contradictions their tenets spring from a common aim: the identification of Man with the Universe. To be sure this aim is a little difficult to discover in contemporary religions. There is a reason for this. Contemporary religion is based on the religious teachings of bygone eras, often teachings that are very much older than the adherents of the modern religions realize, so old indeed that they belong to days when men understood comparatively little either about themselves or about the Universe. It was natural therefore that serious mistakes were made, mistakes that cannot survive a modern scrutiny by the rationally minded. But instead of recognizing this, contemporary religion has preferred to stick to the letter, rather than to the spirit, of the old beliefs. Faced then with outrageous contradictions it has become necessary to be increasingly vague about the meanings of the labels that describe the religious concepts—a point that we have already noted. It is to be doubted whether the situation can be retrieved by an attempt to clarify the present confused situation. Rather does it seem far more

profitable to attempt to rebuild our ideas of Man's relation to the
Universe from a new start, putting aside the older beliefs until some
rational basis for discussing them has been achieved.

What then can we say of Man's relation to the Universe? Do we
know that there is any relation at all, except that Man is some curious by-product of the Universe? Yes, I think we do know something
rather surprising on this point. A digression on science and scientific discovery is necessary to make this clear.

To most people the success that has been achieved by science
[155] seems truly remarkable. Take for instance the ability of the
Newtonian theory of gravitation to predict several years ahead
just when and where an eclipse of the Sun is going to occur. Or
again, consider a remarkable outcome of Maxwell's theory of light:
this theory correctly predicted all the properties of radio, long before the existence of radio was discovered experimentally. Einstein's
theory correctly predicted that light passing near the Sun would be
deflected in its path. Dirac's theory of the electron correctly predicted the existence of a new type of particle, the positron. Many
other examples of a like nature could be given.

Now what is so striking about all these cases is the way in which
it was found possible to describe a vast range of physical phenomena in terms of a quite small number of mathematical equations.
Not only this, but in each of the cases just mentioned, first a group
of physical phenomena was discovered experimentally, second it
was found that the observations could be completely represented by
mathematical equations, third the mathematical equations turned
out to have wider implications than the original observations on
which they were based, and fourth these wider implications were
used with complete success to predict new phenomena not known to
exist up to then, and indeed not even suspected to exist. It is no
exaggeration to describe this correspondence between observations
and mathematics as completely astounding. The element of mystery
in it never wears off, no matter how familiar we may become with
the details. We cease to wonder at an ordinary conjuring trick once
we know how it is done. In contrast, the more we [156] know of
how the scientific conjuring trick is done, the more we continue to
be amazed by it.

This astonishing ability of the human brain to guess the workings of the Universe seems explicable only on the basis that in some degree at least our brains mirror the Universe itself. As Lyttleton has said, it looks as though we carry the pattern of the Universe about inside our own heads. Even on the most cautious view the connection must be reckoned a most remarkable one.

Christians say that Man was created in the image of God. Provided we make the association

$$God = The \ Universe$$

the Christian statement becomes very much what we have just been saying. I feel sure that many religious people would object to this association, however, but what would they offer in its place? What concept does the label "God" stand for? Some people would seem to think of "God" as the "maker" of the Universe. The concept here would seem to be analogous to that of a man-made machine, the role of "God" as "He watches" the Universe from "outside" being analogous to that of a girl tending a spinning wheel. Indeed according to Catholics "God" did such a poor job in his "making" of the Universe that it is constantly necessary for "Him" to be making adjustments ("miracles") when things go wrong, rather as the girl may have to keep adjusting her spinning wheel. Ironically it is just those people who hold this flagrant machine concept who refer to themselves as "spiritually minded" and who castigate rational opinions. I would urge most strongly that the notion of something (undefined) "outside" the Universe [157] should be dropped from all our ways of thinking, and that if we wish to use the label "God" it should be used only in the above association of concepts. The Universe constitutes everything that there is.

It is worth adding a few words on incorrect uses of such labels as "matter," "materialistic," "spiritual," and the like. In the old days when very little was known about matter it seemed as if the difference between an inert body (such as a stone) and an active body (such as a human) could only be explained on the basis that the active body possessed some "vitalizing agent" which the stone did not. Thus the following associations became current:

$$stone = matter$$
$$human = matter + vitalizing \ agent$$

the vitalizing agent being described as "spiritual," and being referred to as the "soul."

Nowadays knowing a great deal more about matter we would rewrite the identities in the following way

stone = matter organized in a simple way
human = matter in a highly complex organization

In a sense the former duality is still preserved, with the highly complex human organization taking the place of the vitalizing agent.
In a sense it is correct to think of the organization as something separate from the matter. It is well known that the actual matter of
which a man is made up changes with time. That is to say the identity of the atoms in a man's body changes. But this does not necessarily produce any change in the man, because the change in the
atoms need not cause any change in the organization—one molecule of water can replace [158] another, one atom of phosphorus
can replace another, and so on. There is nothing unduly remarkable about all this. The building of a house is not simply a matter
of ordering a pile of building materials. A structural design is also
required. Indeed when a person builds a house the first thing to
engage attention is the plan, the organization. A house is a collection of materials plus an organization. The distinction will be abundantly clear not only to those who have built a house, but also to
those who have had a house destroyed—as many did during the
late war.

In accordance with these ideas we can give meanings to such
labels as "soul," "spiritual," and so on. These are concepts that relate to the organization, not to the particular materials that constitute a person. Your "personality" is determined by your organization, the difference between one person and another is a difference
of organization.

"You" = "Your organization"
"Me" = "My organization"
"Jack Smith" = "The organized structure of Jack Smith."

Perhaps I can make this clearer by an idealized experiment. Suppose I take you to pieces, disintegrate you into atoms. Then "You"
will cease to exist, "You" will cease to feel, your "Soul" will have

been destroyed, the organization will have gone. But suppose that before I disintegrate you I take a careful record (supposing this to be possible) of how all the atoms of your body are fitted together. In short I prepare a blueprint of the organization which is "You." Let us suppose further that this blueprint survives for many centuries and eventually, say a thousand years hence, comes into the hands of a man who is [159] clever enough to put atoms of matter (of which there are always plenty on hand) back into their original arrangement. What would happen? "You" would come alive again, exactly and precisely as you are at the present moment.

This may not be as comforting as those who follow contemporary religions would like, but it may come as a surprise to many to realize that there is no logical finality about "death." It is true that, at present, blueprints of this sort cannot be made, nor could a blueprint, even if we had one, be used for constructional purposes. But these are failures of technique, not of principle. It may come as a surprise, even to Christians, to realize that resurrection can be placed on a logical footing. Whether it can ever be put on a practical footing is another issue, one to which we know no answer.

But the main point I wish to bring out is that considerable progress can be made toward understanding Man's relation to the Universe. This can be done without any of the ancient beliefs, and without "faith." The purely scientific approach to such issues as "life," "death," "soul," and so on already reveals more in the way of remarkable conclusions than we might have expected. The picture is not yet complete, or anything like complete. Nor should we expect it to be, since it has become clear in recent years that science itself is still only at the beginning of the road. Recent studies of the ultrasmall in nuclear physics and of the ultralarge in astronomy have made it plain that there are whole worlds of understanding still to be opened up to us. And it is scarcely to be supposed that vitally new scientific knowledge will have no relation to the subject of our present discussion. There are some always ready to assert that [160] science is a barren study, and that only by "faith" in the efficacy or ill-understood labels can the "truth" be perceived. How it comes about that the Universe revealed by painstaking scientific investigation is so incomparably grander than anything that the "men of faith" have ever told us about, I have never yet heard tell.

We started the present chapter by saying that life will be found empty unless the continuity of the human species is endowed with a sense of purpose. We saw that aims of economic sufficiency, of national aspirations, may prove an adequate inducement for a time, but for a time only. In the long run a broader perspective is needed. Perhaps an answer can now be offered as to what this perspective might be. By continuing to search out the ways of the Universe and of Man's relation to the Universe we shall be serving our deepest instincts and we shall be following a progressive line of development. In this can lie our aim.

There is some indication that people are moving already in this direction. There is a looking outward from the Earth, a desire of Man to feel that he has a part in the great play of the Universe.

Science and religion as social controls

HALLEN M. BELL

Bulletin of the Atomic Scientists, XIII (January 1957), 32–34

The question of the relative merits of science and religion as guides in the field of human relations is becoming increasingly significant as the destructive potentialities of atomic energy are more fully revealed. It seems quite possible that the atomic age will require more effective social controls than were needed in the past. In former times the world could tolerate an occasional Hitler or Genghis Khan, since the lethal implements available then were capable of only localized or temporary destructiveness. There is reason to believe, however, that atomic bombs cannot be used very extensively without producing undesirable effects that are world-wide and lasting. Preventing irresponsible egocentrics from getting and using the bomb is only one of the new problems that seem to require a technique more effective than moral suasion. Many of the international tensions that might result in the unsafe use of the new weapon arise from economic maladjustments and inequalities, and these present problems that seem to be scientific or technological rather than religious.

In spite of the apparent need for a more practical approach to the social problems of the atomic age, the traditional religious or metaphysical approach still seems to have many champions, and many earnest voices still insist that science or "finite human intelligence" cannot be depended on and even (some say) cannot be used in the field of human relations. The reasoning in support of this attitude can, I think, be boiled down to two main arguments: that social problems are just too complicated for science to handle, and that science cannot deal with certain metaphysical concepts called "values."

SOCIAL PROBLEMS "TOO COMPLICATED" FOR SCIENCE?

The first of these two arguments is a practical one and is perhaps subjectively appealing, but to me it is unconvincing. The methods of science have been effective in solving so many problems, the solution of which was thought to be beyond the power of human intelligence, that it seems foolish not to use them, or at least give them a fair trial, in the field of human relations. Moreover, the assumption that social problems are unmanageably complicated seems questionable. In many cases the complications are obviously not in the problems themselves but in the attitude with which they are approached, and this accounts for the fact that some rather complex social problems have been solved while some simpler but equally urgent ones still await solution. The control of certain epidemic diseases, for instance, is rather difficult technically. Yellow fever, plague, and typhoid presented complicated control problems; yet the incidence of these diseases has been reduced to the vanishing point in many countries. On the other hand, syphilis is relatively easy to control; yet its control has lagged and is still incomplete. In this latter case, the moral complications which prevented and still prevent effective control are not inherent in the problem but are arbitrarily imposed upon it.

It is the imposition of these extraneous complications, not the limitations of human intelligence, that makes scientific work in the field of human relations difficult; and it is the resulting confusion of thought on social questions that accounts, to some extent, for the lack of public confidence in the social sciences and for the meager support given them in comparison with that accorded other scientific disciplines. The fact that science has produced atomic bombs and has not developed adequate social techniques for their control, does not necessarily indicate that the social problem was more difficult than that of the physicist, since there was an obvious difference in the approach to the two problems, a difference evidenced, for instance, by the [32] more generous financing of atomic research and by the virtual exclusion of the social sciences from the NSF.

The apparent failure of the social scientists to produce such spectacular results as those achieved by other scientists, is often cited as evidence of the inefficacy, and even illegitimacy of social science, but this backwardness is not necessarily due to the formidable complexity of social problems. It is largely due to the fact that the social sciences have had to share their field of operations with theology and philosophy, have been hampered by moral restrictions, and have often encountered stout religious opposition—an incubus from which other sciences have been freed for several centuries. As long as the "physical" sciences were dominated by theology and their determinations had to be justified morally, they too made little progress.

SCIENCE AND MORAL EVALUATIONS

The second argument, that science cannot deal with values, simply means that science cannot evaluate anything in moral terms; that is, in terms of *absolute* rightness or goodness. This is undoubtedly true, but it is rather beside the point, since no scientist, qua scientist, would attempt any moral evaluations. The question really is whether the scientist can make *any* meaningful or practically useful evaluations of human behavior and social institutions—and the obvious answer is that he can. For instance, the act of providing food for starving people may have a moral value which scientists cannot determine; but it certainly has other values, physiological, psychological, and sociological, some of which are obviously, all of which are probably amenable to scientific determination. Scientists cannot tell whether a person's behavior is good or bad, but they probably can determine with fair accuracy how it will affect his relations with other people, and I think this information would be more useful practically.

Moral values are not as mysterious and transcendental as they are sometimes made to appear. They are only hypothetically absolute; actually they vary from place to place, from culture to culture, and even from person to person, depending on the training, cultural heritage, and environment of those who conceive them. So the anthropologist, for instance, can deal with moral values and can often determine their nature, origins, motivations, and effects—which is probably more than most moralists can do. After all, a moral system is merely an arbitrary categorization of human activities designed to influence human behavior: it is really a system of symbols

—slogans and epithets—by which we can express our approval or disapproval without having to explain the motivations or appraise the consequences of our judgments. In short, it is merely one *method* of influencing human behavior—and there are other methods, as almost any educator, social worker, psychiatrist or intelligent parent can testify.

THE DETERMINATION OF GOALS

One thing in particular is said to be beyond the capabilities of science; that is, the determination of goals. If this means that science cannot reveal the ultimate end of human existence, it may be admitted (with some reservations based on the apparent potentialities of atomic energy); and here, of course, theology and philosophy are equally helpless. Short of finality, however, our social goals are simply what we want and reflect our ideas of the kind of a world we want to live in. The choice of goals may be subjective and emotional but it need not be unintelligent, and it will probably be more satisfactory if made after an intelligent analysis and correlation of pertinent facts—and of course it will have no moral significance unless that incubus be arbitrarily imposed upon it. Although the determination of social objectives may not be strictly scientific; still, once they are set, there is seldom any doubt that their attainment is a scientific and technological problem.

Certain social objectives are inescapable if we wish to live socially —which is also practically inescapable. A social form of existence requires a certain amount of social order and harmony; and human progress—in any direction—requires a fair degree of individual freedom. So it seems that the natural function of any system of social controls is to promote an optimum degree of order and harmony in society with the least possible restrictions on the freedom of the individual. This is just what science and the pursuit of knowledge require, and it is what the social scientist, if he has the welfare of science at heart, will try to bring about. It is not, of course, the objective of the moralist who commonly requires strict individual conformity to his mores even to the point of disrupting social harmony.

Really any discussion of the applicability of science to social problems is more or less academic—and anachronistic. This was a live question in the eighteenth century when the great political reformers, including the founders of the American republic, were establishing the modern principle that the validity of political institutions was to be determined by intelligent consideration of their effects upon mundane human welfare—life, liberty, and the pursuit of happiness, for instance—rather than by the dictates of autocratic guardians of morals. Since that time the use of more or less scientific techniques in the field of human relations has become a *fait accompli* in most democratic countries. There is no longer any question that they can be used; the only question is whether they will be effective in producing desired results.

INTELLIGENCE VERSUS INTUITION

The achievements of science in the field of human relations are often underrated. Actually the influence of science has been a potent factor in the development of modern social practices and institutions. It must be admitted, I think, that there has been considerable improvement [33] in social conditions and in the general pattern of everyday social behavior in the Western world since the Dark Ages, and I think most of this improvement can be credited to science and technology. The pioneers of modern science not only added new facts to the sum of human knowledge; they introduced a new conception of facts; namely, that they were interrelated, not isolated, phenomena. Moreover, they showed that, in the search for truth, the intellectual methods of science were apparently more reliable than the intuitive techniques of theology, and that these methods could be used by anyone, since apparently no divine credentials —other than those implicit in the possession of adequate mental equipment—were necessary. This naturally stimulated the search for more knowledge and a demand for greater intellectual freedom, and these impulses eventually produced our modern, essentially scientific civilization with its democratic freedoms.

Specifically, science influenced human relations by revealing that unsatisfactory social conditions, and the frequent miseries and disasters that afflicted mankind, were not due to divine wrath or demonic whimsey, but had natural causes that finite human intelli-

gence could ascertain and deal with. One of the obvious results of this discovery has been a much more humane treatment of the sick and insane, the crippled and deformed, and the poor and unfortunate generally, but it has also abated many irrational prejudices and phobias that in the past frequently caused social discord and violence. If to these achievements of science in general, are added those of the specialized social sciences in adjusting individuals to social living and in adapting social practices and institutions to individual needs, the record of science in the social field is rather impressive.

Compared with the record of science, that of religion is at least different; whether it is better or worse depends on how these words are defined. Science requires and tends to promote individual freedom and social harmony; and increases in knowledge naturally produce changes in social attitudes and customs. On the other hand, religion, with its immutable truths, as naturally resists change, tends to restrict individual freedom, and, in practice at least, seems to have a tendency to produce social discord. Lack of harmony between different religious groups is fairly common. This contentiousness seems to be inherent in the religious ethic and arises from the uncertainties of the intuitive method. Faith, as St. Paul said, is a speculative hope which cannot be verified by finite human intelligence; so the existence of two dissident faiths threatens the integrity of both. The most contentious element in religion—or in most religions—is the common religio-moralistic dichotomy of believer and unbeliever—or good people and bad people—a concept that seems almost designed to cause dissension. It naturally encourages a less friendly attitude toward the outsider than toward the fellow sectarian, and this less friendly attitude is easily extended to anyone who is different in any way, in race, color, culture, or in social or economic ideology.

MORALITY OF ATOMIC WAR

One of the major social objectives of the atomic age is the avoidance of atomic war, and this probably requires the complete abandonment of war as an instrument of international policy. That this goal can be attained by moral or religious influences seems doubtful. The morality of war has always been accepted by most religions, and all the wars of the past seem to have been justified morally. Atomic war, I suspect, can be justified *only* morally. Really, war might be considered the ultimate manifestation of the moral approach to social problems; for its outbreak commonly marks the point at which the issues in dispute have been reduced to a simple question of right and wrong, at which point further negotiation becomes impossible. In the past, there have been many purely religious wars and many outbreaks of violence motivated by religion. In recent times, religious motivations have been prominent in the violence attending the disunion of India, in the fighting in the Near East, in the Spanish Civil War, and to some extent in the ever present cold war—which has actually been called a crusade. This record hardly suggests that religion can bring peace to the world; in fact, the antagonisms arising from religion will probably be among the most formidable obstacles to overcome in any attempt to achieve that objective. Although many religious people seem to be sincerely devoted to the ideal of world peace, they usually predicate the attainment of that goal upon the world-wide acceptance of their particular religion, and none of the present religions seem within measurable distance of this preliminary goal.

The attainment of world peace will be a difficult job. It seems rather obvious, however, that the integration of the many divergent cultures of the world into a harmonious world society must be based on principles that are universally acceptable, upon methods of evaluating human activities and institutions that have world-wide validity. That moral judgments based on religion are too uncertain and variable to fill these requirements is indicated by the hopeless confusion of thought among the almost innumerable religious sects in the world. The same objection applies to judgments based on the categorical imperatives of moral philosophy or on economic creeds that have been invested with supernatural infallibility; for the intuitive dogmas upon which such judgments are based cannot be surely verified and will hardly be taken for granted by everybody in the world. On the other hand, scientific determinations do seem to have the necessary universality, since they are based on commonly available knowledge, and the methods by which they are formulated and verified are substantially the same everywhere.

Science and man's freedom

ARTHUR H. COMPTON
The Atlantic Monthly, 200 (October 1957), 71–74

What is the best in life that we can hope for? What shall we do to attain this best?

The very asking of these questions implies that we can do something to change our lot. Can we by trying affect what happens to us? Is it consistent with the laws of science that man shall have such freedom? On this essential point theologians, philosophers, and scientists have had sharp differences among themselves. Yet here is the very basis of man's responsibility. Responsibility has no meaning except as one is free to set his own course of action. If he is not thus free, both the sense of achievement and the feeling of failure are illusions. Indeed it is only as man is free that his aspirations make any difference, that his life has meaning and worth. If we are to discuss science and human responsibility we must thus ask first of all, does science admit that man is a free and responsible being?

One of the crucial episodes in Greek history was Socrates' decision to accept the verdict of death as given by the people of Athens. Socrates was waiting in prison for the appointed day. A friendly jailer had left the door unlocked. His disciples were urging him to flee. Socrates' reply has had an impact on the thinking of nearly a hundred generations. In effect this is what he said:

When I was a young man, I studied Anaxagoras' book on physics. He would have me believe that I am sitting in this crouched position on my cot because of the tension of the tendons over my joints. What Anaxagoras doesn't seem to know is that I sit here because I will not break the law of Athens. The people have condemned me to drink the hemlock. As a man of honor I will not creep stealthily away.

It was not the laws of physics that determined that Socrates should remain in prison; it was the code of honor to which he committed himself. Even in death Socrates was free.

In another notable case the conflict between science and faith in the power of will altered the course of history. In the tenth and eleventh centuries in the Arab world, science was growing vigorously, but in the twelfth century this growth suddenly ceased. I am told by Islamic historians that the reason for the sharp decline was the anti-scientific attitude of Islamic religious teachers from the twelfth century onward. These teachers, in particular the famous al-Ghazali, feared the study of science because it tended toward disbelief in God. The center of the difficulty was that according to science the world obeys laws that cannot be changed. How can this be reconciled with the doctrine that everything happens according to the will of God? Is not God—and man, too—thus reduced to an automaton?

Both of these incidents grew out of the conflict between physical law and man's belief in freedom. The present generation concerns itself little with the limitations imposed by physics. We think rather of the new possibilities that physics and chemistry are continually opening to us. We are, however, alert to the limitations imposed by biological and psychological factors. We see ourselves acting as demanded by our heredity, our psychological conditioning, and the forces of social pressure. But even such factors are irrelevant if in the mechanics of life things happen as they do because of predetermined physical cause and effect. [71]

The accepted view among western scholars until the sixteenth century was that things move because agents make them move. Such was the view of the great Greek teacher, Aristotle. To Greeks and Christians alike, the Unmoved Mover, who makes things go, was one description of God. The remarkably uniform motion of the planets, for example, was seen as evidence both of God's power and his reliability.

Then came Galileo. His experiments showed that no force is needed to keep objects in uniform motion. The effect of a force is rather to change the motion, to slow it down or speed it up or change its direction. Newton found further that the force of gravity, a universal property of matter, was all that was needed to hold the planets in their orbits. When the significance of these discoveries was fully realized it seemed that all that happens in the world was to be accounted for as a result of the mechanical forces between the particles of matter. A classical statement of this conclusion was made in 1812 by Pierre Simon de Laplace, when he said that everything that happens is the mechanically necessary result of what has gone before, and requires of necessity what will come to pass in the future. Such is indeed the implication of Newton's laws of motion.

This scientific view of mechanical determinism did precisely what had been feared by the Moslem fathers of the twelfth century. The hypothesis of a God that governed the motions of the worlds was no longer needed. He was replaced in people's thinking by mechanical forces inherent in the nature of matter. But the scientists had not only taken away the idea of a God that was free to act as he chose. They had also taken from man his most essential character. Man's idea that his efforts had meaning was an illusion. According to this science that was so successful in explaining the motion of the planets, man's actions had been fixed from the beginning of time. Neither blame nor praise for what a person did was justified. There was no such thing as freedom. All events occurred simply as a result of particles moving under mechanical forces, following their inevitable course.

It is these ideas of mechanical determinism that have shaped much of the philosophical thinking with which we still live.

The fault in this theory of mechanical determinism was not discovered until about thirty years ago. It was then found that the laws of Newton do not describe what happens to the atoms of which matter is composed. It was found instead that the properties of these atoms are such that prediction of what happens to them can only be made within certain limits. The amount of this uncertainty is fixed in the very nature of matter itself.

On my laboratory desk I have two simple devices. The first is a freely swinging pendulum. Its beats are regular, repeating themselves uniformly at equally timed intervals. This pendulum is typical of the objects with which the physicists of Laplace's time were familiar.

The second device is a Geiger counter, responding with a click to each ray that enters it from a near-by capsule of radium. The clicks occur at irregular intervals. It may be that about 100,000 clicks will occur each day. But several seconds may pass without any clicks, while during the next second two or three will occur.

Whether in the following second a ray will be counted cannot be foretold. This device responds to the action of individual atoms. Nothing of this kind was known until near the end of the nineteenth century.

The pendulum swings back and forth according to a precise law. The clicks of the counter occur at random.

If such a pair of experiments had been known in Newton's time, it is doubtful whether the idea that events must happen according to precise laws would ever have been formulated. It would have been evident that only under special conditions can one predict definitely what will occur. These conditions are that what we observe shall be the average of a very large number of individual events.

Consider what happens when an atom of radium disintegrates. This event can be recorded by such an instrument as a Geiger counter. The average life of a radium atom is about two thousand years. That is, in any one year from the time the radium atom is first formed, the chance is about one in two thousand that it will disintegrate. It may disintegrate during the present year 1957, but there is roughly one chance in eight that it will remain unchanged six thousand years from now. What the physicists of the twentieth century have shown is that there is no kind of observation that can be made which will tell in what particular year the radium atom will disintegrate. If the atom was in existence six thousand years ago, it was then identical with what it is today. The possibility of disintegration has always been there. Whether it will in fact disintegrate in this particular year is, as far as physics is concerned, a matter of chance —a likelihood of one in two thousand.

There is something comparable with this example in the case of every atomic or molecular event. Thus when light falls on a photographic emulsion, under its stimulus there is a certain chance that any particular grain of silver bromide will be changed so that it can be developed to silver. [72] With a given light exposure, this chance may be one in ten, so that on the average about one tenth of the grains will be transformed. But which particular grain will thus be changed is by the very nature of the process unpredictable.

These examples illustrate a point of critical importance in today's interpretation of the physical world. Nature provides nothing whose precise measurement would make possible the exact prediction of an atomic event. On this limitation that nature sets on our knowledge both experiment and theory are agreed. The average of large numbers of atomic events does indeed follow exact laws. In a large lump of radium in one year almost precisely one part in two thousand will have disintegrated. In a square inch of the photographic emulsion, almost exactly one tenth of the silver bromide, after the light exposure, will be reduced to silver. The number of atoms in my laboratory pendulum is huge, roughly a million billion billion. The statistics of the action of such numbers of particles are very precise—even more so when one observes the moon's regular revolution around the earth.

Not all large-scale events, however, are thus precisely predictable. If at any stage the big event depends on some atomic process, the end result shares in the uncertainty of this small event.

A typical large-scale event of this kind is the explosion of an atomic bomb. Such an explosion is triggered by the appearance of a neutron during the particular fraction of a microsecond when the chain reaction must be started. But this neutron comes from a radioactive process, which cannot be precisely foretold. If the chances were only even that during the critical time interval a neutron would appear, there would likewise be only even chances that the bomb would explode. In order that the bomb shall be sure to fire, it is arranged that during the critical time interval some thousands of neutrons will probably be present. Thus the chance of failure becomes practically zero.

Now most of life's processes are like such an atomic chain reaction. They begin with some very small event and grow. They are in fact chemical chain reactions. What starts these reactions in living organisms is not known in detail; but we do know that the beginning is on a molecular, or in certain cases on a submolecular, scale. Thus when I touch something hot and quickly withdraw my finger, the nerve currents that stimulate the muscular contractions are themselves small-scale reactions. The events that are involved when choices and decisions are made have so far defied physical identification; but in all probability they are reactions involving such small numbers of particles that definite prediction on a physical basis is by the nature of things impossible.

As far as physics is concerned, a person's actions which we think of as free would thus appear to occur simply according to the rules of chance. We find nevertheless that in practical life such actions can be predicted when we know the person's intentions. This implies that something additional to the physical phenomena is involved. What we actually note is that in such a case the person has a kind of firsthand knowledge of his own situation that is not gained from any physical observation. This additional knowledge is the awareness of his own intentions. When he acts he feels that he is acting freely. That is, his action corresponds with what he intends.

Thus, for example, I told the editor that I would have this article prepared in time for the present issue of the *Atlantic*. How could I confidently give him this assurance? Was it on the basis of physical data? Only to the extent that it appeared physically possible that the article could be prepared in time. As a physical event an immense number of other possibilities were equally likely to occur. Was not the primary basis of my prediction rather that I knew my own intention? And this I knew, not through any kind of observation, but by an inner awareness; not through a deduction from data, but because of a choice that I was making from among the various possibilities before me.

After thousands of years of discussion among scientists and philosophers, the place of free acts in a world that follows physical law has thus become clarified. There is nothing known to physics that is inconsistent with a person exercising freedom.

A set of known physical conditions is not adequate to specify precisely what a forthcoming event will be. These conditions, insofar as they can be known, define instead a range of possible events from among which some particular event will occur. When one exercises freedom, by his act of choice he is himself adding a factor not supplied by the physical conditions and is thus himself determining what will occur. That he does so is known only to the person himself. From the outside one can see in his act only the working of physical law. It is the inner knowledge that he is in fact doing what he intends to do that tells the actor himself that he is free.

Knowledge of the physical conditions and of the physical laws that apply to our situation thus opens to us a limited range of possibilities for action. Within this range the biological and psychologi-

cal factors become of ruling importance. That life shall continue
and thrive makes certain types of choice self-defeating and other
choices so successful [73] that they become dominant. Hereditary
and psychological conditioning makes certain types of response difficult and others easy. Much of such conditioning is beyond the control of either the individual or society.

There are physiologists and psychologists who look upon such
conditioning factors as compelling. They would say that the choices
a man makes are required of him by his nature and his circumstances. Whether this type of determinism in fact exists, the physicist
can neither affirm nor deny. Conditions not specified by physical
observation are here taken into account. There is nothing that physics knows which would deny the possibility that these conditions determine precisely the action of an individual in a particular situation.

I believe most physicists would, however, agree with me in making this suggestion: Physical laws, which at one stage seemed so
exact and compelling, are now found to leave open a wide range of
possibilities. May not the physiological and psychological restrictions likewise serve merely to limit further the range and likelihood
of the possibilities left open by the physical conditions? If this is true,
a choice may still be made from within this more limited range. One
may give personal preference to certain relevant psychological factors that affect the course of action. True freedom and responsibility
would thus remain.

To this possibility it is evident that the physiologist and the psychologist are unable to give a firm no. The final test for freedom
must be one's own sense of doing what he intends. Beyond this test,
science has no means of going.

A few years ago in Geneva, Switzerland, I met with an international group of some thirty scientists and philosophers, brought
together to discuss how man sees himself in the light of science. Is
man morally responsible for doing what seems to him good? Can
man in fact choose his course? To such questions the response of
these men was almost unanimous: Man is free and responsible.

There was one possible exception. He was an Italian student of
genetics who was strongly impressed by the effectiveness of inher-

ited tendencies in influencing a person's choices. To myself as a physicist such inherited tendencies correspond simply to a shift in what one scientist calls "the spectrum of action probability." The shift still leaves open the choice of any action that lies within that spectrum.

However, the significant fact was this: whereas in a similar gathering of scientists and philosophers a century or two earlier, freedom would undoubtedly have been denied by a large number in favor of physical determinism, in 1952 with this possible exception not one of the internationally representative group would deny on the basis of scientific law the responsibility that is implied by freedom.

I am not sure that this degree of unanimity would have been present if scientists bound by Communist ideas had attended the meeting. I am told that for a considerable period after the Second World War the teaching of the scientific principle of indeterminacy was under a ban in Russia. Marx, who was a younger contemporary of Laplace, had taught that man is a machine that obeys exact mechanical laws. The scientific idea of physical indeterminacy was dangerous. Who knew? It might open the way to belief that man has some special kind of value, or even to belief in God!

Let me then summarize how a physicist now views man's freedom. It is not from scientific observation that we know man is free. Science is incapable of telling whether a person's acts are free or not. Freedom is not something that one can touch or measure. We know it through our own innermost feelings. The first essential of freedom is the desire to attain something that one considers good. But desire lies outside the realm of science—at least outside of physics. You can't locate desire as somewhere in space. Similarly our recognition that within limits we can do what we try to do is not a matter of measurement or of external observation. It is a matter of immediate awareness. There is nothing in such awareness of freedom that is inconsistent with science. Freedom does, however, involve the additional determining factor of choice, about which science tells us nothing.

For myself, at least, this answer satisfies. Yes, I am free. I say this because I have found in my inner experience that the world does in fact respond to my efforts. And the findings of science, in particular the findings of physics, which at one stage so sharply denied that freedom had any meaning, are completely consistent with this experience.

Thus the way is cleared for our great task. We are free to shape our destiny. In this understanding we will find our greatest freedom.

Concerning the nature of science and religion: a study of presuppositions

HAROLD K. SCHILLING

Lecture. Iowa City, Iowa: State University of Iowa, 1958*

1. ISSUES

A great deal has been said about so-called presuppositions as part of the perennial discussion of "science and religion." Unfortunately, however, the term "presupposition" is a deceptively slippery one whose meaning tends all too easily to slide about in an argument, thus confusing issues. Also in some of its meanings it is loaded with emotional and prejudicial overtones that may actually create false issues and lead to rather curious sorts of polemic. Thus it is often asserted that religion and science are incompatible because the former requires one to begin by accepting prescribed presuppositions, whereas in the latter one starts "only with the facts"; whereupon the frequent counter-charge is that science also has presuppositions and that these are quite as restricting and prejudicial as those of religion. Apparently, according to this kind of argument presuppositions are intrinsically bad, and no less so for science than for religion.

Now if there is an issue here, it certainly cannot be whether there are presuppositions or not—since surely they are inevitable—but rather what they are, and whether they are legitimate, significant, and fruitful. Do they represent truth? How do they affect the methodology and content of science and religion? Obviously, this is a vast subject, and I can discuss only a small part of it. The particular questions I shall consider are, first, what kinds of presuppositions are mentioned in the literature, second, what their roles are, and, third, what a study of them reveals about the nature of science and religion.

* Reprinted by permission of the State University of Iowa, Iowa City, Iowa.

259

In what follows the term science will refer only to the natural sciences. The term religion will stand for both experiential and interpretive religion, i.e., theology. According to this usage, which I understand is one of the standard ones, theology is not separate from, but a part of religion, just as theoretical physics is integrally part of physics.

2. SURVEY OF PRESUPPOSITIONS OF SCIENCE

The literature[1] of our subject is extensive and presents a disconcerting variety of usages of the term "presupposition." These may refer to basic attitudes and capacities of man, or to elements of common knowledge. Some express intuitive insights assumed unconsciously. Others are carefully formulated propositions about, say, nature, truth, reality, method, [3] etc. Some should doubtless be referred to as postulates, others clearly as implicates. In short, the term stands for a wide spectrum of elements upon which the existence of science and of religion is alleged to depend, ranging from common sense points of view to sophisticated theorems of metaphysics and epistemology.

In analyzing this welter of material two kinds of distinctions are useful: one of definition, the other of classification. As to definition, we can recognize two basic meanings of the word presupposition: first, that which is antecedent to formal knowledge; second, a supposition adopted as a basis for logical inference. The latter I shall call formal or explicit, the former informal or implicit. As to classification, the presuppositions I have encountered in the literature seem to me to fall into five rather easily distinguishable classes. While I shall identify all five of these, I shall not have time to discuss more than the first four in this lecture. My survey will take the form of brief lists of typical presuppositions, for which I claim neither logical coherence nor completeness. Nor would I defend all the items in them as being either reasonable or necessary. Indeed some of them I regard as untenable.

We shall survey first the presuppositions ascribed to science. Class I comprises those that seem basic to all knowledge, though they are often cited as fundamental specifically to science. Typical ones are the following:

I, 1. I exist, and have existed prior to the present.
   2. There are and have been other selves more or less like myself.
   3. Selves can communicate meaningfully.
   4. There exist entities independent of minds.
   5. Propositions are true or false, valid or invalid, me͞   ͞or meaningless, etc.
   6. In developing a set of related propositions, the ͞use of indefinables is inevitable and indispensable.
   7. A system of propositions should be internally consistent, i.e., not contradictory.

Obviously this set is neither coherent nor complete. Like the lists that follow, this one is merely an unsystematic assortment of samples.

Some authors label as presuppositional the realization that certain attitudes, habits, interests, and elemental urges of human beings are indispensable to science. Propositions expressing this I put in Class II. The following are illustrative:

II, 1. Basic to science are such human qualities and values as intellectual curiosity, imagination, independence of mind, freedom to follow the truth wherever it may lead, cooperation, mutual confidence.
    2. Science results from the primal human urges to observe, reason, symbolize, [4] conceptualize, generalize, to count, measure, experiment, etc.
    3. These tendencies of man are valid and good, and lead to reliable knowledge.
    4. Man must make choices among alternatives when observing, experimenting, forming concepts and mental constructs, and setting up theoretical systems; and the knowledge he achieves depends in part upon such choices.
    5. The progress of science depends upon the honesty of scientists in making observations, weighing data, drawing conclusions, and reporting their findings.

Further along the spectrum of presuppositions we come to those relating to nature and the methodology of its exploration. The following are examples of Class III:

III, 1. Nature is real.
     2. Nature exhibits orderliness and regularity.

3. Nature is intelligible.
4. Nature is mathematically explicable.
5. When we measure something we know it.
6. Phenomena and events occur in space and time.
7. Nature does not change basically in time, i.e., natural laws are independent of time.
8. Nature's characteristics are the same throughout space, i.e., the natural laws discoverable here are no different elsewhere.

Class IV presuppositions embody particular conceptions, past or present, of the structure of the universe. A few examples:

IV, 1. There are absolute space and relative space.
2. Space is Euclidian (or Non-Euclidian).
3. Matter-energy is quantitatively constant in time.
4. The second law of thermodynamics applies to the universe regarded as a closed system.
5. Objects are localizable in space and time.
6. It is natural for a body once set in motion to move indefinitely far along a straight line without a motor.
7. Matter is atomic rather than continuous (or it is continuous).
8. Radiation is continuous rather than atomic (or it is atomic).
9. Present physical events are the effects of past causes.
10. The future is determined by the present.
11. The universe exhibits the dynamic tendency of evolution.

The last kind of presuppositions I find in the literature are negative ones. Although I shall not have time to discuss them in this lecture I present a few examples simply to complete this survey of the various types:

V, 1. There is no reality aside from the physical. [5]
2. No physical event occurs without a prior physical cause.
3. A given cause cannot produce different effects.
4. Minds are not direct causes of physical events.
5. There can be no "action at a distance."
6. "Observers" cannot "perceive" anything except when by a physical process one or more of the normal sensations are produced.
7. There can be no genuine "foreknowledge" of future events.

3. IMPLICIT PRESUPPOSITIONS

An over-all look at the four classes I intend to discuss reveals that the first three differ fundamentally from the fourth. For one thing, they *play no important role in the thinking of most scientists, as scientists, and are not a significant part of the subject matter of science.* Except for rare, occasional mention, one looks for them in vain in the standard treatises or research journals of science. Many scientists have gone through years of rigorous education and training without ever having heard them mentioned—much less systematically discussed—in science courses or seminars. In other words, scientists ordinarily enter science without benefit of such presuppositions, and once in they go about their business without paying any attention to them explicitly. They don't feel any need for them in their work. It is almost only when they relax from their work in the bull session or at the dinner table, or when they become, so to speak, philosophizers around the potbellied stove and the cracker barrel, that they talk about such basic postulates or assumptions. If anyone were to ask them to discuss such presuppositions formally, most scientists would deny being competent to do so. They would protest that such assumptions are only indirectly relevant to the scientific enterprise, that scientific inquiry would "go on" whether anyone was aware of them or not. Many would even admit finding it distasteful to engage in the kind of thinking they represent and would assert that ignorance in such matters is no serious handicap in scientific endeavor.

This is not to say that they are unimportant. On the contrary, they are very potent. I believe, however, that while they are presented here, as elsewhere, in postulational form, *their actual role in the lives of most scientists is almost exclusively that of unexpressed predispositions*, rather than assumptions. They are, typically, submerged in the subconscious, and do not originate in deliberate cerebration. They represent not a premeditated logical laying of foundations, but a simple, mostly unconscious taking things for granted as being what on the surface they seem to be; and *they may be regarded as expressions of a sort of elemental realistic faith or confidence in nature,* and in man's ability to understand it.

I use the word "faith" here in its most basic meaning, not as intellectual [6] assent to propositions, but as a state of mind, an orientation, an unformulated point of view, and a trusting relationship and commitment. It is in this sense that these presuppositions are determinative in science, and not because they constitute the formal foundation of inferential lines of thought. This is why, I believe, Whitehead has insisted so often that science is an enterprise in which reason is based on a faith, rather than one which has a faith based on reason. This explains why he can say that "it is essentially an antirationalist movement, based upon an instinctive conviction and a naïve faith," and that "this faith cannot be justified by an inductive generalization. It springs," he says, "from direct inspection of the nature of things so disclosed in our own immediate present experience," and "is impervious to the demand for a consistent rationality."[2]

Science is, as I see it, an exciting adventure, an enthusiastic, lusty sport, more than a coldly calculating chess game. It is, first of all, a hearty response to nature, springing from a compelling curiosity about it and from sheer pleasure in observing, and thinking about its phenomena. In part, it is also a yielding to the lure of the world of theory related to nature, and springs from the pleasure of manipulating and exploiting mathematical symbols and theoretical concepts.

Getting into science is much like falling in love. A young man meets a girl. He thinks about *her*, talks about *her*—but not in terms of propositions about her or about love in the abstract. He launches out into the deep without systematic thought. Science is also much like art, which certainly is basically a spontaneous, unpremeditated response to aesthetic reality. I would assert that science is the way of a man with nature, much as love is the way of a man with a maid, or art the way of a man with beauty.

If this is true these presuppositions of the first three types play no formal role in science akin to that of axioms in mathematics. Unlike art, or the business of falling in love, mathematics *is* largely an enterprise of logical development of consequences derivable from presuppositions. Thus, without particular axioms there would be no rational Euclidian geometry. Non-Euclidian geometrics are different from it because their postulates are different. The structure a mathematician develops must conform completely to the postulates implying it.

Sometimes, of course, the superstructure of theorems already exists, at least in part, and the mathematician's job is to construct for it the appropriate foundation of postulates, the goal being to establish logical consistency of the total system. Certainly the unformulated predispositions and presuppositions I have spoken of thus far have a very different relationship to the total system of a science.

4. EXPLICIT PRESUPPOSITIONS

Having dealt with certain presuppositions in so far as they are implicit in science, we must now look at them in their more formal role. After all, one [7] does find them stated in print explicitly. Apparently our hidden, elemental predispositions do somehow rise from the subconscious levels and appear in the open, where they are analyzed and given conceptual content. Several things should be said about them.

First, these explicit postulational formulations are the products, rather than the bases of inquiry. Furthermore, they come into being as answers not to *scientific* queries, but to *metascientific* ones; to questions not *of* science, but *about* science. Certainly they do not arise as part of the scientist's inquiry into the behavior of light, the isotopic structures of the chemical elements, or the mechanics of genetics. Rather they come out of an analytic search for the postulates that should, perhaps, underlie science, and represent the kind of thinking that is native to metaphysics.

Next, such analysis, even if it is mostly philosophic rather than scientific, is of great value to science. It is always desirable to unearth hidden assumptions, and to strive for logical consistency. It clears away the cobwebs and removes barriers to progress. This is why increasing numbers of scientists are showing interest in such questions, and why some are insisting that such self-analyses are an important responsibility of science itself. It is important, however, to realize that such precisely formulated presuppositions are mostly afterthoughts, actually post-suppositions that come from a study of science already in being. They are seen by looking backward. Paradoxical as it may sound, they represent, it seems to me, a "fitting" of the "foundation" to the superstructure *ex post facto*. Far from being propositions that consciously predetermine thinking in science, their nature is such, I believe, that they are achievable explicitly only by him who is already competent in such thought. That they are important to philosophers is obvious, but to most men of science they take on significance only when, after having engaged in considerable productive work, they stop to put their houses in order logically and philosophically. Up to that point there has been no compelling need for them.

Before proceeding to the next subject, let me repeat, for emphasis, that though some scientists find it necessary some time or other to formulate presuppositions of the first three classes, most of them, I believe, never do. Moreover, for the few that do, the urge to do so only rarely arises from their scientific work. The situation with respect to the fourth kind of presupposition is very different—but more of that later.

5. PRESUPPOSITIONS OF RELIGION

Now let us turn to religion. It seems to me that the situation there is surprisingly like that in science, and that virtually everything said thus far applies in principle equally well to religion. Thus both have presuppositions of the first three classes. Looking at these in turn, those of the first, referring to common knowledge, appear to be essentially the same for both. [8] Certainly religious thought—at least that of the Judaeo-Christian tradition[3]—also assumes the existence of communicating selves; the reality of entities independent of minds; the possibility of truth, validity, and meaningfulness; the inevitability of indefinables; the need for logical consistency; and so on.

Likewise, religion is said to have presuppositions of the second class, those asserting its dependence upon such elemental human qualities as curiosity, imagination, cooperation, trust, freedom, and honesty. Furthermore, religious thought could not exist any more than could science without the primal urges of men to reason, symbolize, conceptualize, generalize, and systematize. Here, too, we assume the capacity and need of choosing among alternatives of hypothesis, mental construct, and conceptual system.

It is, however, at this point in the spectrum of presuppositions that we must also notice, in addition to the similarities, certain significant differences between those of science and of religion. This is, of course, to be expected since science and religion do represent different aspects of human experience, and therefore involve certain different human capacities and urges. For example, man's universal tendency to worship and pray is fundamental to religion, but not to science; whereas his predilection for experimentation and measurement is basic to science, but not to religion.

In the third band of the spectrum also we find many presuppositions common to both science and religion. Here it was that we encountered the assumptions about the reality, intelligibility, and orderliness of nature. These are regarded as basic also to Jewish and Christian theology. In this class, however, the bifurcation of the spectrum separating the scientific from the theological presuppositions becomes even more evident than in the second. Here we find, aside from those common to both fields, a series of presuppositions that are distinctively characteristic of religious thought, but completely irrelevant to science. Some of these are analogous to those referring to nature, which we have just said are accepted by both religion and science. What they assume is a "realm of the spirit" transcending the physical world of space and time. Here are a few examples:

III (R), 1. The realm of the spirit, the holy or numinous, is real.
2. The realm of the spirit exhibits orderliness, regularity, and cause-and-effect relations.
3. The realm of the spirit is intelligible.
4. The realm of the spirit is religiously explicable.
5. When we worship we gain spiritual insight.
6. God is real and can be known.
7. God and the realm of the spirit are basically unchanging in time. [9]

It is evident, then, that religion is said to have the same first three classes of presuppositions as science—and in many cases even identical presuppositions. The next thing to note is that in religion too these are basically implicit and unformulated. They express a faith-relationship to God analogous, though clearly not identical, to the scientist's relationship to nature. They represent, first of all, insights derived not from speculative or inferential thinking, but from direct experience of the individual and the religious community with the realm of the holy and the divine—with God. Certainly they are not like mathematical postulates, and they do not constitute evidence that religion is "based" logically on metaphysical assumptions or religious dogmas to which assent is required in advance. It cannot be emphasized too much that the primary justification of religion, as of science, is *not* rationalistic or logical. The way one enters religion is by yielding to a pull which acts upon one. It too resembles falling in love and art. It is this experience of encounter and response that constitutes the determinative religious faith in its deepest meaning. Certainly this is the foundation of Christianity.

That these first three types of presuppositions do indeed function mostly implicitly in religion is evidenced by what I regard as a fact, namely that most believers (so-called) have never heard of most of them, and seem not to need them explicitly. Like the corresponding ones of science, they are regarded widely as belonging mostly to philosophy. The thinking they represent is more metaphysical than religious. They become explicitly formulated mostly in their "post" phase, as afterthoughts or postsuppositions, when the individual believer or the church seeks to systematize thinking *about* religion or to establish a logical foundation for it *ex post facto*.

Professor F. S. C. Northrop has distinguished between concepts-by-intuition and concepts-by-postulation.[4] The former result from immediate apprehension of experience, the latter from deliberate, systematic thought. Thus the term "light" as a concept-by-intuition represents something known with experiential immediacy, though as such it is not precisely definable; whereas "light" as a concept-by-postulation is something carefully defined and postulated as a basis for theorizing. I suspect that Professor Philipp Frank is making essentially the same point in his book, *The Philosophy of Science,* when he points out repeatedly that the language of science operates at two levels, first, that of common sense experience, and, second, that of general principles and formal theory.[5] Newton's Laws, for example, may be regarded, first, as potentially providing a description in a common sense way of the experiences people have with moving bodies, and, second, as determining by postulation, the abstract, mentally constructed world of theoretical mechanics. [10]

The same situation, with regard to concepts and linguistic levels, prevails, I think, in religion. Moreover, presuppositions also function there—as in science—in two ways, as presuppositions-by-intuition and presuppositions-by-postulation. Thus the assumption that God is real and can be known is a presupposition-by-intuition when it expresses something experienced directly. It is a presupposition-by-postulation when it is something inferred. In the latter case it is what I have called a *post*supposition coming out of religion more than a *pre*supposition underlying it. Important as is this distinction relative to the first three types of presuppositions it is even more so for the fourth, to which we now turn.

6. CREEDAL PRESUPPOSITIONS

Mr. Lucien Price, in his *Dialogues of Alfred North Whitehead*,[6] reports Whitehead as saying repeatedly that all of the basic assumptions of science he learned as a student at Cambridge were set aside during his lifetime. What he was talking about, apparently, was the kind of presuppositions I have designated as the fourth class, those, for example, that refer to the structure of space and time, of matter and radiation. Here we encounter for the first time in our discussion the kind of truly scientific fundamental assumptions upon which logical developments are actually based formally and which are consciously and inextricably entwined with all aspects of the everyday work and thought of the scientist. These are the formally postulated ideas on which others are built, and that are more than feeling and attitudes and instinctive taking things for granted. These are the ones that are native to science itself, *are* expounded explicitly in the scientific treatises, and are indispensable to adequate exposition. Without them we could have no science, conceived now as a tough-minded, rigorous, and intellectual discipline.

Now the presuppositions of religion that correspond to these of science are, it seems to me, those embodied in the so-called creeds, those I-believe statements that are basic explicitly in religious thought and refer to the nature and structure of divine reality. These are the assumptions upon which the theoretical structures of theology are founded. Without them we could have no theology, conceived now also as a tough-minded, rigorous and intellectual discipline. These are the presuppositions that are native to religion, rather than philosophy. It is, however, at this point that religion, at least Christianity, is probably misunderstood more than at any other. Let us consider, for example, the so-called Apostles' Creed: "I believe in God, the Father Almighty, Maker of heaven and earth; and in Jesus Christ His only begotten Son our Lord; who was conceived by the Holy Ghost, born of the Virgin Mary . . ." While not all Christian churches include the recitation of this creed in their ritual and many, indeed, deny that they have any such "fixed creed," yet for most Christians this series [11] of creedal affirmations does, I believe, express in varying degrees the essentials of their own basic beliefs. Therefore I feel justified in using it here as truly representative of Christian faith and thought.

As I pointed out in my introductory remarks, it is often said that one of the irreconcilable differences between religion and science is that the former demands at the outset an unquestioning submission to arbitrary creeds established by authoritarian decree, whereas science has no creeds at all. But this completely misrepresents the situation. While creeds certainly have been tragically misused in the history of the church, it must be admitted that fundamentally they are not arbitrary and authoritarian. The key to understanding them lies, it seems to me, in recognizing that creeds, like other presuppositions, have both an implicit, informal pre-aspect and an explicit, propositional post-phase; an experiential faith phase, and an interpretive theory phase. To borrow Mr. Northrop's language again, we have creeds-by-intuition and creeds-by-postulation. Without doubt the affirmations of the relatively simple and brief Apostles' Creed are in essence expressions of an intuitive, experiential faith, in contrast to the later and much more extensive, philosophico-theological creedal formulations and catechetical systems of propositions.[7]

The Apostles' Creed is, above all, a symbolic expression of what Christianity has always maintained, namely, that its foundation is empirical, and that it is rooted in the facts and events of history. The Gospels and the Book of Acts are not systematic theological treatises. One looks there in vain for expositions of a metaphysical nature. They are accounts of historical events, and especially of the greatest event, Jesus Christ. When the Apostles went forth to preach, what they preached about primarily was what they had experienced. To be sure, they also tried in a modest way to provide conceptualized explanations of what had happened; but when they did they often got themselves into trouble. While the "Logos concept," for example, was indeed suggestive and useful, over and over again they failed to get anywhere with it and were then driven back to fundamentals of which they were sure. "That which was from the beginning, which *we have heard,* which *we have seen* with our eyes, *which we have looked upon and touched* with our hands . . . , *that which we have seen and heard we also proclaim to* you." (I John 1:1,3) I understand that most of the phrases of the Apostles' Creed were individually current in the early church as expressions of a simple faith long before theological speculation and theorizing about their content and meaning became current. They were regarded not as metaphysical propositions, but as statements of experienced fact. Indeed, it required several centuries to bring them together, to accept some and reject others, and to weld them into a unified, coherent statement that was acceptable to the church—acceptable in that it was held widely to [12] represent truthfully what the church had experienced and *knew factually.* By the term "church" I do not mean an ecclesiastical hierarchy or organization, but the religious community of men and women who had witnessed and experienced something tremendous, something they all knew was real, something that had revolutionized their lives to such an extent that they thought of themselves as having been "born again." The creed is first of all an expression of this experience. Its authority resides not in ecclesiastical edict or arbitrary fiat, but in its compelling nature as a truthful description of what was known to have happened to the community. It is today held to be true primarily not because of convincing theological proof or ecclesiastical decree, but because it is regarded as empirically established.[8] Therefore it is meaningless to say that in religion one is confronted with a choice between creeds and facts. Here, then, we have the intuitive pre-aspect of religious creeds.

Inevitably, deep experience and faith eventually seek articulate expression, theoretical "explanation," and doctrinal formulation. Thus arise the post-phases and functions of religious creeds, and this is why in time they become sophisticated and replete with metaphysical intrusions. In this manner, the simple, confessional statement "I believe in God the Father, etc," accumulated in time such non-confessional concepts as absolute, ultimate, infinite, incomprehensible, perfect, indivisible, omnipresent, omniscient, transcendent, and many others, all of which appear in the later creeds. When we become impatient with this verbiage, and are inclined to shrug it off as meaningless and pointless, we would do well to remind ourselves that they represent the perfectly natural and legitimate post-phase kind of thinking, in search of logical coherence and theoretical interpretation, that goes on in all fields of scholarship.

Nor is it true that science has no creeds. It does; namely, those assumptions belonging to Class IV that we considered earlier in this section. They are statements of basic truths that have come to light and won acceptance in the life and thought of the science community. As in the case of their religious counterparts, it took a long time to bring some of them together and to formulate them acceptably— acceptable in the sense of expressing truthfully what the scientific community has actually experienced and *knows factually*. There is no good reason why they should not be referred to as scientific creeds. Both the way they came into being, and the role they have played in science subsequently, are essentially the same as those of religious creeds. And these, like their religious counterparts can be understood adequately only in so far as their dual nature, their pre- and post-aspects are recognized. To recognize this is to realize that science and religion are not incompatible in this regard. [13]

Consider, for example, the presupposition (IV, 9) about cause-and-effect. As commonly understood, it represents implicit ideas corresponding closely to immediate experience. As such it expresses, in common sense language, an elemental faith in the dependability of nature, and a belief that successive events hang together and are not chaotically independent. Thus regarded it is a scientific creed-by-intuition. With the historical growth of scientific experience and thought, and in response to the need for articulation and interpretation, this simple creed has gradually been transformed by the emergence of highly sophisticated meanings far removed from those of ordinary usage. What is technically called the "causality principle" in modern physics certainly says much more than the common sense view of cause-and-effect would imply. Its full explication requires reference to a large variety of concepts, such as efficacy, uniformity, identity, contiguity, simultaneity and succession; dynamical and statistical causality; absolute necessity and probability of connection. Moreover, it requires us to distinguish carefully between the world of conceptual structures and that of common experience, between propositions about cognitions and those concerning things and events.[9] Here in its explicit post-phase, we have a scientific creed-by-postulation.

I suggest then that in the matter of creeds science and religion are not fundamentally incompatible, but are, on the contrary, remarkably alike.

7. CIRCULARITY IN SCIENCE AND RELIGION

There is at least one wrong impression my discussion may have created, namely, that the intuitive and postulational aspects of presuppositions and assumptions can be distinguished or differentiated sharply, or that in the experience of individual and community they operate independently, and are necessarily separated temporally. While, as I see it, there can be no doubt that they may be separated at times, it is equally true that sometimes they are not. Perhaps they are never actually completely apart. In any case, one encounters in both science and religion an existential circularity that suggests that the prefixes pre- and post- are not altogether appropriate. The great, all-embracing generalizations, such as Newton's Laws and the Apostles' Creed are at once the most indispensable assumptions underlying, and the most consequential conclusions resulting from scientific and religious thought and experience. In so far as they represent experiential findings they determine and control interpretation. As interpretation they affect and to a large extent determine the meaning and the further extension of that experience. Our faiths determine our beliefs, and our beliefs greatly affect our faiths—just as experimentation determines theory, while theory largely determines experimentation. Our presuppositions have profound influence upon the formation of our postsuppositions, [14] and our postsuppositions profoundly affect our presuppositions. It is impossible to say which is in any real sense the foundation of the other. There seems to be no way of avoiding these circularities, or feedback interactions and modulations—in either science or religion.

I find that many people have grave difficulty understanding these circular relationships. They seem so illogical. Logic and intuition seem to be mixed together irresponsibly. The difference between the antecedent and the consequent seems to be washed out. It seems impossible to put one's finger on a particular place to begin. I suspect that true understanding of these existential situations may be possible only to him who sees science and religion respectively from within, i.e., learns to see them and know them by actual participation in the life and thought of the scientific or religious communities.

8. CONCLUSION

Science and religion are fundamentally much more alike than is commonly supposed. Neither is essentially a logical structure deriving like a geometric system from underlying assumptions by syllogistic processes, though both do require rational systems of thought for their complete development and expression. Neither demands as a first step assent to prescribed formal assumptions. Of course, both do have presuppositions, and their attitudes toward them are essentially alike. In kind these presuppositions are surprisingly similar. Moreover, in both they appear in two different aspects or phases, which I have referred to as the pre- and post-phases. In the former they are implicit, function as presuppositions-by-intuition, and are "basic" psychologically, representing fideistic pre*dispositions* more than pre*suppositions*. In the latter they are explicit, function as presuppositions-by-postulation and are "basic" logically, expressing a critical demand for coherence, authentication, and interpretation. Implicitly they are part of the so-called "foundations"; explicitly they are actually postsuppositions and part of the "superstructure." Unfortunately, however, the analogy of foundation and superstructure, and the terminology of "pre" and "post" are misleading, since no part of either scientific or religious experience and thought is necessarily prior to, or the indispensable foundation of, any other. Therefore I suggest that science and religion are both circular.

In closing let me say that I realize that I have only scratched the surface of my subject. Many interesting, and some vexing, problems and aspects of the subject have remained completely untouched by my remarks.

EPILOGUE

I realize also that I have not said anything profound. I am not, however, going to apologize for this. One of the basic principles of the great teacher in whose memory this lecture was prepared and delivered was that each of us is responsible to work and produce up to his own capacities, but no more. He used to say that not all of us can be equally profound or equally creative. What he considered important was that each of us *be* creative in some way, according to his own ability. His famous summer colloquia for college physicists were designed with great ingenuity to encourage and stimulate the ordinary run-of-the-mine physics teacher to bestir himself and to contribute something, no matter how humble, which would constitute for him an original contribution. Many a time have I seen him put somebody at ease who was apologetic about, say, a gadget he was exhibiting, by saying "Look here! Did you make that? (Yes.) Has anybody else ever made it? (No, not that I know of.) Then it is original with you? (Yes.) Is it good for anything? (Yes, it really helps students to understand something better.) Well, then, be proud of it. Don't apologize for it. You will see that all sorts of people will be interested in it." At the same time, since he had a marvelous sense of humor, his eyes would twinkle just the right amount, so that with his praise and encouragement would go a judicious amount of kindly deflation of any tendency toward over-evaluation of his praise.

I am neither a philosopher nor a theologian, and what is worse, after only seven years of deaning, even my friends now speak of me as *having been* a physicist. Why, in view of these pertinent, and disillusioning facts, did I accept the invitation to give this lecture? Because Professor Stewart would have wanted me to in spite of my limitations—since it presented an opportunity for me to make a modest contribution—as best I could. I knew of no better way to honor his memory than to do what he would have wished. Believe it or not, if he were here, he would manage to say some nice things about my lecture, though I am quite sure it would be with that kind but completely meaningful twinkle in his eyes. [16]

Notes

1. I suggest the following books as being more or less representative of the literature. All of them consider basic assumptions and presuppositions explicitly, though they differ widely in purpose, content, scope, and point of view.

Broad, C. D., *Religion, Philosophy and Psychical Research,* (and other of his books), (Routledge & Kegan Paul, London, 1953).

Burtt, E. A., *Metaphysical Foundations of Modern Physical Science,* (Harcourt, Brace, New York, 1927).

Caldin, E. F., *The Power and Limits of Science,* (Chapman & Hall, London, 1949).

Cassirer, E., *Determinism and Indeterminism in Modern Physics,* (Yale University Press, New Haven, 1956).

Coulson, C. A., *Science and Christian Belief,* (University of North Carolina Press, Chapel Hill, 1955).

Dotterer, R. H., *Postulates and Implications,* (Philosophical Library, New York, 1955).

Polanyi, M., *Science, Faith and Society,* (Oxford University Press, London, 1946).

Whitehead, A. N., *Science and the Modern World,* (Macmillan, New York, 1925).

International Encyclopedia of Unified Science, (University of Chicago Press, Chicago).

Aside from the above, the standard treatises on the philosophy of science and on the nature and methodology of religion are, of course, also relevant.

2. Whitehead, A. N., *Science and the Modern World,* pp. 12 and 23 (Macmillan, 1926).

3. Throughout this paper I shall be speaking of religion in terms of the Judaeo-Christian tradition, since I know virtually nothing about any other.

4. Northrop, F. S. C., *The Logic of the Sciences and the Humanities,* pp. 36, 62 (Macmillan, 1947).

5. Frank, Philipp, *Philosophy of Science,* pp. 1, 2, etc. (Prentice-Hall, 1957).

6. Price, L., *Dialogues of Alfred North Whitehead,* pp. 131, 215 (Little, Brown, 1954).

7. This difference between the earlier and later creeds becomes very evident when one studies such works as: Schaff, P., *Creeds of Christendom* (3 Vols.) (Harper, 1905), Harnack, A. V., *Dogmengeschichte* (Mohr-Siebeck, Tübingen, 6th ed., 1922), Matthews, W. R., *God in Christian Thought and Experience* (Nisbet, London, 1930). [17]

8. Actually the Apostles' Creed contains also affirmations of a fideistic hope, e.g., "life everlasting," aside from these concerned with experienced fact.

9. For an excellent critical review of this subject see Victor F. Lenzen, *Causality In Natural Science* (Charles C Thomas, 1954).

The role of modern physics in the present development of human thinking

WERNER HEISENBERG
Physics and Philosophy. New York: Harper & Brothers, 1958, pp. 187–206*

The philosophical implications of modern physics have been discussed in the foregoing chapters in order to show that this most modern part of science touches very old trends of thought at many points, that it approaches some of the very old problems from a new direction. It is probably true quite generally that in the history of human thinking the most fruitful developments frequently take place at those points where two different lines of thought meet. These lines may have their roots in quite different parts of human culture, in different times or different cultural environments or different religious traditions; hence if they actually meet, that is, if they are at least so much related to each other that a real interaction can take place, then one may hope that new and interesting developments will follow. Atomic physics as a part of modern science does actually penetrate in our time into very different cultural traditions. It is not only taught in Europe and the Western countries, where it belongs to the traditional activity in the natural sciences, but it is also studied in the Far East, in countries like Japan and China and India, [187] with their quite different cultural background, and in Russia, where a new way of thinking has been established in our time; a new way related both to specific scientific developments of the Europe of the nineteenth century and to other entirely different traditions from Russia itself. It can certainly not be the purpose of the following discussion to make predictions about the probable result of the encounter between the ideas of modern physics and the older traditions. But it may be possible to define the points from which the interaction between the different ideas may begin.

* Copyright © 1958 by Werner Heisenberg. Reprinted by permission of Harper & Brothers.

In considering this process of expansion of modern physics it would certainly not be possible to separate it from the general expansion of natural science, of industry and engineering, of medicine, etc., that is, quite generally of modern civilization in all parts of the world. Modern physics is just one link in a long chain of events that started from the work of Bacon, Galileo and Kepler and from the practical application of natural science in the seventeenth and eighteenth centuries. The connection between natural science and technical science has from the beginning been that of mutual assistance: The progress in technical science, the improvement of the tools, the invention of new technical devices have provided the basis for more, and more accurate, empirical knowledge of nature; and the progress in the understanding of nature and finally the mathematical formulation of natural laws have opened the way to new applications of this knowledge in technical science. For instance, the invention of the telescope enabled the astronomers to measure the motion of the stars more accurately than before; thereby a considerable progress in astronomy and in mechanics was made possible. On the other hand, precise knowledge of the mechanical laws was of the greatest value for the improvement of mechanical tools, [188] for the construction of engines, etc. The great expansion of this combination of natural and technical science started when one had succeeded in putting some of the forces of nature at the disposal of man. The energy stored up in coal, for instance, could then perform some of the work which formerly had to be done by man himself. The industries growing out of these new possibilities could first be considered as a natural continuation and expansion of the older trades; at many points the work of the machines still resembled the older handicraft and the work in the chemical factories could be considered as a continuation of the work in the dyehouses and the pharmacies of the older times. But later entirely new branches of industry developed which had no counterpart in the older trades; for instance, electrical engineering. The penetration of science into the more remote parts of nature enabled the engineers to use forces of nature which in former periods had scarcely been known; and the accurate knowledge of these forces in terms of a mathematical formulation of the laws governing them formed a solid basis for the construction of all kinds of machinery.

The enormous success of this combination of natural and technical science led to a strong preponderance of those nations or states or communities in which this kind of human activity flourished, and as a natural consequence this activity had to be taken up even by those nations which by tradition would not have been inclined toward natural and technical sciences. The modern means of communication and of traffic finally completed this process of expansion of technical civilization. Undoubtedly the process has fundamentally changed the conditions of life on our earth; and whether one approves of it or not, whether one calls it progress or danger, one must realize that it has gone far beyond any control through human forces. One [189] may rather consider it as a biological process on the largest scale whereby the structures active in the human organism encroach on larger parts of matter and transform it into a state suited for the increasing human population.

Modern physics belongs to the most recent parts of this development, and its unfortunately most visible result, the invention of nuclear weapons, has shown the essence of this development in the sharpest possible light. On the one hand, it has demonstrated most clearly that the changes brought about by the combination of natural and technical sciences cannot be looked at only from the optimistic viewpoint; it has at least partly justified the views of those who had always warned against the dangers of such radical transmutation of our natural conditions of life. On the other hand, it has compelled even those nations or individuals who tried to keep apart from these dangers to pay the strongest attention to the new development, since obviously political power in the sense of military power rests upon the possession of atomic weapons. It can certainly not be the task of this volume to discuss extensively the political implications of nuclear physics. But at least a few words may be said about these problems because they always come first into the minds of people when atomic physics is mentioned.

It is obvious that the invention of the new weapons, especially of the thermonuclear weapons, has fundamentally changed the political structure of the world. Not only has the concept of independent nations or states undergone a decisive change, since any nation which is not in possession of such weapons must depend in some way on those very few nations that do produce these arms in large quantity;

but also the attempt of warfare on a large scale by means of such weapons has become practically an absurd kind of suicide. Hence one frequently hears the optimistic [190] view that therefore war has become obsolete, that it will not happen again. This view, unfortunately, is a much too optimistic oversimplification. On the contrary, the absurdity of warfare by means of thermonuclear weapons may, in a first approximation, act as an incentive for war on a small scale. Any nation or political group which is convinced of its historical or moral right to enforce some change of the present situation will feel that the use of conventional arms for this purpose will not involve any great risks; they will assume that the other side will certainly not have recourse to the nuclear weapons, since the other side being historically and morally wrong in this issue will not take the chance of war on a large scale. This situation would in turn induce the other nations to state that in case of small wars inflicted upon them by aggressors, they would actually have recourse to the nuclear weapons, and thus the danger obviously remains. It may quite well be that in about twenty or thirty years from now the world will have undergone so great changes that the danger of warfare on a large scale, of the application of all technical resources for the annihilation of the opponent, will have greatly diminished or disappeared. But the way to this new state will be full of the greatest dangers. We must as in all former times, realize that what looks historically or morally right to the one side may look wrong to the other side. The continuation of the status quo may not always be the correct solution; it may, on the contrary, be most important to find peaceful means of adjustments to new situations, and it may in many cases be extremely difficult to find any just decision at all. Therefore, it is probably not too pessimistic to say that the great war can be avoided only if all the different political groups are ready to renounce some of their apparently most obvious rights—in view of the fact that the question of right or wrong may look essentially [191] different from the other side. This is certainly not a new point of view; it is in fact only an application of that human attitude which has been taught through many centuries by some of the great religions.

The invention of nuclear weapons has also raised entirely new problems for science and scientists. The political influence of science has become very much stronger than it was before World War II, and this fact has burdened the scientist, especially the atomic physicist, with a double responsibility. He can either take an active part in the administration of the country in connection with the importance of science for the community; then he will eventually have to face the responsibility for decisions of enormous weight which go far beyond the small circle of research and university work to which he was wont. Or he may voluntarily withdraw from any participation in political decisions; then he will still be responsible for wrong decisions which he could possibly have prevented had he not preferred the quiet life of the scientist. Obviously it is the duty of the scientists to inform their governments in detail about the unprecedented destruction that would follow from a war with thermonuclear weapons. Beyond that, scientists are frequently requested to participate in solemn resolutions in favor of world peace; but considering this latter demand I must confess that I have never been able to see any point in declarations of this kind. Such resolutions may seem a welcome proof of goodwill; but anyone who speaks in favor of peace without stating precisely the conditions of this peace must at once be suspected of speaking only about that kind of peace in which he and his group thrive best—which of course would be completely worthless. Any honest declaration for peace must be an enumeration of the sacrifices one is prepared [192] to make for its preservation. But as a rule the scientists have no authority to make statements of this kind.

At the same time the scientist can do his best to promote international co-operation in his own field. The great importance that many governments attach to research in nuclear physics nowadays and the fact that the level of scientific work is still very different in different countries favors international co-operation in this work. Young scientists of many different countries may gather in research institutions in which a strong activity in the field of modern physics is going on and the common work on difficult scientific problems will foster mutual understanding. In one case, that of the Geneva organization, it has even been possible to reach an agreement between a number of different nations for building a common laboratory and for constructing by a combined effort the expensive experimental equipment for research in nuclear physics. This kind of co-operation will certainly help to establish a common attitude toward the problems of science—common even beyond the purely scientific problems—among the younger generation of scientists. Of course one does not know beforehand what will grow out of the seeds that have been sown in this way when the scientists return into their old environments and again take part in their own cultural traditions. But one can scarcely doubt that the exchange of ideas between young scientists of different countries and between the different generations in every country will help to approach without too much tension that new state of affairs in which a balance is reached between the older traditional forces and the inevitable necessities of modern life. It is especially one feature of science which makes it more than anything else suited for establishing the first strong connection between different cultural traditions. This is the fact that the ultimate decisions about the value of a [193] special scientific work, about what is correct or wrong in the work, do not depend on any human authority. It may sometimes take many years before one knows the solution of a problem, before one can distinguish between truth and error; but finally the questions will be decided, and the decisions are made not by any group of scientists but by nature itself. Therefore, scientific ideas spread among those who are interested in science in an entirely different way from the propagation of political ideas.

While political ideas may gain a convincing influence among great masses of people just because they correspond or seem to correspond to the prevailing interests of the people, scientific ideas will spread only because they are true. There are objective and final criteria assuring the correctness of a scientific statement.

All that has here been said about international co-operation and exchange of ideas would of course be equally true for any part of modern science; it is by no means confined to atomic physics. In this respect modern physics is just one of the many branches of science, and even if its technical applications—the arms and the peaceful use of atomic energy—attach a special weight to this branch, there would be no reason for considering international co-operation in this field as far more important than in any other field. But we have now to discuss again those features of modern physics which are essentially different from the previous development of natural science, and we have for this purpose once more to go back to the European history of this development that was brought about by the combination of natural and technical sciences.

It has frequently been discussed among the historians whether the rise of natural science after the sixteenth century was in any way a natural consequence of earlier trends in human thinking. [194] It may be argued that certain trends in Christian philosophy led to a very abstract concept of God, that they put God so far above the world that one began to consider the world without at the same time also seeing God in the world. The Cartesian partition may be called a final step in this development. Or one may point out that all the theological controversies of the sixteenth century produced a general discontent about problems that could not really be settled by reason and were exposed to the political struggles of the time; that this discontent favored interest in problems which were entirely separated from the theological disputes. Or one may simply refer to the enormous activity, the new spirit that had come into the European societies through the Renaissance. In any case during this period a new authority appeared which was completely independent of Christian religion or philosophy or of the Church, the authority of experience, of the empirical fact. One may trace this authority back into older philosophical trends, for instance, into the philosophy of Occam and Duns Scotus, but it became a vital force of human activity only from the sixteenth century onward. Galileo did not only *think* about the mechanical motions, the pendulum and the falling stone; he tried out by experiments, quantitatively, how these motions took place. This new activity was in its beginning certainly not meant as a deviation from the traditional Christian religion. On the contrary, one spoke of two kinds of revelation of God. The one was written in the Bible and the other was to be found in the book of nature. The Holy Scripture had been written by man and was therefore subject to error, while nature was the immediate expression of God's intentions.

However, the emphasis on experience was connected with a slow and gradual change in the aspect of reality. While in the Middle Ages what we nowadays call the symbolic meaning of a [195] thing was in some way its primary reality, the aspect of reality changed toward what we can perceive with our senses. What we can see and touch became primarily real. And this new concept of reality could be connected with a new activity: we can experiment and see how things really are. It was easily seen that this new attitude meant the departure of the human mind into an immense field of new possibilities, and it can be well understood that the Church saw in the new movement the dangers rather than the hopes. The famous trial of Galileo in connection with his views on the Copernican system marked the beginning of a struggle that went on for more than a century. In this controversy the representatives of natural science could argue that experience offers an undisputable truth, that it cannot be left to any human authority to decide about what really happens in nature, and that this decision is made by nature or in this sense by God. The representatives of the traditional religion, on the other hand, could argue that by paying too much attention to the material world, to what we perceive with our senses, we lose the connection with the essential values of human life, with just that part of reality which is beyond the material world. These two arguments do not meet, and therefore the problem could not be settled by any kind of agreement or decision.

In the meantime natural science proceeded to get a clearer and wider picture of the material world. In physics this picture was to be described by means of those concepts which we nowadays call the concepts of classical physics. The world consisted of things in space and time, the things consist of matter, and matter can produce and can be acted upon by forces. The events follow from the interplay between matter and forces; every event is the result and the cause of other events. At the same time the human attitude toward nature changed from a contemplative [196] one to the pragmatic one. One was not so much interested in nature as it is; one rather asked what one could do with it. Therefore, natural science turned into technical science; every advancement of knowledge was connected with the question as to what practical use could be derived from it. This was true not only in physics; in chemistry and biology the attitude was essentially the same, and the success of the new methods in medicine or in agriculture contributed essentially to the propagation of the new tendencies.

In this way, finally, the nineteenth century developed an extremely rigid frame for natural science which formed not only science but also the general outlook of great masses of people. This frame was supported by the fundamental concepts of classical physics, space, time, matter and causality; the concept of reality applied to the things or events that we could perceive by our senses or that could be observed by means of the refined tools that technical science had provided. Matter was the primary reality. The progress of science was pictured as a crusade of conquest into the material world. Utility was the watch word of the time.

On the other hand, this frame was so narrow and rigid that it was difficult to find a place in it for many concepts of our language that had always belonged to its very substance, for instance, the concepts of mind, of the human soul or of life. Mind could be introduced into the general picture only as a kind of mirror of the material world; and when one studied the properties of this mirror in the science of psychology, the scientists were always tempted—if I may carry the comparison further—to pay more attention to its mechanical than to its optical properties. Even there one tried to apply the concepts of classical physics, primarily that of causality. In the same way life [197] was to be explained as a physical and chemical process, governed by natural laws, completely determined by causality. Darwin's concept of evolution provided ample evidence for this interpretation. It was especially difficult to find in this framework room for those parts of reality that had been the object of the traditional religion and seemed now more or less only imaginary. Therefore, in those European countries in which one was wont to follow the ideas up to their extreme consequences, an open hostility of science toward religion developed, and even in the other countries there was an increasing tendency toward indifference toward such questions; only the ethical values of the Christian religion were excepted from this trend, at least for the time being. Confidence in the scientific method and in rational thinking replaced all other safeguards of the human mind.

Coming back now to the contributions of modern physics, one may say that the most important change brought about by its results consists in the dissolution of this rigid frame of concepts of the nineteenth century. Of course many attempts had been made before to get away from this rigid frame which seemed obviously too narrow for an understanding of the essential parts of reality. But it had not been possible to see what could be wrong with the fundamental concepts like matter, space, time and causality that had been so extremely successful in the history of science. Only experimental research itself, carried out with all the refined equipment that technical science could offer, and its mathematical interpretation, provided the basis for a critical analysis—or, one may say, enforced the critical analysis—of these concepts, and finally resulted in the dissolution of the rigid frame.

This dissolution took place in two distinct stages. The first was the discovery, through the theory of relativity, that even [198] such fundamental concepts as space and time could be changed and in fact must be changed on account of new experience. This change did not concern the somewhat vague concepts of space and time in natural language; but it did concern their precise formulation in the scientific language of Newtonian mechanics, which had erroneously been accepted as final. The second stage was the discussion of the concept of matter enforced by the experimental results concerning the atomic structure. The idea of the reality of matter had probably been the strongest part in that rigid frame of concepts of the nineteenth century, and this idea had at least to be modified in connection with the new experience. Again the concepts so far as they belonged to the natural language remained untouched. There was no difficulty in speaking about matter or about facts or about reality when one had to describe the atomic experiments and their results. But the scientific extrapolation of these concepts into the smallest parts of matter could not be done in the simple way suggested by classical physics, though it had erroneously determined the general outlook on the problem of matter.

These new results had first of all to be considered as a serious warning against the somewhat forced application of scientific concepts in domains where they did not belong. The application of the concepts of classical physics, e.g., in chemistry, had been a mistake. Therefore, one will nowadays be less inclined to assume that the concepts of physics, even those of quantum theory, can certainly be applied everywhere in biology or other sciences. We will, on the contrary, try to keep the doors open for the entrance of new concepts even in those parts of science where the older concepts have been very useful for the understanding of the phenomena. Especially at those points where the application of the older concepts seems some-what forced or [199] appears not quite adequate to the problem we will try to avoid any rash conclusions.

Furthermore, one of the most important features of the development and the analysis of modern physics is the experience that the concepts of natural language, vaguely defined as they are, seem to be more stable in the expansion of knowledge than the precise terms of scientific language, derived as an idealization from only limited groups of phenomena. This is in fact not surprising since the concepts of natural language are formed by the immediate connection with reality; they represent reality. It is true that they are not very well defined and may therefore also undergo changes in the course of the centuries, just as reality itself did, but they never lose the immediate connection with reality. On the other hand, the scientific concepts are idealizations; they are derived from experience obtained by refined experimental tools, and are precisely defined through axioms and definitions. Only through these precise definitions is it possible to connect the concepts with a mathematical scheme and to derive mathematically the infinite variety of possible phenomena in this field. But through this process of idealization and precise definition the immediate connection with reality is lost. The concepts still correspond very closely to reality in that part of nature which had been the object of the research. But the correspondence may be lost in other parts containing other groups of phenomena.

Keeping in mind the intrinsic stability of the concepts of natural language in the process of scientific development, one sees that—after the experience of modern physics—our attitude toward concepts like mind or the human soul or life or God will be different from that of the nineteenth century, because these concepts belong to the natural language and have therefore [200] immediate connection with reality. It is true that we will also realize that these concepts are not well defined in the scientific sense and that their application may lead to various contradictions, for the time being we may have to take the concepts, unanalyzed as they are; but still we know that they touch reality. It may be useful in this connection to remember that even in the most precise part of science, in mathematics, we cannot avoid using concepts that involve contradictions. For instance, it is well known that the concept of infinity leads to contradictions that have been analyzed, but it would be practically impossible to construct the main parts of mathematics without this concept.

The general trend of human thinking in the nineteenth century had been toward an increasing confidence in the scientific method and in precise rational terms, and had led to a general skepticism with regard to those concepts of natural language which do not fit into the closed frame of scientific thought—for instance, those of religion. Modern physics has in many ways increased this skepticism; but it has at the same time turned it against the overestimation of precise scientific concepts, against a too-optimistic view on progress in general, and finally against skepticism itself. The skepticism against precise scientific concepts does not mean that there should be a definite limitation for the application of rational thinking. On the contrary, one may say that the human ability to understand may be in a certain sense unlimited. But the existing scientific concepts cover always only a very limited part of reality, and the other part that has not yet been understood is infinite. Whenever we proceed from the known into the unknown we may hope to understand, but we may have to learn at the same time a new meaning of the word "understanding." We know that any understanding must be based finally upon the natural language because it is only [201] there that we can be certain to touch reality, and hence we must be skeptical about any skepticism with regard to this natural language and its essential concepts. Therefore, we may use these concepts as they have been used at all times. In this way modern physics has perhaps opened the door to a wider outlook on the relation between the human mind and reality.

This modern science, then, penetrates in our time into other parts of the world where the cultural tradition has been entirely different from the European civilization. There the impact of this new activity in natural and technical science must make itself felt even more strongly than in Europe, since changes in the conditions of life that have taken two or three centuries in Europe will take place there within a few decades. One should expect that in many places this new activity must appear as a decline of the older culture, as a ruthless and barbarian attitude, that upsets the sensitive balance on which all human happiness rests. Such consequences cannot be avoided; they must be taken as one aspect of our time. But even there the openness of modern physics may help to some extent to reconcile the older traditions with the new trends of thought. For instance, the great scientific contribution in theoretical physics that has come from Japan since the last war may be an indication for a certain relationship between philosophical ideas in the tradition of the Far East and the philosophical substance of quantum theory. It may be easier to adapt oneself to the quantum-theoretical concept of reality when one has not gone through the naïve materialistic way of thinking that still prevailed in Europe in the first decades of this century.

Of course such remarks should not be misunderstood as an underestimation of the damage that may be done or has been done to old cultural traditions by the impact of technical progress. [202] But since this whole development has for a long time passed far beyond any control by human forces, we have to accept it as one of the most essential features of our time and must try to connect it as much as possible with the human values that have been the aim of the older cultural and religious traditions. It may be allowed at this point to quote a story from the Hasidic religion: There was an old rabbi, a priest famous for his wisdom, to whom all people came for advice. A man visited him in despair over all the changes that went on around him, deploring all the harm done by so-called technical progress. "Isn't all this technical nuisance completely worthless," he exclaimed, "if one considers the real values of life?" "This may be so," the rabbi replied, "but if one has the right attitude one can learn from everything." "No," the visitor rejoined, "from such foolish things as railway or telephone or telegraph one can learn nothing whatsoever." But the rabbi answered, "You are wrong. From the railway you can learn that you may by being one instant late miss everything. From the telegraph you can learn that every word counts. And from the telephone you can learn that what we say here can be heard there." The visitor understood what the rabbi meant and went away.

Finally, modern science penetrates into those large areas of our present world in which new doctrines were established only a few decades ago as foundations for new and powerful societies. There modern science is confronted both with the content of the doctrines, which go back to European philosophical ideas of the nineteenth century (Hegel and Marx), and with the phenomenon of uncompromising belief. Since modern physics must play a great role in these countries because of its practical applicability, it can scarcely be avoided that the narrowness of the doctrines is felt by those who have really understood modern [203] physics and its philosophical meaning. Therefore, at this point an interaction between science and the general trend of thought may take place. Of course the influence of science should not be overrated; but it might be that the openness of modern science could make it easier even for larger groups of people to see that the doctrines are possibly not so important for the society as had been assumed before. In this way the influence of modern science may favor an attitude of tolerance and thereby may prove valuable.

On the other hand, the phenomenon of uncompromising belief carries much more weight than some special philosophical notions of the nineteenth century. We cannot close our eyes to the fact that the great majority of the people can scarcely have any well-founded judgment concerning the correctness of certain important general ideas or doctrines. Therefore, the word "belief" can for this majority not mean "perceiving the truth of something" but can only be understood as "taking this as the basis for life." One can easily understand that this second kind of belief is much firmer, is much more fixed than the first one, that it can persist even against immediate contradicting experience and can therefore not be shaken by added scientific knowledge. The history of the past two decades has shown by many examples that this second kind of belief can sometimes be upheld to a point where it seems completely absurd, and that it then ends only with the death of the believer. Science and history can teach us that this kind of belief may become a great danger for those who share it. But such knowledge is of no avail, since one cannot see how it could be avoided, and therefore such belief has always belonged to the great forces in human history. From the scientific tradition of the nineteenth century one would of course be inclined to hope that all belief should be based on a [204] rational analysis of every argument, on careful deliberation; and that this other kind of belief, in which some real or apparent truth is simply taken as the basis for life, should not exist. It is true that cautious deliberation based on purely rational arguments can save us from many errors and dangers, since it allows readjustment to new situations, and this may be a necessary condition for life. But remembering our experience in modern physics it is easy to see that there must always be a fundamental complementarity between deliberation and decision. In the practical decisions of life it will scarcely ever be possible to go through all the arguments in favor of or against one possible decision, and one will therefore always have to act on insufficient evidence. The decision finally takes place by pushing away all the arguments—both those that have been understood and others that might come up through further deliberation—and by cutting off all further pondering. The decision may be the result of deliberation, but it is at the same time complementary to deliberation; it excludes deliberation. Even the most important decisions in life must always contain this inevitable element of irrationality. The decision itself is necessary, since there must be something to rely upon, some principle to guide our actions. Without such a firm stand our own actions would lose all force. Therefore, it cannot be avoided that some real or apparent truth form the basis of life; and this fact should be acknowledged with regard to those groups of people whose basis is different from our own.

Coming now to a conclusion from all that has been said about modern science, one may perhaps state that modern physics is just one, but a very characteristic, part of a general historical process that tends toward a unification and a widening of our present world. This process would in itself lead to a diminution [205] of those cultural and political tensions that create the great danger of our time. But it is accompanied by another process which acts in the opposite direction. The fact that great masses of people become conscious of this process of unification leads to an instigation of all forces in the existing cultural communities that try to ensure for their traditional values the largest possible role in the final state of unification. Thereby the tensions increase and the two competing processes are so closely linked with each other that every intensification of the unifying process—for instance, by means of new technical progress —intensifies also the struggle for influence in the final state, and thereby adds to the instability of the transient state. Modern physics plays perhaps only a small role in this dangerous process of unification. But it helps at two very decisive points to guide the development into a calmer kind of evolution. First, it shows that the use of arms in the process would be disastrous and, second, through its openness for all kinds of concepts it raises the hope that in the final state of unification many different cultural traditions may live together and may combine different human endeavors into a new kind of balance between thought and deed, between activity and meditation.

A scientist ponders faith

WARREN WEAVER
Saturday Review, January 3, 1959, pp. 8–10, 33

I believe that faith plays an essential role in science just as it clearly does in religion. I further believe that there are elements of perfection in religion that do not have counterparts in science. It is the purpose to develop here these two statements of belief—the first rather briefly, since many scientists agree on this point, and the second in somewhat more detail, since scientists tend to be shocked at a claim that religion is in any sense superior to science.

What do I mean by "faith"? The dictionary says, "the act or state of accepting unquestioningly the existence, power, etc., of a supreme being and the reality of a divine order."

I do not understand the inclusion here of the word "unquestioningly," for *acceptance* seems to me a process necessarily preceded by questioning. But, in any event, I use the word faith to refer to beliefs held so deeply, so completely, and so without reservation that one is prepared to base his life on these beliefs, even though they cannot be justified by so-called rational proof. I do not at all imply that an element of "faith" is to be established by virtue of external authority, and I most certainly do not refer to formal and formally imposed ecclesiastical dogmas. Faith is something I accept, not something which is forced upon me. Faith arises, I believe, in various and almost unanalyzable ways. Partly it arises by virtue of inner mystical experiences to which can probably be fairly applied the word "revelation." In large part, however, it develops and is sustained by actual experience.

Now, in science, is any role played by this kind of faith? The dictionary definition gives the proper beginning of the answer, when it says that faith is a belief in the existence of a divine order. For the great underlying, and essentially unprovable, assumption on which all of science is based is that nature is orderly. A second great dictum of scientific faith is that the order of nature is discoverable by man. A third great element of the scientific faith of Western science, and one which many accept without realizing that they do so, and without realizing that there are alternative possibilities, is the assumption that the whole quantitative time-space-mass-energy set of concepts which have been developed within the Greco-Judaic system is capable of capturing the variety and subtlety of nature. Fourthly, science assumes that logic is to be trusted as a mental tool. I hope that the reader is curious about the idea that anyone needs faith to believe in logic, for I will be saying more about this point.

Fifthly, although scientific thought has never been able to construct any generally acceptable basis for probability theory, and although we realize that science can in general make no quantitative statements about the external world other than probability statements, science proceeds on the calm faith that its statements do nevertheless have meaning and beauty. (Science, of course, has the added comfort that its statements clearly have utility.)

Sixthly, in the last thirty-five years or so it has come to be realized that—speaking of course in terms of detailed and ultimate accuracy—science actually has no capacity to deal directly with the external world. We now know that when we observe any object—an electron, a molecule, a [8] flatiron, or a star—the process of observation inescapably affects the thing observed. It will not be misleading to say that what happens is a little like asking questions of an exceedingly delicate and sick person through a crack in the door to his room in the hospital. You call in, "How are you?" He answers, "OK." But if he is very weak indeed the effort of making that answer may result in his death, so that the reply completely and automatically invalidates its own meaning.

When a physicist asks an electron, "Where are you?" the electron replies; but the effort of replying always moves the electron—and unpredictably—into a new location so that the answer is automatically invalidated. With large-scale objects, like the flatiron or the star, the effect is normally very small indeed, and for that reason most of us live out our lives, dealing with ordinary objects, without noticing, or having to notice, this effect. But it is a large effect when one deals with electrons, neutrons, and the other ultimate particles;

and remember that every object in our universe is, after all, made up of these particles; so if they elude description, then in a very real ultimate sense, everything does. And this effect can be of great consequence in the case of large-scale objects, as in nuclear events that lead by a chain process to very large-scale explosions. So the shocking fact is that science simply does not have detailed and precise access to what we ordinarily call the external world. Thus here again science is not "dealing with hard facts" as so many suppose, but is rather playing a subtle game with nature, all based on an unproved and unprovable faith that this procedure is meaningful and rewarding.

I think it neither necessary nor appropriate that I spend any considerable time speaking of religious faith. But may I merely call your attention to the close parallelism between some of the items of scientific faith I have just mentioned, and items of religious faith. Where the scientist has faith that nature is orderly, the religionist has faith that God is good. Where the scientist believes that the order of nature is discoverable to man, the religionist believes that the moral nature of the universe is discoverable to man—some would wish to say, has been revealed to man. Where the scientist has faith that his Western system of scientific thought is capable of dealing with nature, the religionist has faith that the moral concepts of the great religions—and for us particularly the concepts of Christianity —are capable of dealing with the ethical and moral problems of man. None of these propositions can, in any formal logical sense, be "proved." But in both sets of cases, these are the kinds of belief— the articles of faith—that men are prepared to live by.

Now, to pass to another aspect of this subject, I claim that it can suggestively, and I think convincingly, be argued that religion enjoys a certain superiority over science, in that religion has attained an actual identification with perfection, whereas science has to content itself with a never-ending, and hence never realized, approach to perfection.

I want to say at once that, in stating that religion has had experience with finality and perfection, I do not at all wish to question the reality or the desirability of progress in religious thinking. I do not hold with those fundamentalists who think that the last i was dotted and the last t crossed, centuries ago. The religion of the New Testament is to me a distinctly purer and finer doctrine than the religion of the Old Testament. As science reveals more and more of the complicated and orderly beauty of nature, our religion should become richer and richer. Scholarly study of the history of man's record of religious thought and experience does in fact reveal flaws in our previous understanding, and does result in real change—real progress—in our interpretation of religious ideas.

So far, then, one can say that both science and religion are dynamic activities, both advancing towards deeper and better understanding. But I think that there is nevertheless a real difference in the two situations; and that in the comparison, religion comes out on top.

I will offer three interrelated arguments: first, that scientific thinking always expands out to face an ever larger area of unsolved questions whereas religion closes in, more and more securely, on an inner core of truth; second, that as the external successes of science grow, it becomes more and more clear that there are unavoidable and inescapable inner imperfections in the underlying structure of science; and third, that there is a quality of permanence to religious thought which is not to be found in science.

First, then, which—science or religion—is really gaining in its assault on the totality of the unsolved? As science learns one answer, it is characteristically true that it also learns several new questions. It is as though science were working in a great forest of ignorance, making an ever larger circular clearing within which, not to insist on the pun, things are clear. The cleared circle is ever expanding—there is continuous progress in clearing away further ignorance. But as that circle becomes larger and larger, the circumference of contact with ignorance also gets longer and longer. Science learns more and more. But there is an ultimate sense in which it does not gain; for the volume of the appreciated but not understood keeps getting larger. We keep, in science, getting a more and more sophisticated view of our essential ignorance.

I do not think that a similar or comparable thing happens in advancing religious thought. It is almost as if the progress in religious thought were centripetal, aimed toward decreasing a central core of ignorance, rather than centrifugal, aimed out into the limitless unknown. In religious thought we progress toward known and recognizable goals; whereas in scientific thought we have really no way whatsoever to guess where we are heading.

Next, let us look briefly at the logical structure of scientific thought. If there is any aspect of science which is universally considered as basic, and which is usually considered to be unassailable, it is the logical nature of scientific reasoning. The relentless, austere precision of logic is, in fact, often held up to shame those who admittedly proceed, at least in part, through more emotional and intuitive modes of thought. But what is the situation, if one looks far within and says, "I do not in the least question the magnificent practical usefulness of this logical technique, but I am asking whether or not it is, in any ultimate sense and at its core, impregnable."

We remember that there are two great divisions of logic—deductive and inductive. In deductive logic one starts by making a certain number of pure assumptions—technically speaking, he adopts the postulates of the system under examination. Then with the addition of a certain accepted vocabulary of signs, certain assumed formation rules for combining the signs, and certain assumed transformation rules for deriving new formulas from old ones—with this assumed machinery one then proceeds to—to do what?

Of course, all he can possibly do is to unroll, in all its lovely and unsuspected complexity, the truths—or more properly, the formally correct [9] relationships—which were inherent in what he originally assumed. This procedure is, of course, quite powerless to create truths—it can only reveal previously and unconsciously assumed truth.

But this is not the limitation of deductive logic which I wish to emphasize. I wish rather to speak of shocking discoveries concerning deductive logic which have been recently made by an amazing genius named Kurt Gödel.

Let me start by quoting from a recent paper by Nagel and Newman on Gödel's work:

The axiomatic method invented by the Greeks has always been regarded as the strongest foundation for erecting systems of mathematical thinking. . . . Until recent times the only branch of mathematics that was considered by most students to be established on sound axiomatic foundations was geometry. But within the past two centuries powerful and rigorous systems of axioms have been developed for other branches of mathematics. . . . Mathematicians came to hope and believe that the whole realm of mathematical reasoning could be brought into order by way of the axiomatic method.

Gödel's paper put an end to this hope. He confronted mathematicians with proof that the axiomatic method has certain inherent limitations which rule out any possibility that even the ordinary arithmetic of whole numbers can ever be fully systematized by its means. What is more, his proofs brought the astounding and melancholy revelation that it is impossible to establish the logical consistency of any complex deductive system except by assuming principles of reasoning whose own internal consistency is as open to question as that of the system itself.

Indeed, Gödel obtained two results, each of which is of the most massive importance. He proved first of all that it is impossible— theoretically impossible, not just unreasonably difficult—to prove the consistency of any set of postulates which is, so to speak, rich enough in content to be interesting. The question "Is there an inner flaw in this system?" is a question which is simply unanswerable.

Secondly, he proved that any such deductive logical system inevitably has a further great limitation. Such a system is essentially incomplete. Within the system it is always possible to ask questions which are undecidable.

"This remarkable conclusion," and again I am quoting the Nagel-Newman article, "makes evident an inherent limitation in the axiomatic method. Contrary to previous assumptions, the vast 'continent' of arithmetical truth cannot be brought into systematic order by way of specifying once for all a fixed set of axioms from which all true arithmetical statements would be formally derivable."

If deductive logic has serious and built-in limitations, how about inductive logic? This is the branch of reasoning which examines all the observed cases recorded in the evidence, and seeks to induce therefrom general laws. This is the way in which the mind of man attempts to reach universals by the study of particulars.

Over 200 years ago David Hume bluntly denied the propriety of inductive logic. Ever since, certain skeptics have urged the necessity of practicing induction without pretending that it has any rational foundation; certain deductionists have vainly tried to prove Hume wrong; certain philosophers have optimistically hoped that a mild and friendly attitude towards such words as "rational" and "reasonable" could of itself sanction their application to statements referring to future and hence unexamined cases; and certain scientists have felt that it is vaguely sensible to suppose that future phenomena would conform to past regularities.

Deep and troublesome questions are involved here. Consider, just for a moment, the question: When and why does a single piece of past evidence give useful information about a future situation? If one takes a single piece of copper and determines that it conducts electricity, then it seems sensible to suppose that all other future pieces of copper will also conduct electricity. But if we pick out a man at random and determine that his name is John, this does not at all lend credence to the idea that all other men are named John. The first of these seems to lead to a "lawlike statement," and the second to an "unlawlike" one; but no one, so far as I know, has ever been able to give workable form to this distinction.

In fact, in spite of many attempts to make induction intellectually tolerable, the matter remains a mess. If you think I exaggerate, may I urge you to examine an article by Israel Scheffler in *Science* in which he summarizes recent work of N. Goodman.

He points out that the attitude of scientists toward induction, just referred to, has seemed to some to justify the claim that "in principle, we have our answer to the challenge of induction."

But Dr. Scheffler goes on to say:

It is this sanguine estimate which has been thoroughly upset by Goodman's researches. . . . Appearing at a time when logicians had been making considerable progress in analyzing other aspects of scientific method, these results came as a shock. Goodman's investigations, it seemed, had sufficed to undermine all the usual formulas concerning the most basic concepts of the logic of science, but his repeated and ingenious efforts to supply a positive alternative had all turned out fruitless. In the philosophic discussions that followed, every attempt was made to skirt Goodman's disheartening results. They were declared unimportant for the practicing scientist. The initial questions were asserted to be insoluble, hence worthless. Many papers, on the other hand, proposed what seemed perfectly obvious solutions that turned out to be question-begging. Only a very few authors fully recognized the seriousness of the situation for the philosophy of science and tried to cope with it directly.

Although the result will be almost incredible to one who has not read the original papers, the reader should face, from a specific example, just how surprising is the weakness of inductive logic as one now sees the matter. Let us look at the simplified case of the way in which one piece of evidence can be used in making inductions; for after all, if we cannot establish some gain from a single piece of evidence, then the prospect is most dubious that we could gain from more evidence.

A given piece of copper is tested, and it is found to conduct electricity. This item of evidence supports the statement: "All specimens of copper conduct electricity," but it also and equally logically supports the statement: "All specimens of copper are either such that they have been previously examined and have been found to conduct electricity, or are such that they have not yet been examined and do not conduct." And by invoking exactly the same logical machinery in the two instances the former statement leads to the conclusion: "A new and untried piece of copper will conduct electricity," whereas the latter, with precisely equal cogency, leads to the conclusion: "A new and untried piece of copper will not conduct electricity." The ability of induction to deal with a future case thus collapses; and since this is the only useful aspect of induction, we are faced by total collapse.

Thus I must report to you that discouraging news has leaked out of the citadel of logic. The external walls appear as formidable as ever; but at the very center of the supposedly [10] solid fortress of logical thinking, all is confusion. As practical tools, no one doubts the continuing value of the armaments. But in terms of ultimate and inner strength, the revelations are astounding indeed. The ultimate basis of both types of logical thinking is infected, at the very core, with imperfection.

Finally, I would argue that there is a different texture of finality to religious thought. Let me illustrate. I believe that fifty years ago essentially every well-trained scientist would have said that the principle of conservation of mass, and the principle of conservation of energy, were both perfect and doubtless unchangeable. Fifty (or 500 for that matter) years ago there were persons who believed that the basic principles of the Sermon on the Mount were perfect and unchangeable. Now the two scientific principles I have mentioned have been discarded. To be sure they have joined to form a broader new principle, but the fact remains that each, considered separately, simply is known today to be untrue. The newspapers of the past months have told us of the recent collapse of another scientific principle—that of parity. One confidently expects further really revolutionary changes in our present scientific conceptions of time, space, mass, continuity vs. discreetness, etc., which will simplify and unify the present almost intolerable confusion in modern atomic physics.

But although I hope that there will be ever deeper understanding, ever more realistic interpretation in modern-day terms, ever more clarifying light from all sectors of modern scholarship, I myself find it impossible to contemplate any fundamental change in or improvement on the basic principles of the teaching of Christ. Which, then, science or religion, has the harder inner core?

Sir Richard Gregory, until recently the distinguished editor of one of the world's leading scientific journals, *Nature*, has written his own epitaph. It begins:

> My Grandfather preached the
>   Gospel of Christ,
> My father preached the Gospel
>   of Socialism,
> I preach the Gospel of Science.

On the contrary, I think that the day has already come when one may proudly say:

> I preach the Gospel of Science and
>   the Gospel of Christ.

The future of man

JULIAN HUXLEY

Bulletin of the Atomic Scientists, XV (December 1959), 402–404, 409*

Science provides increased control over the forces of nature, and so gives us the means of realizing our aims in practice. But it also provides fuller understanding and a truer vision of natural reality. This is in the long run the more important, for our vision of reality helps to determine our aims.

HUMANIST ERA

By discovering how to control intra-atomic energy, science has launched us into the Atomic Era, with all its attendant hopes and fears. But by giving us fuller comprehension of nature as a whole, it has set us on the threshold of a greater and more revolutionary age, which I will call the Humanist Era. It is the era in which the evolutionary process, in the person of man, is becoming purposeful and conscious of itself.

Today, for the first time in man's long and strange history, science is revealing a comprehensive picture of the natural universe and of man's place and role in it—in a word, of his destiny.

Thanks to the patient labors of thousands of scientists—biologists and astronomers, geologists and anthropologists, historians and physicists—the universe of nature in which man lives is now revealed as a single process of evolution, vast in its scales of space and time. Man is part of this universal evolving world-stuff. He is made of the same matter, operated by the same energy, as all the stars in all the galaxies.

Most of the universe is lifeless and its portentously slow evolution

---

* This article was originally delivered as one of a series of presentations on "The Future of Science" at the Day of Science at the Brussels Exposition.

has produced only simple patterns of organization and little variety. But on our earth (and doubtless on other planetary specks) conditions permitted the appearance of the self-reproducing and self-varying type of matter we call life. With this, natural selection could begin to act and the biological phase of evolution was initiated.

CHANGE BECOMES MORE RAPID

Through natural selection, change—though still slow by human standards—could become much more rapid, and surprising new possibilities could be realized by the world-stuff. From the uniformity and relative simplicity of submicroscopic particles, there was generated the astonishingly rich variety of life, from sea-anemones and ants to cuttlefish and lions, from bacteria and toadstools to daisies and giant trees; the astonishingly high organization of a beehive or a bird; and most astonishing of all, the emergence of mind, living matter's increasing awareness of itself and its surroundings.

But there are restrictions on what the blind forces of natural selection can accomplish. A few million years ago, it now appears, living matter had reached the limits of purely material and physiological achievement: only the possibilities of mind remained largely unrealized.

By exploiting the possibilities of mental advance, man became the latest dominant type of life, and initiated a new phase of evolution, the human or *psychosocial* phase, which operates much faster than biological evolution, and produces new kinds of results. Man's capacity for reason and imagination, coupled with his ability to communicate his ideas by means of the verbal symbols of language, provided him with a new mechanism for evolution, in the shape of cumulative tradition. Pre-human life depended only on the transmission of material particles, the genes in the chromosomes, from one generation to the next. But man can also transmit experience and its results. With this, mind as well as matter acquired the capacity for self-reproduction. Natural selection became subordinate to psychosocial selection, and the human phase of evolution could begin. [402]

Science has also shown man his position in evolutionary time. Life has been evolving on the earth for over two thousand million years. Man-like creatures have existed for only about one million years, and human civilization, with all its achievements, for a bare five thousand. But evolving man can reasonably expect an immensity of future time—another two thousand million or more.

The psychosocial phase of evolution is thus in its infancy: man as dominant evolutionary type is absurdly young. I may adapt a simile of Sir James Jeans: If you represent the biological past by the height of St. Paul's cathedral, then the time since the beginning of agriculture and settled life equals one postage stamp flat on its top. And, unless man destroys himself by nuclear war or other follies, he can look forward to evolving through at the least the time-equivalent of another St. Paul's.

ROLE OF MAN

Man's place and role in nature is now clear. No other animal can now hope to challenge his dominant position. Only man is capable of further real advance, of major new evolutionary achievement. He and he alone is now responsible for the future of this planet and its inhabitants. In him evolution is at last becoming conscious of itself; his mind is the agency by which evolution can reach new levels of achievement. Man's destiny, we now perceive, is to be the agent of evolution on this earth, realizing richer and ampler possibilities for the evolutionary process and providing greater fulfillment for more human beings.

The revelation of fulfillment as man's most ultimate and comprehensive aim provides us with a criterion for assessing our own psychosocial evolution. Already in its brief course psychosocial evolution has produced real progress—increased expectation of life, less disease, more knowledge, better communications, increase of mechanical power and decrease of physical drudgery, more varied interest, and enrichment through creative achievement—in buildings and works of art, in music and spectacle, in discovery and ideas. But it has also produced poverty and crime and slavery and organized cruelty, and its course has been accompanied by constant exploitation, indignity, and slaughter.

In this new perspective, we see that what Père Teilhard de

Chardin called the process of hominization—the better realization
of man's intrinsic possibilities—has barely begun. Few human
beings realize more than a tiny fraction of their capacities, or enjoy
any but the most meager degree of possible satisfaction and self-
fulfillment. The majority are still illiterate, undernourished and
short-lived, and their existence is full of misery and indignity. Nor
have human societies realized more than a fraction of their capacities. They provide inadequate opportunities for expression and enjoyment, they still produce more ugliness than beauty, more frustration than fulfillment; they can easily lead to the dehumanization of
life instead of its enrichment.

SCIENCE AND THE FUTURE

What has all this to do with science? I would say a great deal.
First let us remember that most of what we can properly call advance in psychosocial evolution has stemmed from new or better
organized knowledge, whether in the form of traditional skills, sudden inventions, new scientific discoveries, technological improve-
ments, or new insights into old problems.

Science is a particularly efficient method for obtaining, organizing, and applying knowledge. Though modern science is barely three
centuries old, it has led to the most unexpected discoveries and the
most spectacular practical results. Scientific method involves controlled observation of fact, rational interpretation by way of hypothesis, the publication and discussion of procedures and results, and
the further checking of hypothesis against fact. The use of scientific
method has proved to be the best way of obtaining fuller intellectual
understanding and increased practical control, in all fields where it
has been tried. It leads inevitably toward more and fuller truth, to
an increasing body of more firmly established factual knowledge,
and more coherent principles and ideas.

Science is often used to denote only the natural sciences; but this
is a false restriction, which springs from the historical fact that
scientific method could be more readily applied to simpler subjects,
and so first became effectively applied in non-human fields. But it
can be applied to all natural phenomena, however complex, provided

that we take account of their special peculiarities and go to the trouble of devising appropriate methods for dealing with them.

PSYCHOSOCIAL SCIENCE

Today, the time has come to apply scientific method to man and all his works. We have made a piecemeal beginning, with psychology, economics, anthropology, linguistics, social science, and so forth. But we need a comprehensive approach to the human field as a whole. We already have physical science, chemical science, and biological science: to deal with man as a natural phenomenon, we must develop psychosocial science.

The primary job of psychosocial science will be to describe and analyze the course and mechanism of psychosocial evolution in scientific terms. It will also include a science of human possibilities. What are the possibilities of man and his nature, individually and collectively? How is their realization helped or hindered by different types of psychosocial environment? How can we estimate human fulfillment; in what ways and to what extent can it be promoted by changes in psychosocial organization? In particular, such a science will involve a radical re-thinking of man's systems of education, their aims, content, and techniques. [403]

The value of such an approach and such criteria is clear when we look at concrete problems. Two new challenges have recently appeared on the evolutionary scene—the threat of over-population and the promise of excess leisure. The population problem obstinately resists solution in terms of power-politics, economics, or religion, but the criterion of greater fulfillment immediately lights it up and indicates the general lines of the policy we should pursue in reconciling quantity with quality of human life.

The new possibilities opened up by science are exerting two effects on psychosocial evolution. Increased scientific control over the forces of nature has produced a flood of new conveniences and comforts, and has led directly to death-control and the recent alarming increase of human numbers. But the knowledge that healthier and longer life is possible, and that technology can provide higher standards of living and enjoyment, has changed the attitude of the vast underprivileged majority: they are demanding that the new possibilities shall be more abundantly realized.

LIMITED POSSIBILITIES

The next step must be to grasp the fact that the quantitative possibilities are not unlimited. Unless present-day man controls the exploitation of natural resources, he will impoverish his descendants; unless he supplements death-control with birth-control, he will become the cancer of the planet, ruining his earthly habitation and himself with it.

The leisure problem is equally fundamental. Having to decide what we shall do with our leisure is inevitably forcing us to re-examine the purpose of human existence, and to ask what fulfillment really means. This, I repeat, involves a comprehensive survey of human possibilities and the methods of realizing them; it also implies a survey of the obstacles to their realization.

Let me summarize the new picture of human destiny from a slightly different angle.

Man is the latest dominant type of life, but he is also a very imperfect kind of being. He is equipped with a modicum of intelligence, but also with an array of conflicting passions and desires. He can be reasonable but is often extremely stupid. He has impulses to sympathy and love, but also to cruelty and hatred. He is capable of moral action but also has inevitable capacities for sin and error.

As a result, the course of psychosocial evolution has been erratic, wasteful, and full of imperfection. It is easy to take a pessimistic view of man's history in general, and of his present situation in particular, where force and fear have become magnified on a gigantic scale.

HOPEFUL PROCESS

But when we survey the process as a whole, it looks more hopeful. During its course, there has been progress. Progress has always been the result of the discovery, dissemination, or application of human knowledge, and human knowledge has shown a cumulative increase. Furthermore, the erratic course of past psychosocial evolution was largely due to man as a species being divided against himself, and not having discovered any single overriding aim.

There is now a dramatic change in process. The human world has become inextricably interlocked with itself; the separate parts of the psychosocial process are being forced to converge toward some sort of organized unity. We are at last able and indeed compelled to think in terms of a single aim for mankind, while our increasing knowledge is enabling us to define our aim in relation to reality instead of in terms of wish-fulfillment: our knowledge of our imperfections and limitations is helping to define the possibilities of our improvement.

This marks a critical point in history. We have discovered psychosocial evolution as a complex but natural phenomenon, to be explored and controlled like other natural phenomena. Up till now, it has operated in erratic and often undesirable fashion, with self-contradictory aims. We now see that it could be transformed into an orderly mechanism for securing desirable results.

The idea of greater fulfillment for all mankind could become a powerful motive force, capable of influencing the direction of future evolution, and of overriding the more obvious motives of immediate personal or national self-interest. But it can only do so if it and its implications are properly understood, and made comprehensible to the bulk of men, all over the world. For this we need not only an extension of science but a reorientation of education; not only more knowledge, but also a better expression and a wider dissemination of ideas.

We must not imagine that the fuller realization of possibilities will be accomplished without effort, conflict, or suffering. This is inherent in the nature of man and of the psychosocial process; but so is hope.

The individual human brain and mind is the most complicated and highly organized piece of machinery that has ever existed on this earth. So-called electronic brains can perform extraordinary tasks with superhuman rapidity: but they have to be given their instructions by men. The human organism can give instructions to itself; and can perform tasks outside the range of any inanimate machine. Though at the outset it is a feeble instrument equipped with conflicting tendencies, it can in the course of its development achieve a high degree of integration and performance.

HOW SHALL WE USE IT?

It is up to us to make the best use of this marvellous piece of living machinery. Instead of taking it for granted, or ignorantly abusing it, we must cherish it, try [404] to understand its development, and explore its capacities.

The collective human organism, embodied in the psychosocial process, is an equally extraordinary piece of machinery. It is the mechanism for realizing human destiny. It can discover new aims for itself, and devise new methods for realizing them; but it is still primitive and inefficient. It is up to us to improve it, as we have improved our inanimate machines. Our ignorance about its potentialities is profound; therefore our immediate task is to understand the first principles of its operation, and think out their consequences.

Thus the new vision we owe to science is one of real though tempered optimism. It gives us a measure of significance and rational hope in a world which appeared irrational and meaningless. It shows us man's place and role in the universe. He is the earth's reservoir of evolutionary possibility; the servant of evolution, but at the same time its youthful master. His destiny is to pursue greater fulfillment through a better ordering of the psychosocial process. That is his extraordinary privilege, and also his supreme duty.

Our new vision assures us that human life could gradually be transformed from a competitive struggle against blind fate into a great collective enterprise, consciously undertaken. We see that enterprise as one for greater fulfillment through the better realization of human possibilities.

It is for us to accept this new revelation given us by science, examine it, and explore all its implications, secure in the knowledge that ideas help to determine events, that more understanding leads to more appropriate action, that scientific truth is an indispensable weapon against stupidity and wickedness and the other enemies of fulfillment, and true vision the parent of progress.

Theme topics

1. According to Hallen Bell, what makes "scientific work in the field of human relations" so difficult? Why? What solution does he propose?
2. What does James B. Conant mean when he states that a scientific theory is a policy and not a creed?
3. What similarities and differences does Harold Schilling find in the presuppositions of science and religion?
4. Why does Warren Weaver believe that "faith plays an essential role in science"?
5. Compare Aldous Huxley and Julian Huxley's attitudes toward science and man.
6. Which writers would agree with Schilling's conclusion that "science and religion are fundamentally much more alike than is commonly supposed"? Which writers would disagree? On what grounds? Can these differences of interpretation, if they exist, be reconciled? How?
7. Why does Conant believe that the analogy between the scientist and map maker is inadequate? Which writers would agree? Which ones would disagree? On what grounds? Can these differences of interpretation, if they exist, be reconciled? How?
8. According to Heisenberg, what have been the influences of the discoveries in modern physics upon modern thought? Does he maintain the objective definition and attitude which Jones, Rotblat, and Whitrow call for? (This paper may substitute Compton for Heisenberg, or it may be expanded to include both men.)
9. What does Hoyle believe man's relationship to the universe to be? What role does, or should, purpose play? Would Julian Huxley agree or disagree?

part VI   THE REFERENCE PAPER

The reference paper

Most of the papers you prepare for freshman and sophomore composition courses draw solely upon your personal experience and opinion. Frequently even though you base your paper upon some outside reading—a novel, a play, an article—you are asked to evaluate it in terms of your own experience, as in the Assignments in Parts I and IV of this volume. In contrast stands the reference, or research, paper. Ideally, its purpose is to bring together authoritative discussions of specific topics, from these sources to assemble and analyze data in an orderly fashion, and, finally, to reach any conclusions possible after an examination of the available data. For example, you might assemble articles by scientists and educators discussing the adequacy of the science curriculum in American high schools; after interpreting the body of material, you would state such conclusions as could be drawn from the evidence. Such a paper is essentially informational. It is paralleled by the written report stating the results derived from a laboratory experiment. The element of evaluation enters into a reference paper in much the same manner as it does in the critical summary; that is, the evaluation is based upon the completeness, logic, objectivity, and accuracy of the data available. In short, evaluation appraises the worth of the material. But at no time is evaluation based upon your unsupported personal opinion.

Your paper drawn from the sources in this volume will begin a method of study and writing which will continue through the "term" papers of upperclass courses, the original research of graduate school, and the reports which are so much a part of many businesses and professions.

The chief problem you face in writing the reference paper is the choice of topic. All too often the student chooses a subject that is far too broad and nebulous to be treated adequately in a few thousand words. One professor still tells the story of a student who announced his intention of writing about the influence of the nineteenth century upon the twentieth. Even a paper entitled "Science and Education" or "Science and Religion" and based only upon the selections included in this volume would create innumerable problems. Such proposals ignore at least two basic principles of the first-rate research paper. First, they are so general that no sharp focus, or limitation, can be maintained throughout the paper. Second, they ignore the fact that the more specific the topic is, the more thorough and valuable will be its treatment. Think of your topic as a specific problem to be solved, a question to be answered, as illustrated by the suggestions in both "Shorter Documented Papers" and "Final Documented Papers." You must be able to develop your subject thoroughly, with no loose ends, within the prescribed length of your paper, whatever that may be.

The distinction between primary and secondary sources also deserves your attention. Diaries, journals, letters, autobiographies, court records, and all legal documents—these provide some of the best examples of primary sources. The laboratory experiment and such a survey as that made by Mead and Métraux provide counterparts in the physical and social sciences. In short, primary materials which involve first-hand observation and reflection are the raw materials of original research. Any article or book written about these materials, particularly the documents, is usually described as a secondary source. But this traditional definition oversimplifies somewhat, for it glosses over the fact that your primary and secondary sources are frequently determined by the nature of your topic. For example, an historian might consider Shakespeare's *Macbeth* and *Hamlet* secondary materials because they are based principally upon accounts found in Holinshed's *Chronicles* and Belleforest's *Histoires Tragiques*, respectively, but the literary scholar will consider those plays as primary sources. In literary study the literary work itself joins the historical and biographical documents as primary sources, while reviews of these works are considered secondary sources. But to the student doing a study of the critical reception of Shakespeare's plays during a given period, the reviews and commentaries become primary sources. In short, your primary sources will be determined by the nature of your topic—by the problem to be solved, the question to be answered.

The traditional distinction between primary and secondary sources also glosses over the fact that the results of laboratory experiments and surveys such as that of Mead and Métraux are of little value if no one knows about them. The articles reporting and interpreting their results are of tremendous importance to other specialists as well as the general public. These articles therefore assume primary significance. When you write a senior "thesis" or when you are a graduate student, undoubtedly you will be expected not only to conduct an experiment (survey) yourself, if the nature of your subject requires it, but also to draw upon previous studies of your topic. But the facilities for original research are not always available to the underclassman. As a result the underclassman has too often written his paper from the accounts of his topic in encyclopedias and history books. That is why such a volume as this presents primary sources for you to work with, so that you will gain experience in analyzing and evaluating the raw materials of research. Your most important task, then, is to learn to assemble authoritative sources and both interpret and evaluate the data contained in them. And this process, as noted, begins with your statement of the central problem, the central question.

Documentation

Documentation, or footnoting, serves two basic functions in the reference paper, both essentially for the convenience of your reader. First, it provides exact references to the documents in order to substantiate significant facts or to identify the direct quotations which you include in your paper. Second, it permits your reader to go to the sources from which you have taken your material in order to inform himself more fully about a specific point or to ascertain whether you have presented and interpreted the material accurately.

If you footnoted every statement in your paper, you would certainly hinder, not aid your reader. Thus arises the question of what to footnote. Direct quotations, of course, for these must be credited to their authors. A widely known fact, however, one to which all or many of your authorities refer, need not be annotated; on the other hand, data and opinions unique to a single source and essential to the development of your analysis and conclusions must be noted in order to verify them. For example, there is no need to document Heisenberg's discovery of the uncertainty principle, but in certain papers there may be need to annotate the specific details, or steps, leading to that discovery. In addition, you will want to paraphrase and condense long passages from your sources, or you will present briefly the sequence of thought that occurs in some source. All such passages in your paper should be footnoted so that you can both acknowledge your indebtedness and allow your reader to go to your source in order to gain fuller information and to make certain of the original context. In short, documentation establishes your indebtedness to your sources.

Because the various academic disciplines employ styles of annotation that vary slightly in their detail, no universally standardized forms for footnotes exist. Whatever style you use, be clear, brief, and consistent. The forms recommended below have been taken from the *MLA Style Sheet* published by the Modern Language Association. Over seventy journals in various disciplines, particularly the Humanities, have adopted these forms. The examples cited be-

low include not only those forms you will need in referring to the
selections in this volume but also several common forms, especially
for books, that you will need if you choose to do additional reading
outside this volume.

1. Books
    a. Aldous Huxley, "Education for Freedom," *Brave New World
       Revisited* (New York, 1958), pp. 125–126.
    b. Ernest Jones, *The Life and Work of Sigmund Freud* (New
       York, 1953), I, 145.
    c. Fred Hoyle, "Continuous Creation and the Expanding Uni-
       verse," ed., Milton K. Munitz, *Theories of the Universe*
       (Glencoe, Illinois, 1957), pp. 419–433.
    d. Robert Jungk, *Brighter Than a Thousand Suns,* trans. James
       Cleugh (New York, 1958), pp. 185, 203.

Entry *a* indicates that only one chapter has been read; if the entire book had been read and made use of, the chapter citation would
be omitted. Entry *b* indicates the volume number as well as the
page. Entry *c* cites a single article within a symposium, an anthology
of any kind. Note that the editor is named and identified by *ed.* before the surname. His name must be included because libraries will
catalogue the book under the name of the general editor rather
than the individual contributor. Entry *d* includes the name of the
translator. In each case the name of the publisher has been omitted
but will be given in the bibliography.

2. Periodicals
    a. J. Bronowski, "The Creative Process," *Scientific American,*
       199 (September 1958), 59–65.
    b. Warren Weaver, "A Scientist Ponders Faith," *Saturday Re-
       view,* January 3, 1959, pp. 8–10.

The only difference between these two entries is the substitution in
b of the exact date for the volume number and more general date in
a. Most periodicals will be cited according to *a,* but some few which
publish weekly, together with newspapers, will be cited according
to *b.*

1. Books
    a. Huxley, p. 128.
    b. Aldous Huxley, *Brave New World Revisited*, p. 129.
    c. Jones, II, 234.
    d. Hoyle, in Munitz, *Theories of the Universe*, p. 423.
2. Periodicals
    a. Bronowski, *Scientific American*, 199 (1958), 61.
    b. Weaver, *SR*, January 3, 1959, p. 9.

In recent years Latin abbreviations, such as *op. cit.* and *loc. cit.*, have been omitted more and more from documentation; the principal exception is *ibid.*, which is still retained by many journals. The feeling has grown that they are superfluous. In addition, they may create problems of clarity. Since footnotes are numbered consecutively throughout the paper (or chapter of a book), the use of a Latin abbreviation may force the reader to waste time paging through the article trying to find the citation to which the Latin refers. Thus, after the initial citation, your reference to the author's surname and page number(s) in books or to the author's surname, title of periodical, and page number(s) is completely clear. As soon, however, as you refer to two authors with the same surname (Aldous and Julian Huxley) or to two works by the same author (Bronowski, Weaver), a more complete entry is necessary. A note similar to *b* will be needed for books, while the entry for periodicals will duplicate the original entry, since the articles may be from the same journal.

Although many editors have abandoned *ibid.* in favor of the author's name, it may be used to refer to the book or article cited in the *immediately preceding* note:

[24] Ernest Jones, *The Life and Work of Sigmund Freud*, II, 107.
[25] *Ibid.*, II, 178.

Notice that the volume and page numbers must be included.

Some journals exclude the year from *a* under periodicals and place a colon between the volume and page numbers:

Bronowski, *Scientific American*, 199:61.

Whatever form the citation takes, exact page references should always be given.

BIBLIOGRAPHY

Organize your bibliography alphabetically by the surname of the author or, if no author is given, as in newspapers and some periodicals, by the first word, excluding articles, of the title. Normally, you will include only those items to which you have referred in your discussion. (You may, for example, have read a "background" article in the encyclopedia without making actual use of it in your paper. It should usually be excluded from your bibliography.) A standard practice divides the bibliography according to books and periodicals, although if your bibliography is short, no division whatsoever need be made. Typical entries for books and periodicals are as follows:

Heisenberg, Werner. *Physics and Philosophy*. New York: Harper & Brothers, 1958.

Rabinowitch, Eugene. "Responsibilities of Scientists in the Atomic Age," *Bulletin of the Atomic Scientists*, XV (January 1959), 2–7.

Weaver, Warren. "A Scientist Ponders Faith," *Saturday Review*, January 3, 1959, pp. 8–10.

Assignments related to the reference paper

The following exercises are designed to acquaint you with stand-ard reference works and standard procedures in library research. They will provide you with material that may be incorporated into your annotated paper(s).

1. Who are the authors of these selections? Consult such refer-ences as the *Dictionary of American Biography* and *Current Biography* to learn something of their lives. Do you find any reference books devoted exclusively to biographical sketches of American scientists? Are any of the men listed in the *Dictionary of American Scholars* or *Who's Who in American Education?* Have any of them been the subject of full-length biographies? If they have, compile a bibliography of such works for any one man.

2. Many of the writers represented here have published other books and articles. Consult the *Readers' Guide to Periodical Literature, International Index to Periodicals,* and other ap-propriate sources to compile a bibliography of any one man's writings. Did he publish in both learned journals and popular magazines? Do you find a bibliography devoted solely to the writings of scientists or to writings about science and its rela-tionship to different phases of society?

3. Take any one of the problems discussed in these selections, such as the so-called crisis in science education, and using such sources as the *Readers' Guide,* compile a bibliography of recent articles pertaining to it. What is the date of the earliest article dealing with the problem? What periodical, or periodicals, has published the greatest number of articles relating to it? Did journals in specialized fields, such as education, give it atten-tion before the popular magazines did?

4. What has been the critical reception given the books from which excerpts have been taken? Take one book—Oppenheimer's *The Open Mind,* Heisenberg's *Physics and Philosophy,* Bridg-

man's *Reflections of a Physicist*, to cite several possibilities—and consult such publications as *Book Review Digest, The New York Times Book Review*, and *Saturday Review* to compile a bibliography of reviews of the book. Remember that almost all of the scientific journals, such as *Science*, publish reviews. Did all of the articles appear soon after the book's publication, or was the book discussed long after its appearance? (You may vary this assignment by using a book which one of the writers has mentioned, like Robert Jungk's *Brighter Than a Thousand Suns*, or by compiling reviews given all the books of such a man as Conant or Oppenheimer.)

5. As illustrated by the Mead-Métraux article, readers sometimes respond in letters to the editor. Take any one article and see if it has gained attention in the letters-to-the-editor columns of the journal in which it appeared.

6. Have any of the scientists referred to by the authors written about the relationship of science and society? Choose a man like Max Planck, Niels Bohr, Albert Einstein, or Max Born and compile a bibliography of his writings on nontechnical topics.

7. Many past scientists and historical incidents have been referred to by the writers. Compile a bibliography of publications from the last five or ten years dealing with one such man or event.

8. Reference has been made to Aldous Huxley's novel *Ape and Essence*. Consult such references as *Book Review Digest* to compile a bibliography of recent fiction dealing with the relationship of science and society. Are most of the authors scientists or nonscientists?

9. What was the reception given any one of the discoveries or theories, such as the uncertainty principle, discussed by the writers? What is the date of the earliest article? Did a number of articles appear immediately in the popular magazines or were they published solely in the learned journals? If there was a time lapse, when did the popular magazines take notice of the discovery?

10. Consult one scientific journal, such as *The Scientific American*, for a period of five or ten years and compile a bibliography of articles dealing with some phase of the relationship of science and society.

11. Consult the *New York Times Index* to find out what newspaper coverage some event such as the development of the Salk Polio Vaccine or the launching of Sputnik received. (Although the *New York Times Index* refers only to the *Times,* it can guide you to other newspaper articles because it gives the dates of events. Presumably most newspapers cover a major news item on the same date.)

II. SHORTER DOCUMENTED PAPERS (700–1000 WORDS)

Many of the topics suggested after each division of the text may be used as the basis for a preliminary, shorter annotated paper. The majority of them require material to be taken from more than one article. They by no means exhaust the possible topics.

III. PROSPECTUS

In no more than three hundred words write a *prospectus,* or plan, for a long annotated paper based upon some topic derived from *Science and Society: Midcentury Readings.* Naturally you cannot know what your findings will be before you complete your research. In presenting your plan, therefore, you should concentrate upon a statement of purpose to indicate the specific problem you will investigate, the limitations of the paper, and the nature and scope of the material to be considered. Remember that while this plan should be your guide in preparing the final paper, if, after you have completed your reading, you find that altering the plan somewhat will produce a better paper, by all means do so. Slavish adherence to a *prospectus* can distort the data, and result in the impression that you have tried to prove a preconceived thesis rather than interpreted your material objectively.

IV. FINAL DOCUMENTED PAPERS (APPROXIMATELY 2000–3000 WORDS)

The following topics illustrate the type of paper which may be based upon a larger selection from the text. Group A includes suggestions that would be based solely upon the text; Group B would involve some additional library research. Students may use these topics, or they may devise their own with the approval of the instructor.

Group A

1. From these writings what picture does one gain of the twentieth century scientist? What are his values, his goals? How does he picture the public's concept of him and his goals?

2. How do the various writers define science and the scientific method? Do they agree among themselves? If not, why not? How are their ideas similar to and different from the ideas held by scientists of past centuries?

3. What do the writers feel are the major problems facing American education? What caused these problems to arise? What measures do they suggest be adopted? What is their attitude toward the Humanities?

4. Some of the writers, like Bronowski, have discussed science as a creative action or art. Do all of the writers have this concept of science? What part does the imagination play in science? Is it as important to modern science as empirical observation?

5. A number of the writers discuss progress—past, present, and future. How do they define it? What illustrative evidence do they include to show that progress has taken place in past centuries and is taking place now? Do they believe the doctrine of progress has created special problems for modern society? Do they agree on the course of progress in the future?

6. In the view of these writers what responsibilities does the scientist have to society? What responsibilities do government and the public have to science and scientists?

7. Conant speaks of "conceptual schemes"; other writers emphasize concepts and man's position as a part of nature. How important are these ideas to man's understanding of himself and his universe? What influence do they have upon modern science? Upon modern philosophy? Upon modern religious thought?

8. What are the basic difficulties between science and government during the present period? What caused them to arise? Is fric-

tion between science and governmental authority something unique to this period? What measures do the writers suggest be adopted?

9. Do these selections leave the impression that the wants and needs of society during a given period have dictated the course of scientific research? Has there always been a separation between applied science and a science "for its own sake"? Is this division detrimental to both science and the general public? What has brought it about? Should there continue to be such a division?

10. What do the writers believe the philosophical implications of modern science to be? Do they agree upon their nature? Do they agree that man is justified in finding philosophical implications in scientific theory and discovery?

11. Several of the writers have stated that science prospers best in a free society. What is their basis for this view? What problems occur in a totalitarian state, such as Nazi Germany, that do not occur in a democracy? Have any of these problems occurred in countries like Britain and the United States? Are these problems unique to the present period?

12. Several of the writers have asserted that many people do not believe science has an ethical content, that it is merely a mass of facts. Do the scientists agree or disagree with this view? If they disagree, what ethical content is there in science? Is it of such a nature that individuals and institutions could base their own ethical behavior on it?

13. What influence has science had upon the writers' attitudes toward religion? Are the writers chiefly sectarian or nonsectarian in their views? What elements of formal religion do they stress most, least? What place in man's life do they believe religion has?

14. Many of the writers have emphasized such periods of history as Classical Greece, the Renaissance, and the eighteenth and nineteenth centuries. Are they interested in these periods solely for their contribution to the history of science? What forces, or motives, do the writers believe have given direction to Western history? Do they idealize the past?

15. Drawing for your evidence upon the proposals made by the

writers in regard to the problems they discuss, predict the role that science will play in society in general or in some specific area such as education during the next twenty-five or fifty years.

Group B

1. A number of great political figures of the past, such as Jefferson and Franklin in America, have been sympathetic toward science. Consult the writings of one such man to discover both what knowledge he had of science and what he said about the relationship of science and society.

2. What did the scientists of the 1920's (or any one decade) regard as the chief problem(s) in the relationship of science and society? How did they propose these problems be solved? Have any of their proposals been carried out? If they have, with what success?

3. Several of the articles, such as the unsigned editorial in *The Christian Century* and the two articles from *Saturday Review* for January 4, 1958, cite a number of cases in which a scientist has been in difficulty with the American government. Investigate one such case. What caused the difficulty to arise? What were the issues involved? What action was taken? Has there been any modification of this action?

4. How well does such a program as the development of the atomic submarine or of the ICBM illustrate the problems in the relationship between science and government? What were the problems specific to the project? Were they of such a nature as to be unique to the project? How have they been solved? If no problems arose in a particular project, what measures were taken to prevent them?

5. Most of the writers represented in this volume are themselves scientists. Choose one of the problems they discuss and assemble articles in which nonscientists deal with it. What are the issues as seen by the nonscientists? If different from those emphasized by the scientists, how can the difference be explained? What solutions do they offer? How do these differ, if they do, from the solutions proposed by the scientists?

6. Many scientists of earlier periods—Bacon, Newton, and

Thomas Huxley, for example—have been mentioned by various writers. Choose one and read his writings on the subject of the relationship of science and society. Do his views reflect the tensions of his own period? Are his views regarding science similar to or different from those of current writers? How were his ideas received by his contemporaries?

7. Read several other writings by Conant, Oppenheimer, Weaver, or Bronowski. Do all of the man's writings reflect the same attitudes and problems? What ideas, if any, have changed? Can these changes be accounted for? What new issues, if any, have entered his latest works? (Someone like Bohr or Einstein, who has been mentioned but not included in this volume, may serve as the basis for this paper.)

8. What was the critical reception given such books as Conant's *Modern Science and Modern Man,* Oppenheimer's *The Open Mind,* or Heisenberg's *Physics and Philosophy?* Was the reaction of the reviewers who were also scientists different from that of reviewers who were not scientists? (This paper may be expanded to include all of the major nontechnical books by one author.)

9. What was the significance of some single historical event, like Galileo's trial or Madame Curie's discovery of radium, to the development of scientific thought? What was the reaction of men of the period? What is the attitude of present-day writers to it?

10. Read such a novel as Aldous Huxley's *Brave New World* or *Ape and Essence,* or Fred Hoyle's *The Black Cloud.* What picture does the novelist give of science and the scientist? Of the relationship of science to society? Of the philosophical implications of science? Do his views reflect the same concerns shown by the writers included here? In the case of either Huxley or Hoyle, are his views the same in his fiction as in his nonfiction?

11. Although the public clamor about the inadequacy of science education has grown louder since Sputnik, several writers spoke of a crisis much earlier. Did others join them? What factors explain the lag in public response? What have the educators had to say about the problem? Are their solutions the same as those proposed by the scientists?

12. Although several British and Continental writers have been included in this collection, articles from British and Continental journals have not. If they are available in your library and if you read German or French, examine them to see what attention they give to the relationship of science and society. Do they focus on the same problems and suggest the same solutions that American writers do? If not, what causes the difference in emphasis?

13. Extend one of the topics suggested in Group A beyond the writers represented here. Do the additional authors agree or disagree with the writers represented in this volume?

Index of Authors and Titles